THE GREA

BY THE SAME AUTHOR

Six Steps Back to the Land

Why Genes Are Not Selfish and People Are Nice

Good Food for Everyone Forever:
A People's Takeover of the World's Food Supply

Consider the Birds: Who they are and what they do

The Secret Life of Trees

The Variety of Life:
A Survey and a Celebration of All the Creatures That Have Ever Lived

Neanderthals, Bandits, and Farmers

Last Animals at the Zoo

Future Cook

The Famine Business

Colin Tudge

THE GREAT RE-THINK

A 21st Century Renaissance

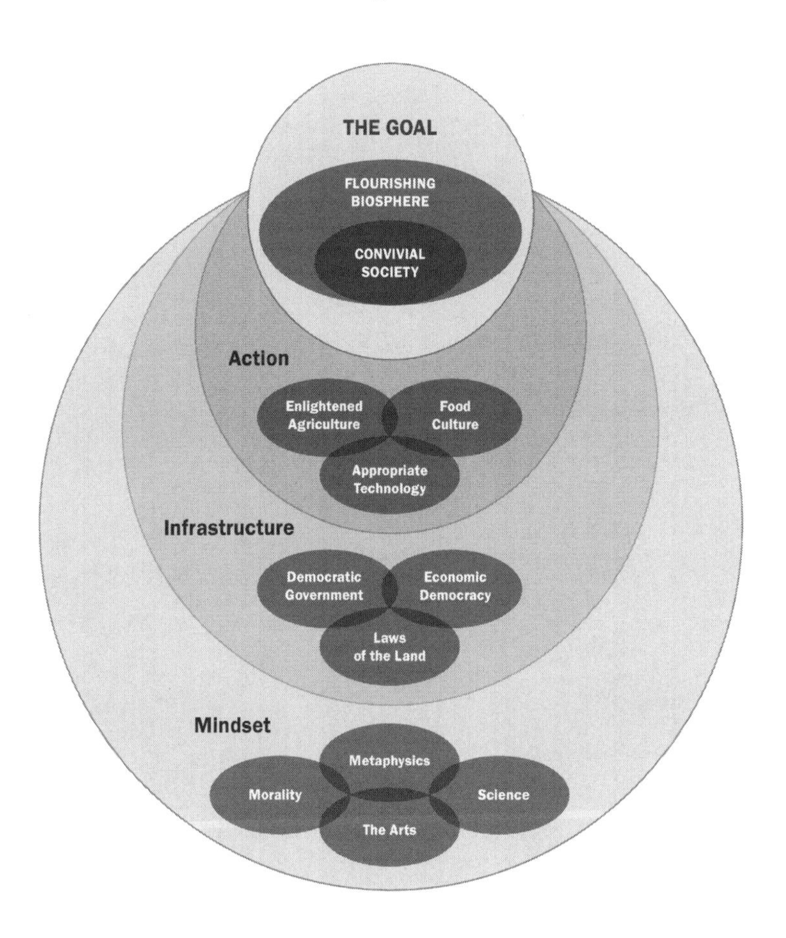

PARI PUBLISHING

Colin Tudge is a biologist by education (Peterhouse, Cambridge) and a writer by inclination and by trade. For some decades he worked for *World Medicine, Farmers Weekly, New Scientist,* and the much-missed Agricultural and Food Research Council, and then had his own science programme on BBC Radio 3 before becoming a full-time author in 1990. In 2010 he co-founded the Oxford Real Farming Conference which in 2021 becomes 'ORFC Global'; and he is now helping to set up the College for Real Farming and Food Culture to develop and disseminate the ideas outlined in this book.

Only the most unthinking farmer, citizen or cook can support the madness of modern farming and the food industry it supplies. The future of our planet and our children depends on an urgent re-evaluation of practices from seed to plate and the science, economy, beliefs and philosophy that have driven us to the edge of self-destruction. Colin Tudge, one of our great rural thinkers, argues with eloquence, love and an extraordinary depth of knowledge for a better path, and, with inspirational hope, asserts that such a renaissance is do-able. Let's get on and do it.

Guy Singh Watson, organic farmer, founder-creator of Riverford Organic Farmers

The Great Re-think *is more than a book. It is a beautiful blueprint for a new renaissance. Colin Tudge has written a simple, succinct and clear guidebook for durable and regenerative culture for now and for the future generations. It is a book of profound wisdom as well as a practical roadmap. At the time when humanity is confronted with multiple crises, such as loss of biodiversity, soil erosion, climate catastrophe and narrow nationalism we need to head to the insights of this timely book.*

Satish Kumar, founder of Schumacher College, editor emeritus of *Resurgence & Ecologist*

Unquestionably, we need a great and urgent rethink of how we organize human affairs for our own wellbeing and for planetary health, starting with our food and farming systems but radiating out to just about everything else. Colin Tudge has long been in the forefront of this work, and in his new book he joins the dots between farming, nutrition, politics, science, economics, philosophy and religion in an easy and accessible style. The challenges are enormous, but with Colin as our tour guide directing attention to where it needs to go, they start to seem a little less daunting. Read his book, then get to work!

Chris Smaje, small farmer in Somerset, UK, for the last 15 years, previously a university-based social scientist at the University of Surrey and Goldsmiths College, University of London

Hope is rare. Clear-sighted, exhaustively audited hope, presented as an immensely accessible, congenial conversation, is unheard of outside the covers of The Great Re-Think. *A vital, compelling and urgent read for everyone who wants to stave off despair, who wants to be useful, and who knows that the future is far too important to be left to the politicians.*

Charles Foster, author of *Being a Beast*, visiting professor of the Oxford University Law Faculty

As governments the world over seek to put profit before both people and planet Colin Tudge offers us a realistic, just and humane alternative which could deliver a secure and convivial future. Here is a programme for survival which we can and should all sign up to. Excellent, as always!

Tim Gorringe, emeritus professor of Theology at Exeter University and also a smallholder

Colin Tudge offers a fresh way of thinking, being and doing to shape hopeful, viable, and humane futures. Read to survive.

Ziauddin Sardar, writer, renowned futurist, editor of *Critical Muslim*

To rethink how as a society we restoratively feed ourselves is to examine and reimagine how we think, act and interact with all of life. What Colin has served us is a potential roadmap into the future, a positive legacy to adopt and a call to action.

Rebecca Hosking MBE, former television producer turned farmer—a leading exponent of agroecological agriculture

For our species, 'believing is seeing'; and where Colin Tudge excels is enabling us to crack open deadly belief systems so that we can see the new emerging—precisely what the world needs now.

Frances Moore Lapé, author of *Diet for a Small Planet*, a Right Livelihood Laureate

Colin Tudge is especially skilled at interpreting and setting science in the wider context of our civilisation. He is a biologist who has spent decades explaining scientific topics to non-specialist audiences.... In The Great Rethink *he takes bridge rebuilding a step further into the world of metaphysics, essentially the study of mind, including our understandings of reality, and importantly what we do not know and can never know. In this respect,* The Great Rethink *is a work of philosophy as well as of anxiety at the current trajectory of Earth mismanagement.*

Patricia Racher, *Ecopolitics Today*

First published in Italy in 2021 by Pari Publishing Sas.

A catalogue record for this book
is available from the British Library

ISBN 978-88-95604-34-3

Book and cover design: Andrea Barbieri
Cover graphic: Andrea Barbieri, based on an idea by Alex Towler

Printed and bound in Italy

Finito di stampare nel mese di dicembre 2020
presso Universal Books, Rende (CS)
per conto di Pari Publishing Sas di Eleanor F. Peat & C.

Pari Publishing
Via Tozzi 7, 58045 Pari (GR), Italy
www.paripublishing.com

Table of Contents

Acknowledgements

To be truly fair and accurate I would have to acknowledge everyone who has helped to shape my ideas throughout my life including many excellent teachers at school and university and especially the admirable Miss Crichton (felicitously named!) at primary school who had a true sense of values and became a Christian missionary; and quite a few at Dulwich College, especially Doug Hillyer and Brian Jones; and the scores—hundreds?—of doctors, scientists, farmers, and miscellaneous academics I have interviewed and sometimes become friends with over 50 years of science journalism with various magazines and the BBC. Outstanding among these were Profs Bob Orskov, who I knew in his days at the Rowett Institute in Aberdeen and then at the James Huttton Institute; and the late and much missed Prof Martin Wolfe, first at the old Plant Breeding Institute at Cambridge and then at Wakelyns Farm, Suffolk, which features in this book. Also to Graham Harvey who alerted me (and the world) to the advantages of pasture feeding and suggested twelve years or so ago that we—Graham, me, and my wife Ruth West—should set up the Oxford Real Farming Conference which now attracts more than 1200 delegates and has given rise to many new initiatives.

Over the past few years of writing this book I have also been particularly indebted to the Revd Peter Dewey and Profs Tim Gorringe and John Lennox, and to Dr Timothy Bartel, for insights into many aspects of Christianity; to Rabbis Jonathan Wittenberg and Jeffery Newman; and to my former *New Scientist* colleague and Muslim scholar Ziauddin Sardar. Friends with various areas of expertise who read various passages of this book and offered cogent comments both on style and content include (in alphabetical order) Georgina Ferry; Mary Franklin, who has helped in many ways, over endless hours; Harry Greenfield; Jamie Hartzell; Rebecca Hazell; Becks Hosking; Barrie Lees; Peter Marsh; John Meadley; and Hugo Spowers. Right now I am heavily engaged in conversation with geneticist and farmer John Letts, who is re-thinking arable farming, than which nothing is more important or in greater need of reform; and with conservation biologist Ian Rappell, with whom I hope to be working on our College for Real Farming and Food Culture, not least in collaboration with Ben Rawlence and Libby Pearson at the newly-founded Black Mountains College in Brecon; and I continue to learn from Tom Curtis about the politics and intricacies of land ownership and management. I am indebted also in various ways to all the trustees and executives of the Real Farming Trust, who include some of the above, plus Robert Fraser, Clare Horrell, Francesca Price, and Samrawit Mariam. I am also particularly grateful to Martin Stanley for all his help and advice over the past decade and more. Thanks to you all—with the usual disclaimer on your behalf; that they don't all agree with everything I say and are not responsible for my mistakes.

I owe a special debt to Maureen Doolan, Eleanor Peat, and Andrea Barbieri at the Pari Center, in Tuscany. Pari promotes big and important ideas in all fields in various ways and I feel privileged to be published by them.

Finally, I am eternally grateful to my wife, Ruth, without whose love and support I would never have contemplated this book, let alone written it. She, more than anybody, has made the Oxford Real Farming Conference a major presence and also (with Pete Riley) helped to set up the All-Party Parliamentary Group on Agroecology, and is a co-founder of the Real Farming Trust, which oversees all our endeavours. Writing on the whole is a solitary trade but this particular endeavour is embedded very sociably in what is now a worldwide, highly eclectic movement that truly has the potential to make the world a better place.

Colin Tudge, Wolvercote, Oxford, July 2020

Preface:
WHAT IS AND WHAT COULD BE

We should therefore act on the basis of global interest with clear understanding of the oneness of humanity: we must develop a big 'we'. That way, we can develop a genuine sense of the well-being of all.

The Dalai Lama May 22, 2020: a letter in anticipation of World Localization Day June 21, 2020

No problem can be solved from the same consciousness that created it.

Albert Einstein (1879-1955) Physicist

You never change things by fighting the existing reality. To change something, build a new model that makes the existing model obsolete.

Buckminster Fuller (1895-1983) American architect and seer

EVEN AT THIS LATE HOUR, with the world warming and the waters rising and popes, scientists, and armies of activists queuing up to tell us that we'll be lucky to survive the present century in a tolerable state, humanity and our fellow creatures could still be looking forward to a long and glorious future. Ours is a young species, versatile and genetically various, and our descendants should still be here in a million years' time—personally fulfilled, at peace, and in the company of wild creatures of wondrous diversity and in great abundance.

As things are, of course, for many millions of people life is already intolerable—it could hardly be worse—and we are losing species of all kinds almost by the hour. The particular horrors of 2020—Covid-19, racial turbulence, the rise and rise of autocratic governments from the US to China and Russia, and from India to Brazil—are only symptoms of far deeper ills.

To turn things around we, humanity, need to re-think everything that we do and take for granted, from first principles: what we aspire to—what are we trying to achieve?; how we do things; how we organize our affairs; what we think is good and bad; what we value. Where necessary—not always, but often—we need to re-structure and re-build. Overall, we—the world—need transformation; metamorphosis and metanoia; nothing less than a Renaissance—re-birth—even more deep-rooted and far-reaching than the Renaissance of the 14th to the 16th centuries that brought the European Middle Ages to a close (more or less, for better or worse).

Furthermore: whereas the Renaissance of past centuries was led by bankers, intellectuals, and artists—who nowadays we might call 'the Establishment'—the Renaissance we need now must be led and driven by us, people-at-large, Ordinary Joes and Jos. We have to believe in ourselves—to recognize that an ordinary human being is a good thing to be; and then we have to do what needs doing. The present powers-that-be are an oligarchy of big governments, corporates, financiers, and their chosen intellectual and expert advisers, and the oligarchs see it as their role in life to defend the status quo, by whatever means are deemed necessary. The Renaissance we need now should be as painless as we can make it and in that sense conservative but it must inescapably be radical, in the proper sense of the word; get down to the roots. Oligarchs don't do radical, except to purge whatever gets in their way: drain wetlands and burn forests; demolish monasteries and temples; close down agencies that challenge the orthodoxy and the hierarchy; assassinate those they call 'dissidents.'

Clearly, the task before us is huge—and is never-ending: a perpetual journey. Yet there is good news. Many millions of individuals and many thousands of organizations in all societies all around the world are already in tune with what's needed, and are already on the case. Always we need more good ideas and more research but already there is enough good thinking and expertise and good will out there to form a critical mass and to bring about the necessary change. What's lacking now is coordination—more networking; a network of networks—which is now made easier, not to say possible, by modern IT. It surely can be done.

I don't presume to offer a prescription for the next million years but I hope this book may help to provide a preliminary agenda; at least a sketch of the Renaissance to come which we, individually and collectively, must bring about.

Part I

THE NATURE OF THE TASK

1

WHAT'S THE PROBLEM? THE HUMAN CONDITION AND THE STATE OF THE WORLD

ABOVE ALL I WANT THIS BOOK TO BE POSITIVE—to suggest ways forward; to show, as far as now is known, why we should and could be planning for the next million years and not, as now, wondering if we can get to the end of the century in a tolerable state. But we do need to know what we are up against, the size and nature of the task, so here is a brief check-list of the main issues.

Can we produce enough food?

The United Nations tells us that out of the present world population of around 7.8 billion almost a billion are chronically undernourished while another two billion or so suffer from 'diseases of affluence'—too much food, though often with too little of the right things. Notably, the world population of diabetics, mostly diet-related, is now thought to exceed 400 million—greater, by far, than the total population of the United States.

Unfortunately, the orthodox responses both to world hunger and to excess are horribly misconceived and so too are the solutions proposed by some of the world's most influential food lobbies. Thus in 2009 The Food and Agriculture Organization of the United Nations (FAO) produced a discussion document called 'How to Feed the World in 2050' in which they suggested that the world will need to produce 50% more food by 2050 to keep pace with rising human numbers and rising demand; and in 2011 a 'Foresight' report from the British government called 'The Future of Food and Farming' made the same claim. Indeed this idea has apparently become embedded in the psyche both of governments, which seek above all to achieve economic 'growth'; and of the food industry, which is always seeking to expand. Some since have upped the ante and declared that we will need to double present food output by 2100. Furthermore, it seems to be accepted in high places that this can be achieved only by high tech on a vast scale—big machines, industrial chemistry, biotech, robots and remote sensing, and whatever else may be lurking in the pipeline, each innovation to be welcomed as a world-saver until it all starts to go wrong, and another technology is pulled from the wizard's sleeve to correct, up to a point, the shortcomings of the one before.

But all this is the most dreadful, destructive nonsense. High-tech, high-input agriculture geared to production, production, production is a prime cause of ecological disaster and of poverty and injustice. It is also unnecessary—for in truth, as Hans Herren of the Millennium Institute, Washington, points out, ***the world already produces enough to feed 14 billion people.*** This is about twice as much food as we really need and at least 40% more than we should ever need. You can work this out for yourself on the back of an envelope. For the FAO website tells us that the world now produces around 2.5 billion tonnes of cereal a year. One tonne of cereal provides enough macronutrient (food energy and protein) to sustain three people for a year, so 2.5 billion tonnes is enough for 7.5 billion people. But although cereals (mainly wheat, rice, and maize) are by far the most important crops worldwide they nonetheless provide us with only half our food. The other half (including most of the essential micronutrients) comes from pulses (beans, peas, etc.); root and stem tubers (notably potatoes); non-cereal seeds including nuts; fruit and vegetables; meat, eggs, and dairy products; and fish, prawns, etc. In total, then, we produce enough for 7.5 x 2 = 15 billion people. Professor Herren's estimate if anything is conservative.

Of course we need agriculture to be productive but if we really care about the future then emphasis must shift from quantity to quality, and to provenance and the means of production. Farming above all needs to be kinder to people and animals, and far more wildlife-friendly. We need in fact '***Enlightened Agriculture***'—farming that is actually designed to provide us all with good food, as opposed to making a few people rich (chapter 6). Neither do we need to be particularly austere—for ***there is a perfect, one-to-one correspondence between Enlightened Agriculture, sound nutrition, and great cooking*** (chapter 7). Thus we need only to emulate the world's finest cuisines—which surely is no great hardship. Neither, on a significant point of detail, do we need to be vegan.

Above all else, food and farming are the things we absolutely have to get right—the *sine qua non*, as the lawyers say—and present strategies are taking us in quite the wrong direction. If we farmed properly and cooked accordingly we need have no food problems, and much else that is wrong with the world would be put right in passing. But, as so often seems to be the case, we do need to do more or less the complete opposite of what the powers-that-be now recommend.

But can all this really be true? After all, the world population has almost quadrupled since 1920—within the lifetimes of many people who are still on Earth. Numbers have increased by about 1.5 billion since 2000—an amount not far short of the total world population in 1900. Why should the numbers not just keep on growing? The present stats provide some comfort—but what of the future? Do we—can we—really produce enough for everyone who is likely to be born?

The answer ought to be 'Yes—easily.' For modern demographic studies as opposed to the musings of yesteryear suggest that although some further increase is inevitable, the world population is reaching a peak. It is however an unfortunate fact that the people with most influence in the world tend to believe whatever they find most expedient, however out-dated. The economy is geared to production, production, and more production, so they latch on to the statistics that seem to show that this is necessary.

Human numbers

Alarm bells were first rung in earnest at the turn of the 18th and 19th century with a gloomy cleric turned economist called Thomas Robert Malthus (1766-1834), known cosily as 'Bob.' Specifically Malthus pointed out that while human numbers increase exponentially, agricultural output can increase only arithmetically. Exponential growth means a small *percentage* increase each year, so that as the population grows the actual number of people added each year is larger and larger. Arithmetical growth implies a fixed amount of increase each year. Sooner or later exponential growth must outstrip arithmetical growth and then the food supply will be inadequate and the population must crash. This was a dire prediction indeed but, based as it was on the logic of maths, it seemed inescapable, for maths, it was and is assumed, can never lie (but see chapter 13). This belief was taken to justify the indifference of many people of wealth to the appalling suffering of the poor. For as Ebenezer Scrooge remarked in Charles Dickens's *A Christmas Carol* of 1843:

> *If they would rather die... they had better do it, and decrease the surplus population.*

With similar reasoning, as the Irish journalist and historian Brian Inglis recorded in *Poverty and the Industrial Revolution* (1971), the English government more or less refused to help the Irish peasants who starved in vast numbers in the potato famine of the 1840s. Material assistance would only postpone the inevitable, the thinking went. It would also encourage laziness—which has long been a standard excuse for not helping people. In present-day Britain, it still is. Benefits have been cut to encourage people who can barely get out of the door to get on their bikes and find work. Britain is not the worst by any means but by any worthwhile standards much of its official policy these past few centuries has been cruel, and to a large extent still is.

Charles Darwin (1809-1882) was profoundly influenced by Malthus, at least in his biology. In his seminal *Origin of Species* of 1859 Darwin observed that what applies to human populations must apply to all living creatures. All seem bound to reproduce beyond the carrying capacity of their environments. There is, therefore, he said, a constant 'struggle for existence' or a 'struggle for life.' All are obliged to compete for the inevitably limited resources from conception to the compost heap. But no two kittens in a litter or peas in a pod are quite identical. So, inevitably, some individuals will be better adapted to the conditions than others—and the ones that are best adapted will be the most likely to survive and reproduce in their turn. This is the essence of one of the most important insights of modern biology and indeed in all of science: ***natural selection***. Competition for inevitably limited resources plus natural variation led to what the philosopher Herbert Spencer (1820-1903) later summarized as the 'survival of the fittest,' where 'fittest' means 'most suited,' as in 'fit for purpose.' Darwin's younger contemporary Alfred Russel Wallace (1823-1913) arrived at the same idea by a somewhat different route and is often given less credit than he deserves; and, even earlier, the forester and landowner Patrick Matthew had clearly grasped the principle. But Darwin thought of it first or at least was first equal and was certainly the first to explain the idea clearly and in depth, in *Origin of Species.*

Natural selection seemed to explain what had long been a huge problem both for biologists and for theologians (and biologists in Darwin's day commonly had a foot in both camps). Why are there so many different creatures, and how and why are they all so well adapted to the places where they live? Some—including many or most biologists—simply assumed that God had made them that way, as recorded in *Genesis.* A few invoked some form of evolution. But no one before Darwin and Wallace had suggested a plausible mechanism by which evolution could occur, and scientists do like ideas to be plausible.

Darwin was a modest man and a cautious scientist and in *Origin of Species,* he suggested that natural selection was probably not the only mechanism of evolution. He also stressed, particularly in later books, the importance of cooperation in nature. But natural selection is at least a major force in evolution and competition emerged as the great and necessary spur; competition made necessary by the tendency of all populations to out-grow their resources. The ideas of Malthus were already popular in the mid-19th century and Darwin's endorsement boosted his reputation still further. Malthus seemed justified both by his own apparently inexorable logic and by Darwin's biology—the added kudos of *bona fide* science. Many intellectuals of all stripes took the ideas of Darwin and Malthus as gospel, the irrefutable truth, and many still do. The notion that people at large out-breed resources was, and is, also politically convenient. People have only themselves to blame if there are shortages. The economic philosophy of neoliberalism as discussed in chapter 10 is rooted in what I call the 'metadarwinian' idea that all creatures including human beings must compete, compete, compete for Earth's limited resources. That, we are told, is just the way life is.

Darwin in daily life and in his politics was a kindly and liberal gentleman, indulgent father, a vigorous opponent of slavery, and unofficial financial adviser to the local villagers. Wallace was of humbler birth, self-taught and modest to a fault—in many ways a model human being.

But their idea of natural selection with its stress on competition is used to justify the foulest of right-wing politics, and an economic system that threatens the survival of the whole world. Their success has also served to give Malthus a far higher profile than he deserves. Many people in high places still take his ideas as a given, based as they are in what seems like inexorable logic and ratified, we are told, by science.

Yet, it seems, Malthus was wrong. For, modern studies show that most animal (including human) populations do not rise and rise until they crash. This does apparently happen in some creatures, like lemmings and blow-flies, but in many creatures there are mechanisms of one kind or another that tend to reduce birth rate and hence reduce population growth before disaster strikes. Many birds, for example, simply lay fewer eggs when their habitats feel too crowded. We human beings, we like to think, plan our life strategies more consciously. Whatever the mechanisms at work, it seems that most populations of most animals follow a 'sigmoid'—S-shaped—curve. Numbers do rise rapidly after a slow start, in exponential fashion, for a time—but then the *percentage* rate of growth begins to tail off. So it was that in 1974 when the United Nations held the world's first ever Global Food Conference, after a series of famines in Asia and Africa, world numbers were rising at almost two per cent per year which means, because of compound interest, that numbers were on course to double every 40 years. Since numbers already stood at around four billion it seemed we would reach eight billion by 2010. If the trend continued there would be 16 billion by 2050 and well over 30 billion by the end of century. As we have seen, the world should be able to accommodate 10 billion-plus but no technophilic zealot in his or her wildest dreams could suppose that we could manage 30 billion. Long before we got anywhere near—sometime around the mid-century in fact—we would surely experience Malthusian meltdown, the mother of all dystopias.

But things have not turned out like that. By 2010 we were up to about seven billion; a lot, but a billion short of the 1970s prediction. A decade on from 2010, we still have not reached eight billion. Numbers are still increasing more rapidly than ever (because of compound interest) but the percentage growth rate is slowing. In some countries, including Italy and the UK, *actual* numbers would now be going down were it not for immigration (which in the short term at least should be welcomed because, as outlined below, falling populations cause problems of their own).

Human numbers are still rising nonetheless so that until recently the

UN was predicting that the population would reach 10 or 11 billion before it plateaued, somewhere around the end of this century. Yet some thinkers have been doubting for some time whether that is really the case. Thus in 2010 the British journalist Fred Pearce wrote in *Peoplequake* that numbers were unlikely to rise even to 9 billion. Latest research seems to show that he was right. Thus, on July 14, 2020 the British medical journal *The Lancet* published a report by the Norwegian Professor scientist Stein Emil Vollset of the University of Washington and his colleagues which predicted that human numbers will peak before the end of this century and then fall rapidly—in some countries by more than 50 per cent. Thus Japan's population peaked at 128 million in 2017 but seems likely to fall to below 53 million by 2100. China could peak at 1.4 billion in 2024—and then plummet to around 730 million by the end of the century. Italy reached 61 million in 2017 but is on course to fall to around 28 million. And so on.

There is nothing sinister about this. It's just that women are choosing to have fewer children, and a very small tweak in the statistics makes all the difference. Thus, for one reason or another, whatever the circumstances, not everyone chooses or is able to reproduce and because of this a population does not generally increase if women on average have fewer than 2.1 to 2.3 children. If each woman has 1.9 children on average then the population starts to fall remarkably rapidly—at least within decades. Thus, family planning policies that aim to reduce population in the long term do not need to be draconian. We merely need to think broadly and to be patient.

There is one further—enormous—serendipity. ***The strategies that curb population growth most effectively are all benign.*** The methods that have sometimes been tried—encouraging conflict, spreading disease, allowing people to starve, draconian, forced family planning, or out-and-out genocide—are not only obviously foul, but are also counter-productive. People tend to respond to sudden set-back by having more children (which surely in part accounts for the baby boom that followed World War II), and any attempt at genocide that falls short of total wipe-out leaves a residual population that tends to nurse a perfectly justified resentment against their conquerors that may endure for centuries or in effect forever. Such discontented populations are found the world over (the Kurds, the Basques, the Republican Irish, the Maoris, and so on).

The methods that really do work include good obstetrics and childcare, so that people can be as certain as life can be that their children will live—and do not feel they need to have five or six children just to ensure that one or two pull through. Reproductively speaking human beings are natural 'K-strategists'—like orangutans, elephants, rhinos and eagles (and in contrast to mice, lions, or sparrows). They produce only a few children but take good care of them. Huge families in large part are a sign of biological disarray. Then again, if people have financial security—especially pensions—they don't need children just to take care of them in old age. Demonstrably, too, if women are given more opportunities to do more things in life—if motherhood is not their only route to status—then mostly they opt to have fewer children. Only bigots, mountebanks, and religious zealots oppose women's liberation which, after all, in the long term is good for men as well as for women. (Religion is very necessary as I will argue in chapter 14 but as most religious people agree, zealotry is a menace). Safe, effective, and freely available contraception is hugely important too, not to say vital. Religious opposition to it is bad biology (see below) and also, I suggest, bad theology. In short, all the measures that really do encourage smaller families are surely desirable in their own right. Each is an aspect of what 'progress' ought to mean. Their role in family planning and ultimately in curbing population growth can almost be seen as a bonus.

As numbers fall we can begin to ask, what would be the optimum size for the human population? How large, or small, do we want it to be? A few years ago I put this very question to leading thinkers when I worked on a programme on human population for BBC Radio 3. Most suggested somewhere between one and two billion people—a number we could get down to within a few centuries if we followed the currently projected demographic curve. The one outstanding exception was the Californian ecologist Michael Soule, who suggested 300 million as the desirable goal. After all, he said, this was the probable global population at the time of Christ—which was also a time of enormous cultural diversity; none more so. Paradoxically, indeed, there may be *more* cultural diversity with smaller numbers. Crowds tend to become homogenous.

Some, though, suggest that to think along such lines is to be anti-humanity. How dare anyone suggest that some people should not be born? Some religious zealots have suggested (though surely with very little textual evidence) that God *wants* us to breed maximally to supply Him with more souls. However, while a world population of around one billion should easily be able to survive for another million years, and then draw breath and think about the following million, a population of 10 billion-plus would be hard-pressed to survive for much more than another 100 years in a tolerable form. This should be eminently possible but in practice we are already wrecking the world with only seven-and-a-bit billion. Ten billion souls for 100 years means one trillion person-years (where one trillion equals one thousand billion). One billion souls for a million years is a thousand trillion person years. In short, the human species will give itself a far better crack of the whip if we spread ourselves out through time. Our fellow creatures have no chance at all unless we do.

Unfortunately, not everyone agrees with this kind of analysis or the conclusions it leads to. As we all know, many Roman Catholics in particular oppose contraception—which, they say, thwarts God's purpose. This among other things is seriously bad biology for a prime function of sex among intelligent animals is not simply to produce babies but to reinforce bonding—which is vital in those species in which both parents contribute to childcare. If God is indeed the benign Creator then he surely had this in mind. Family planning in a state of nature is taken care of mainly by *lactational amenorrhea*. Lactating women on low-calorie diets cannot conceive.

Probably even more significantly, for one reason or another, *governments* from time to time become pro-natalist (encouraging childbirth) including, in recent memory, Tanzania (under Julius Nyerere), Romania (under Nicolae Ceausescu), and France. The women who in China these past few decades have been encouraged (though 'encouraged' is a euphemism) to have only one child or none at all are, to a large extent, the daughters and granddaughters of the women who under Mao Zedong were encouraged to have as many children as possible—to help Mao build an army of 100 million soldiers. Right now Vladimir Putin is rewarding big families as he attempts in effect to re-create the USSR, or something very like it. Russian women with half a dozen children or more can expect free holidays by the Black Sea. As in all human affairs, too, fashion and the kudos that comes with being fashionable play a huge part in determining family size. In the US before World War II, smart people had two children or fewer. Only hillbillies had more. But when the Catholic Kennedy family rose to prominence big families were back in vogue.

However: although it seems highly desirable and indeed essential to reduce human numbers (by benign means) this is no panacea, for there are no panaceas. It raises problems, too, at least in the short term—and governments and big business tend to be geared to the short term. These problems are surely soluble but they do need to be addressed.

Life, death, and the problem of falling numbers

For the world as a whole total human numbers are less important than total consumption—and as the American ecologist Paul Ehrlich pointed out in the 1970s the model Californian family with Mom, Pop, and two abundantly nourished children consumes far more than the average Bangladeshi village. Yet the global economy is geared, still—or indeed ever more so—to greater and greater consumption. As argued in chapter 10, we need to develop a minimalist economy: ask how little we really need for a satisfying life, rather than seeking obsessively to maximize our own material possessions.

It seems to be widely accepted too (although it is not politically acceptable to say so) that almost a billion go hungry because there are too many people in the world—that there is, as Scrooge said, a 'surplus population.' Like so much that is taken to be obvious in the present world, this simply is not true. What is true is that in a maximally competitive economy like the one we have now some people are bound to miss out however large or small the population may be because in all competitions there are losers as well as winners. Even if we did encourage the population to dwindle to around two billion some would still go hungry if we persisted with the present economy and the mindset behind it.

Falling birth rate raises problems too—especially when coupled, as now, with longer life-spans. With fewer children and more oldies the average age of the whole population must increase. In Japan the birth rate has fallen to 1.4 children per woman and by 2040 on present trends 35% of the population will be over 65. Already in Italy nearly a quarter are over 65. Fewer children means fewer young adults a few years' later which means a smaller workforce—all trying to maintain a population in which more and more people are too old for a full days' work (while the young spend more and more time in full-time education). Life in Britain was much easier to organize when men retired at 65 and, commonly, died before they were 70, or not much after. Now 80-plus is the norm and the Queen must grow tired of signing telegrams for the growing cohort of Britain's centenarians (currently more than 14,500).

Fear of a dwindling workforce is a prime reason for government pro-natalism. As Fred Pearce points out in *Peoplequake* countries with ageing populations would do well to *encourage* immigration from countries that are still producing more and more children, whose populations are skewed towards the young. You don't have to be born in France or Russia in order to live and work there—or to feel very Russian or very French. Chinese children in Newcastle have impeccable Geordie accents. Britain, of course, did encourage its commonwealth citizens to come to the home country in the 1950s and '60s although recent governments have been trying to kick them out again (and their children too).

In the long term, as a matter of urgency, we need a different attitude to work. Work should in general be made more agreeable—and seen not as a burden to be displaced as quickly as possible by 'leisure' but as a vital component of a fulfilled life. As argued in chapter 5 the role of technology should not be to replace human beings with robots but simply or primarily to take the grind out of human endeavour. More generally we need to take the heat out of the economy—to move away from the idea that it is necessary and virtuous to maximize wealth and to work harder and harder in order to do so. Perhaps in particular we need to find more ways of employing people usefully and enjoyably who are past the first flush of youth. I continue to type away happily at the age of 77 but at this stage of life I would not fancy being a plumber or a lorry driver (although the latter, I believe, would be against the law. Sometimes the law is sensible). We need to find ways to engage people usefully who can no longer follow their main profession, and to make use of their skills, at least for a few hours a week.

Oldies are definitely a good thing—on the whole we don't have the awful ambition and ego of youth—but (and I speak as one who is nearer the end than the beginning) I do think we need a more civilized and sensible attitude to death. I for one would far rather shuffle off this mortal coil while I am still more or less in control, than spend a decade in a 'rest home,' going steadily downhill, and I know many others of my kind of age who feel the same, including some who are in rest homes. A well-regulated death is not the worst thing that can happen to people, not by any means. Great thinker and humanitarian that he was, Dylan Thomas was surely wrong to urge his father to rage against the dying of the light. We *ought* to go gentle into the good night, with minimum disturbance to those we leave behind; and to make it easier or possible for people who want to, to do so. Many other societies have had a much more enlightened attitude to death than we have.

The natural, mainly benignly-inspired levelling off of human numbers ought to be hailed as the greatest benison for humankind, and indeed for the whole world, in modern history. The Malthusian apocalypse, which once seemed inevitable, now seems illusory. Such is the mentality of modern politicians, however, that the ones I have heard so far seem to care more about the short-term economic difficulties. If we need leaders at all (chapter 9) then we need them to take serious things seriously.

Disease

I am second to none in my admiration for modern, high-tech medicine, and for the people who make it work. Contrast modern childbirth with the awful traumas described in Victorian novels. Many and perhaps most people now reading this would surely be dead were it not for vaccination. Gravestones in churchyards around Britain commonly record the deaths of half a dozen children, and hint at the grief of their helpless parents. I think it likely that two of my own three children would no longer be with us if it weren't for modern antibiotics. At the time of writing (April 2020) there is no vaccine against Covid-19 and perhaps there never will be one that is both effective and safe but goodness knows where we would be without modern intensive care.

Even without modern medicine the world population might still be roughly as big as it is now but only if people had much larger families than is now usual, and endured many more deaths along the way. That we can now *expect* our children to survive childhood is a wonderful step forward. That is true progress.

High tech medicine tends to be expensive—yet again prompting many of the world's most influential people to argue that all countries must strive above all to be rich, and to focus on 'economic growth' measured as GDP (chapter 10). To be sure, worldwide, the greatest cause of ill health by far is poverty and injustice: poor food, poor hygiene, a grinding job in a sweatshop or a mine or—even worse—unemployment. But high tech and wealth *per se* are not the answer. After all, a great deal of ill health, mental as well as physical, is caused by the stress and excesses of modern, high-tech living. Some diseases are *aided* in their evil course by high-tech. Covid-19 became a world problem almost overnight in early 2020 because of high-speed mass transport—and the same applies to animal diseases. More generally, there is no simple relationship between accountable wealth and human wellbeing. The US is by far the richest country in the world *per capita* and spends the most on healthcare, and yet ranks only 35th in the world's league table of healthiness—behind Cuba (30th) and Costa Rica (33rd). Spain is top of the global health league and the UK is 19th. The United Arab Emirates are $46^{th.}$.

Often, too, as outlined in chapter 5, the simplest technologies can often achieve the most. Millions of children in poor countries die from infant diarrhoea yet many could be saved with simple replacement of electrolyte-balanced fluids. Treatments to save a child's eyesight may cost a few pennies. But, often, the money is not spent. In general, far more is spent on the chronic irritations of the rich than on life-saving measures for the poor.

In the end, though, we should not set our sights too high. Disorders of one kind or another will always be with us. Perfection is too much to ask for. The eugenicists of the 19th and early 20th centuries sought perfection but the endeavour was and is a huge mistake. So too was and is the mid-20th century idea that we should attempt to create a germ-free bubble for ourselves, spraying our homes with disinfectant, as ads on day-time television still encourage young mums to do. Of course in times of emergency, as in the Covid-19 pandemic, special measures of hygiene may well be necessary, or indeed vital. But in normal times we need to see ourselves not as isolated beings warding off the world at large but as part of an ecosystem, in which microbes are key players, whose relationship with us is mostly symbiotic. We *need* the small creatures that we try so hard to kill, or most of them. Only a few are rogues—and they, for the most part, are kept in check by the good guys, as long as we don't kill off the good guys as we attack the baddies. Truly modern nutritional and agricultural science are in line with this idea. In agriculture, the same principle applies to weeds; not simply to be obliterated but by and large to be adapted to.

More generally, we should not seek to avoid all stress for the mind and body are evolved to cope with challenges. Our bodies are damaged by obsessive cleanliness: the Devil finds work for an idle immune system. Our minds are damaged by too much leisure and in particular by the forced leisure of involuntary unemployment. Yet at the other extreme, we do need to avoid the stress of overwork and the anxiety that goes with it. Worse of all perhaps are the awful void of loneliness or the burning sense of social injustice. Above all, as social creatures—indeed as *eu*social ('super-social') creatures (chapter 3) —we need *each other*. We need to feel that we belong, that we are truly members of a society, of a community, and that we, individually, *matter*. This point is expanded not least by John Macmurray in *Persons in Relation* (1961); by David Jenkins (and Rebecca Jenkins) in *Free to Believe* (1991); by Satish Kumar in *You Are, Therefore I Am* (2002); and Sue Gerhardt in *Why Love Matters* (2003). Karl Marx coined the term 'alienation' to describe the utterly destructive sense that what we do as individuals is of no consequence, and that we ourselves are of no account. Racism, sexism, social snobbery, bullying, and what Hamlet called 'the proud man's contumely'—the sense of being looked down upon—foment such feelings. Nothing is more erosive.

In short, medicine in all its forms (traditional as well as high-tech) is indispensable but it is only a part of what is needed to keep us in good fettle. In the cause of good health it should be seen primarily as the back-up.

Poverty, inequality, injustice

Humanity is still dogged by poverty: the sheer inability to buy even the necessities of life, in a world where nothing is free, except perhaps, for the time being, air. The World Bank suggests that an income of less than $1.90 a day should be classed as 'extreme poverty'—yet 1.3 billion people worldwide live on less than $1.25 and almost three billion, around 40% of the world population, are near to the mark on less than $2.50 per day. UNICEF tells us that 22,000 children die every day simply through poverty. Poverty is rife even in the richest countries including the UK and, even more strikingly, the US.

Nevertheless, we are given to understand, the powers-that-be are on the case. The World Bank tells us that almost 1.1 billion people worldwide were 'lifted out' of extreme poverty (less than $1.90 a day) between 1990 and 2013. The rise of the Chinese middle classes in the early 21st century has been spectacular. So too has the worldwide increase in billionaires, not least in China.

Ever-increasing production, trade, and consumption have brought about this improvement—all made possible, we are told, by the operation of the allegedly 'free' ***'neoliberal'*** market: maximally competitive and increasingly global. Markets are the medium through which trade happens and trade is essential—a key part of being human; enabling us to share the good things the world has to offer. Markets work best when they are conceived and operate simply as mechanisms of exchange and exchange is perceived as symbiosis, an exercise in what biologists call *mutualism*. If the trade is fair then everyone should benefit, and no one should lose out. But in the prevailing economy it is taken for granted that the market is and should be a giant, all-out, ruthless competition in which the aim is not to benefit all the participants and still less to benefit the world as a whole but to *win*. The market, as indeed all life, is reduced to a global dogfight and in a dogfight there are many more losers than winners. Under the neoliberal economy and the mindset that goes with it the rich grow richer and the poor grow poorer, even though the stats can be manipulated to make it seem otherwise. Overall I suggest that ***the modern combination of neoliberal economics and uncritical technophilia are the greatest threat by far to the future of humanity and the biosphere.*** Yet both prevail. More in chapters 10 and 5.

Conflict

In *The Better Angels of Our Nature* (2011), the Canadian psychologist Steven Pinker argues that violence in the world at large, is diminishing—that there is less of it now than in centuries past; and he backs up his thesis with an impressive array of statistics and anecdotes. Well—there does seem to be less delight in public hangings, which surely is a step forward. But World War II is within living memory and was the biggest and most deadly conflict in all of history and as James Meek recorded in *The London Review of Books* (September 6, 2011 p 28), since WW II ended in 1945 more than 300 wars have been fought in

> *Indonesia, Greece, Iran, Vietnam, India, Bolivia, Pakistan, China, Paraguay, Yemen, Madagascar, Israel, Colombia, Costa Rica, Korea, Egypt, Jordan, Lebanon, Syria, Burma, Malaysia, the Philippines, Thailand, Tunisia, Kenya, Taiwan, Morocco, Guatemala, Algeria, Cameroon, Hungary, Haiti, Rwanda, Sudan, Oman, Honduras,*

Nicaragua, Mauritania, Cuba, Venezuela, Iraq, Zaire, Laos, Burundi, Guinea-Bissau, Somalia, France, Cyprus, Zambia, Gabon, the IS, Uganda, Tanzania, Brazil, the Dominican Republic, Peru, Namibia, Chad, Czechoslovakia, Spain, the Soviet Union, Britain, El Salvador, Cambodia, Italy, Sri Lanka, Bangladesh, Chile, Turkey, Ethiopia, Portugal, Mozambique, South Africa, Libya, Afghanistan, Jamaica, Ghana, Ecuador, Zimbabwe, Burkina Faso, Mali, Panama, Romania, Senegal, Kuwait, Armenia, Azerbaijan, Niger, Croatia, Georgia, Bhutan, Djibouti, Moldova, Sierra Leone, Bosnia, Tajikistan, the Congo, Russia, Mexico, Nepal, Albania, Yugoslavia, Eritrea, Macedonia, and Palestine. One crude tally puts the number of dead at well over twenty million.

Surely, too, there have in the history of the world been few more horrible conflicts than in present-day Syria and in Yemen and there are so many other wars in the world at large that the standard media cannot keep up; and there is no historical precedent (is there?) for the mass shootings that are now a regular event in the US. For good measure, government-sponsored torture is still routine in many countries. (Where is it not?)

All this, though, can be seen in an even larger context. In *This Changes Everything* (Simon & Schuster, 2014) Naomi Klein argues that in various hotspots around the world—notably the Middle East—conflict, meaning violence, demonstrably increases with climate change, as desertification and consequent crop failures turn the screws on an already difficult existence. The Earth as a whole is becoming less hospitable to all living creatures including us, and violence is a common and very understandable response—to which 'the authorities' commonly respond with even greater violence (and indeed are apt to get their retaliation in first). Some biologists including Jared Diamond in *Guns, Germs, and Steel* (1997) and *Collapse* (2004), raise the spectre of ***ecological collapse***: that we may trigger processes that are no longer reversible and will continue to unfold until we, and most other existing life-forms, can no longer endure. The corrective mechanisms of Gaia (chapter 4) which would keep the Earth habitable and in large part eminently agreeable are simply being overwhelmed.

Portents of collapse are already evident—including:

Mass extinction

Mass extinction is a fact of evolutionary history—the one we are in now is the sixth in the history of the world. It is estimated that we could lose half of all existing species by the end of this century and, the way things are going, that prediction if anything seems conservative. This would not be the biggest wipe-out the Earth has seen—more than 90% of species disappeared in the Permian-Triassic extinction about 250 million years ago—but it would be by far the most rapid and, unlike the others, this one is caused by *us*.

To put things right we need good science—which mainly means good ecology. We need appropriate action—and in particular to create wild-life-friendly farms and cities, with some significant reapportionment of land. For this to happen we need sympathetic governance and an appropriate economy. Above all we need the right *attitude*. Perhaps above all, I doubt if conservation strategies can ever be truly robust until and unless we restore a sense of the sacred. When our fellow creatures disappear we need to feel not just a mild regret (assuming we notice at all) but dread; that it is, as as Shakespeare's Henry V said in a somewhat different context, 'another fall of man.'

Many people are toiling heroically to save what is left of wild nature and to recover at least some of its former glory but the overall mien of the present *Zeitgeist* is very much against. The science of ecology is still not taken seriously enough. The most powerful governments treat the natural world as a resource— 'natural capital'—that can be valued if at all only for its supply of 'ecosystem services' and are content to leave its fate, like everything else, to the market. Again, it just won't do. More on what will do in chapter 4.

Pollution

Pollution of many kinds is as old as civilization—and indeed is older, for there is soot on the ceilings of prehistoric cave-dwellings. Ice cores from Greenland are laced with effluents from metal works that were flourishing in 'ancient' Greece, Rome, and China. Mediaeval cities were cess-pits and middens. By the mid-19th century London was an industrial city and already had three million people and as Charles Dickens recorded in Book 1 chapter 3 of *Little Dorrit* (1855-57):

> *Miles of close wells and pits of houses, where the inhabitants gasped for air, stretched far away towards every point of the compass. Through the heart of the town a deadly sewer ebbed and flowed, in the place of a fine fresh river.*

The Thames became so fetid in 'the Great Stink' of London in the heatwave of August 1858 that the curtains in the Houses of Parliament had to be soaked in chlorinated lime in a desperate attempt to provide breathable air.

London at least has largely cleaned up its act since then, thanks in the main to Joseph Bazalgette's great sewers of the 1860s and '70s and the Clean Air Act of 1956—but the world as a whole has added many hundreds of novel pollutants to the stew largely based on hydrocarbons (oil) but also on heavy metals, including some that are radioactive. Alarm bells were rung in particular in 1961 by the American biologist Rachel Carson (1907-1964) in *Silent Spring* in which she argued, very convincingly, that the ever-increasing dissemination of oil-based organochlorine pesticides—DDT, dieldrin and the rest—and of organophosphorus pesticides was responsible for mass die-offs of birds and fish. Legislation followed to limit their use (though the USA still *exported* DDT) —but what was, and is, truly depressing was the response from big industry and from the scientists that industry employs to justify its policies. Carson offered no 'hard evidence,' they argued. No definitive *proof*. There have been no controlled trials. Should we sacrifice the advantages of these agents—not just to protect crops but also to destroy the mosquitoes that carry malaria and more—and the lucrative industry that they have given rise to just on a hunch? Such arguments can be made to sound good—'rigorous'—but in truth they are just a stalling tactic. The reason there was no hard evidence was that no one had looked for any, basically because it wasn't in the interests of the producers to look for it. This is one of several ways in which science is seriously corrupted (of which more in chapter 13). Besides, said the industrial scientists of the 1960s, Rachel Carson doesn't have a PhD, merely an MSc, and—the last straw! —she was a woman.

This last argument, mercifully, wouldn't wash today but the more general argument—that the pesticides in question should not be banned because there was no definitive proof of harm—is still wheeled out. Thus in our own times the manufacturers have fought tooth and nail to defend glyphosate, a herbicide used to control weeds; neonicotinoids, the nicotine-derived pesticides that many entomologists believe are largely responsible for the 60%-plus die-off of insects these past few decades and in particular for the 'colony collapse' of honeybees; and, more generally, gmos ('genetically manipulated organisms,' meaning novel crops and livestock produced by genetic engineering). Again, the advocates argue, there is no definitive 'proof' of serious collateral damage and besides—the clincher—neonics and gmos in particular are essential, they claim, if we are to practice the kind of agriculture that we need to feed the world—an argument that is almost totally spurious (chapter 6). Among other things, neonics in Britain are largely employed to kill flea beetles on ever-larger fields of rapeseed but rapeseed is not a vital crop and neither rape nor any other crop should be grown in vast monocultures, as is now the norm. In fact, neonics to control flea beetles on industrial rape are yet another example of ever-more fancy technologies that are devised to ameliorate what in effect is malpractice. But what the hell! Industrial-scale rapeseed may not really be necessary but it is certainly lucrative (so long as the economy remains as it is) despite the cost of pesticide (and fertilizer and combine harvesters)—and what else matters?

Indeed, the response of the people with the most power in the world (governments, corporates, financiers) is almost always too feeble by half. Who cannot be aware, by now, of the damage wrought by plastics? According to *Surfers Against Sewage* plastics account for 60-90% of all the debris found in the oceans. There's an average of 150 plastic bottles on every mile of Britain's beaches. We may find sun-cream bottles and abandoned flip-flops on every beach in the world, including those in the far, uninhabitable reaches. Many of the pebbles on the beach turn out to be made of hard plastics worn smooth by the tides, like real pebbles. Every year plastic kills 100,000 marine mammals and turtles and a million seabirds. *All* marine turtles and nearly 60% of whales have plastic in their guts. Under ideal conditions 'biodegradable' plastics may do as they are supposed to do—break down into (relatively) innocuous gases such as carbon dioxide—but conditions often are far from ideal. Plastic debris may endure forever in a desert or a saline lake or in anoxic swamps or ocean mud. The same is true of all organic matter. Human bodies may remain perfectly recognisable after 5000 years or more if they are buried in desert sand or wind up in some acid bog. More seriously, plastics break down if they break down at all to form micro-particles, or nanoparticles, that choke the ocean's many filter feeders, including the single-celled animals of the plankton, which in turn are food for all the creatures higher in the food chain.

Industrial pollution as a whole is thought to kill around nine million people a year—more than malaria, Aids, tuberculosis, war, and violence combined. Few of the ever-growing list of chemical pollutants have been convincingly assessed for possible ecological side-effects and many in the history of the world have been all but ignored until the destruction is too big to ignore—as was the case with DDT and the rest. Traceable death, too, is not all that matters. Today, one of the most pernicious pollutants is or are oestrogens, the excreted remains of contraceptive pills, and a wide range of industrial effluents that are 'oestrogen mimics.' Among other things, rogue oestrogens reduce the fertility of male animals of all kinds, including humans. The sperm counts among human males (men) have fallen by 50% in the last 40 years. A cynic might observe that this is all good business for fertility clinics—'there are no problems, only opportunities,' as the neoliberal zealots like to tell us. But that doesn't quite seem to answer the case. As Meehan Crist observes in 'A Strange Blight,' a review of Rachel Carson's writings edited by Sandra Steingraber:

Carson won, but the planet is awash with poison.

As always when money and power are at stake, the response from governments, and indeed from society at large, falls far short. We could for starters, if we had the will, simply ban all plastic packaging of all kinds. That would account for most of the mess. It isn't enough just to charge 5p or a nickel for a plastic bag in a supermarket. Sure, we would lose what is now a 'major industry.' But industries do and must die, when they are no longer fit for purpose—as the British government was keen to point out when it abandoned Britain's steel industry. There are still plenty of useful jobs to be done, as outlined in Part III. But we really do need to be radical. It's too late for tweaking.

Many pollutants, of course, are all too obvious. Sewage stinks. Plastic debris is all too horribly visible, and tangible, at least till reduced to nanoparticles. But the most dangerous pollutants of all are odourless and invisible. These are the ***greenhouse gases***, GHGs, the cause of global warming and hence of climate change which threatens us all.

Climate change

In 1951—nearly 70 years ago—Rachel Carson wrote in *The Sea Around Us*:

Can the ocean ... also be agent in bringing about the long-period swings of climatic change that we know have occurred throughout the long history of the Earth—the alternating periods of heat and cold, of drought and flood?

She added:

... the long trend is towards a warmer earth: the pendulum is swinging .... In our own lifetime we are witnessing a startling alteration of climate.

She was convinced, too, even back then, that human activity was at least in part responsible for the rising temperatures.

Truly she was a prophet—able to see what the case is even in the absence of cast-iron evidence. For now climate change is all too obvious, and it is clear too that human activity is largely responsible. Some, though, including some in influential places, most notably Donald Trump, are 'deniers' who continue to insist either that the changing weather patterns are just a part of the normal fluctuations; and/or to deny that GHGs are responsible; and/or that human beings are responsible for the rising GHGs; and/or argue that even if we are responsible; it is too late to do anything about it, so we should simply seek to adapt to the difficult times ahead, by the most profitable means available. Some of those deniers attended the United Nations Climate Action Summit in New York in September 2019. To its credit, the New York meeting gave pride of place to the remarkable, 16-year-old Greta Thunberg, leader of the schoolchildren's climate change protest, who reminded the distinguished delegates that

People are suffering. People are dying and ecosystems are collapsing. We are in the beginning of a mass extinction, and all you can talk about is the money and fairy tales of eternal economic growth ... How dare you continue to look away and come here saying that

you're doing enough when the politics and solutions needed are still nowhere in sight!

Donald Trump dropped in briefly to the UN summit and observed that Greta looked a happy little girl and wished her well. But, he implied, the affairs of the world should be left to the grown-ups. Like himself.

Global temperatures have been monitored since 1988 by the International Panel on Climate Change (IPCC) who tell us that since they began the world has already warmed by an average of 1.5°C since—which may not sound much but has profound and diverse consequences. Five of the hottest years on record have occurred in the past 10 years. Rising levels of GHGs in the atmosphere have the effect they do because they allow the short-wave radiation from the sun to penetrate and so warm the land and the oceans, but inhibit the passage of infra-red. But the Earth, once warmed, cools itself down again by radiating infra-red—and if the infra-red cannot easily escape, the continents and the seas stay warm. Greenhouses work on the same principle. The greater the concentration of GHGs, the more the world is warmed.

The principal greenhouse gas by far is carbon dioxide, CO2. CO2 is the principal oxide of carbon and it is of course a natural and vital component of the atmosphere—the food of plants and all other creatures that photosynthesize and hence, in the end, the basic nutrient of animals too, including us. Ice-core samples from Greenland and Antarctica which contain bubbles of air trapped in past ages, show that before the industrial revolution that began in earnest in the late 18th century the atmosphere contained only about 186 parts per million (ppm) of CO2. Then—as the new industrialists burnt more and more coal, and then oil and gas—the concentration rose more and more rapidly. When I first started learning chemistry in the early 1950s we were told that there were 300 or so ppm of CO2 in the atmosphere. Now we are up to around 415 ppm. Again this may not sound much, but very small amounts of potent chemicals can have huge effects. A few potent molecules of the right stuff, or the wrong stuff, can end a life or change the whole world.

The second most important GHG is methane, CH4—carbon in reduced form. Methane is a far more potent GHG than CO2 but it does not persist for very long in the atmosphere because it is rapidly oxidised (to become CO2). In fact, atmospheric CO2 has a half-life of several decades and a proportion may persist for hundreds or thousands of years but CH4 has mostly been oxidized (to form CO2) within a decade.

Ruminant animals belch out methane as they ferment their food which has led various lobbies including the vegans to redouble their campaign against cattle and sheep but in truth, as outlined in chapter 6, well-managed grazing on natural pasture may function as a net carbon 'sink'—*reducing* atmospheric carbon.

Minor but still important players are various oxides of nitrogen, known collectively as NOx, which gust not least from fields that have been plied with more N-rich fertilizer than the crops can readily take up—whether the fertilizer is organic or inorganic. A shortlist of industrial chemicals too, such as CFCs, are also greenhouse gases.

Finally, water vapour is a potent GHG (if vapours can indeed be classed as gases). But it is the joker in the pack. Its effects seem particularly unpredictable. For as the Earth is warmed, more and more water is evaporated from the oceans—and the oceans cover seven-tenths of the planet. That, then, should have a huge GHG effect, setting in train a 'positive feedback loop': the hotter it gets, the more the sea evaporates, and the more the world should heat up. But in the higher reaches of the atmosphere the vapour condenses to form clouds—and clouds blot out the sun, and this is cooling: a 'negative feedback loop.' All in all, then, the effects of water vapour are very difficult to foresee.

There are other complications too. The Earth's surface does not warm uniformly. Some places heat up far more quickly than others. The deep oceans are slow to respond but once warm they are a huge reservoir of heat. Heat tends to shift (in net) from warm places to cool, primarily in ocean currents and winds; and as energy redistributes itself some ocean currents may go into reverse or cease to flow altogether, and places that once were warmed by currents from warmer climes may then become cooler, even though the world as a whole is growing warmer. Some projections show that Britain might lose its warming Gulf Stream and become as cold as Newfoundland. Ice, too, is a great reflector of radiation and hence of heat, so an ice-bound continent warms only slowly. This is the 'albedo' effect. But as the temperature increases the ice must eventually melt and the earth that is thus exposed heats far more quickly, and so sets up another positive feedback loop. Furthermore, glaciers are melted in part by the warming rock beneath and so the undersides become slippery and so they slide into the oceans in great ice floes. Thus the ice is lost far more quickly than the physics of heat would suggest, and the albedo is reduced commensurately. So it is that Greenland and Antarctica are losing ice far more quickly than was predicted a few years ago. Incidentally, too, as the Greenland ice melts it is exposing huge dumps of noxious, toxic, and sometimes radioactive chemicals left by the American military in the expectation that they would remain entombed in ice forever and therefore (it was hoped) out of harm's way. Or at least: 'out of sight, out of mind.'

There are yet more traps in store. Notably, hidden beneath the soil in cold parts of the world, and beneath the ocean beds, are huge deposits of 'methane clathrates': basically ice with bubbles of methane trapped inside. As the subsoil and the oceans grow warmer this ice will melt, releasing millions of tons of methane—enough to set the curve of rising temperature into a new and ever-more threatening trajectory.

Because of all these complications (and more), the main prediction from studies so far is that without a drastic turn-around the climate will become more and more unpredictable in the decades and centuries to come, and more and more extreme; with hotter and more frequent heatwaves. Here and there too like eddies in the tides of shifting heat, there could be deeper and deeper frosts; more and more frequent storms and hurricanes; bigger and more long-lasting droughts with more and more severe and frequent wildfires; and bigger and more frequent floods, with accompanying land-slips. Crops will fail and livestock will die; formerly 'tropical' diseases and pests will spread north and south, towards the poles. Livestock in Northern Europe are now threatened by Bluetongue, a very nasty viral disease carried by midges of a kind that prefer warm climates. The first suspected case in Britain was in 2007. The mass species extinction that is already well in train will gain even more momentum, not least as the creatures that live at Earth's extremes are pushed almost literally over the edge. Polar Bears are running out of suitable habitat. They now symbolise the ecological perils of global warming, just as Giant Pandas in their dwindling bamboo forests symbolise habitat destruction in general.

Unless we take truly radical action the prospects are dire and will be felt well within the lifetimes of the younger generation. If the global temperature rises by another 2°C, as it is well on course to do, we will see wholesale loss of land-locked ice and sea levels must rise as a result by an amount that again is difficult to calculate—perhaps by a metre by 2100 and perhaps, some say, by 10 metres or more in the fullness of time. One more metre, with a few storms, will be enough in effect to wipe out most of the world's small island states and some of the world's major cities, mostly in Asia, including Shanghai with its 12 million inhabitants, but also New York and, probably most of London. With a further 6° rise—perfectly plausible—virtually the whole Earth must become uninhabitable, at least for the foreseeable future. To be sure, in the very long term such a rise would open up vast regions that now are seriously hostile—Greenland, Antarctica, Siberia. But by then most of humanity and our fellow creatures will have disappeared. Some will surely survive but we cannot know which. Perhaps the descendants of rats, which at least are intelligent and versatile, will inherit the Earth. Perhaps, simply, the descendants of tardigrades, also known as water bears: tiny arthropods that live in the soil and in what to them are forests of moss and are the most resilient animals known, able to withstand deep freezing and desiccation. Microbes will always pull through, for which we should be grateful. Where there's life, there's hope.

It is clear, though, once again, that the people with most power in the world are not properly on the case. They hold plenty of high-profile meetings, but then they don't do what's needed. Thus the Paris Convention on Climate Change in 2016 called on all the world's nations to work together and to restrict global warming to a further 1.5°—and that target is already passed. Despite solemn declarations of intent from *most* of the world's rich countries CO2 has risen faster in the first 20 years of the 21st century than in the last 20 years of the 20th. The deniers deny what now seems all too obvious and the powers-that-be in general seem far too complacent partly because the truth is inconvenient—but also, I suggest, because most people in high places are inadequately educated and fail to appreciate what's really going on, or what really matters. Most or many of them went to Oxford or Yale or Stanford or several of the above but very few if any studied ecology or evolution. They simply cannot conceive that the world's climate and landscapes *could* be very different from what they now experience—despite, for example, the near obliteration of New Orleans in 2005 by the floods that came with Hurricane Katrina or the all-too obvious fact that Australia is rapidly becoming uninhabitable. Despite the evidence of their own eyes, those with most power seem to remain incredulous.

Yet the long history of humankind shows that what is happening now is all too plausible, and indeed has been an accident waiting to happen. Over the past 100,000 years or so our ancestors—not our very ancient, ape-like ancestors who are long-since dead as dinosaurs but thoroughly modern people—lived through at least 10 Ice Ages, with tropical weather in between. The causes were purely cosmological—our ancient ancestors had very little influence on global events—but even so, it seems, the world could and did change very rapidly—perhaps within a few decades—from pole-to-pole ice (almost) to pole-to-pole tropics and back again. With the help of modern industry and industrial farming, such changes could happen in a few seasons. If people in high places realized this they surely would not be so complacent. Would they?

What's to be done?

Perhaps above all we need drastically to reduce the use of fossil fuels and, as soon as may be arranged, to phase them out entirely. The world needs many more trees to soak up atmospheric CO_2 (and to help control flooding)—but only of the right kind, in the right places. Tax-breaks insouciantly granted to the rich to plant as many trees as they like wherever they want to may do more harm than good, and sometimes have. Agriculture is a key player. Above all we need universal agroecology, the principal element of Enlightened Agriculture, with emphasis on agroforestry and pasture feeding, as outlined in chapter 6. To accommodate this we must shift the economy—from the present, post-Enlightenment, neoliberal desire and perceived need to maximize wealth and see where it leads, to the 'minimalist' economy: asking how *little* we really need to achieve justice and personal fulfilment. If we acknowledge as most people do that what most of us really care about is family and friends and a sense of purpose then we would find that we could live happily on a great deal less than we are currently encouraged to desire.

All of which demonstrates the main theme of this book: that we need to re-think everything from first principles, and that we need a new kind of education. The next chapter suggests an agenda.

Coda

That, then, is a very rough summary of the human condition and the state of the world at least as I see things. Some people are doing very well, at least materially, but life for most people is far less agreeable or fulfilled than it could be; and if we continue on our present course then we are surely heading for disaster, which no-one will be able to escape. As discussed throughout this book, too, our fellow creatures are even more parlously placed—and that is a tragedy not only for them, and for us, but for the cosmos. Our role in the decline of our fellow species should be seen not simply as a crime, but as a sin. We are geared at best for the short term although we should, and could, if we get our ideas straight, be planning or at least contemplating seriously the next million years—and that's just for starters. The gap between what is and what could be is truly startling. The present state of the world is not only tragic—what could be more so? It is ridiculous.

Even so, it's not too late. There is a great deal that we can do, and many people are already on the case—as discussed in the rest of this book.

2

RENAISSANCE: AN AGENDA FOR ALL HUMANITY FOR THE NEXT MILLION YEARS

IF WE ARE TRULY TO PUT THE WORLD TO RIGHTS—to realize our individual potential, to create agreeable societies, to rescue the natural world, and in general to make what should properly be called 'progress'—then we need to re-think everything on all fronts and at all levels. Specifically, I suggest, we need always to be asking three fundamental questions:

WHAT IS GOOD? (What *should* we be doing? What is it good to do?)

WHAT IS NECESSARY? (if we are truly to do good)

WHAT IS POSSIBLE? (in the ecological sense—meaning 'How much can we really do within the limits of planet Earth, without turning it into a wasteland?')

Clearly if what is necessary exceeds what is possible, then we are in trouble. At present, at least with luck and for the next few years, what is at least theoretically possible seems to exceed what is necessary—so there is no excuse for not giving it our best shot.

The first of the three fundamental questions is most obviously a matter of ***moral philosophy***—and moral philosophy as discussed in part V must be rooted in ***metaphysics***.

The second two fundamental questions in the end are matters of fact and are best approached through ***science***—and in particular through the science of ***ecology***. Ecology has been something of a Cinderella within the life sciences, playing second fiddle in recent decades to genetics and molecular biology. But ecology should be seen as the most subtle of all the sciences—the one that engages most directly with life, and hence must cope as a matter of course with complexity and uncertainty.

From this it follows that:

> **All human action should be guided by moral/metaphysical principles on the one hand, and by the principles of ecology on the other.**

This, I suggest, should be written in letters six feet high in clear sight of everyone in positions of influence. In truth, the principles of moral philosophy and of ecology are the only ideas that properly deserve to be called *principles* at all. What governments call political principles are, at best, mere ideologies, which is not the same thing at all. In reality, although some governments have of course been far better than others, ***no government that has ever been has ever systematically sought to frame its strategy and policies within the necessary guidelines of ecology and morality***. This, in the end, is why the world is in such a mess. We, or our appointed leaders, do not systematically address the questions that really matter or seek conscientiously to operate within the necessary guidelines. This is why we need a complete re-think: a ***Renaissance***.

Even so—'Renaissance 'literally means 're-birth,' and isn't that somewhat over-the-top? Couldn't we get to where we need to be just by a series of well-judged Reforms? On the other hand, some would say that the concept of Renaissance is altogether too mealy-mouthed, not to say timorous. The human race and our fellow creatures are heading for disaster and the clock is ticking and we need to change things fast. Should we not simply acknowledge that the status quo and the oligarchs who now command the heights are beyond redemption, and seek to initiate a full-scale Revolution? Well—let's look briefly at the options:

Reform

Reform is certainly necessary, and can achieve a great deal. In particular it can and sometimes does prepare the ground for more radical approaches.

By themselves, though, the conventional processes of reform are surely not sufficient. Reform implies that we change things step-by-step; and there is no plausible step-by-step route to take us from where we are to where we need to be. Some of the changes we need are of a quantum kind—an all-out leap into a different place with nothing in between. There are bound to be some discontinuities. Some of the world's most powerful and influential institutions just have to go, including some or perhaps all of the transnational corporates, at least as they are now conceived. The agrochemical-biotech industry is largely ill-conceived and yet is deeply entwined and indeed embedded in all the world's affairs and it is hard to see how it could simply be reformed out of existence. If we want a better, kinder, more diverse and yet more secure world, we just have to acknowledge that some companies and industries are not fit for purpose and withdraw support and, if necessary, actively dismantle them.

We should not, though, be more radical than we need to be. The status quo is not all bad, by any means, and we should take pains to retain whatever is truly worthwhile—including many or most of the very clever and expert people who now work for corporates. I have the impression from many conversations over the years that many people who work for big aggressive commercial companies and banks would rather be engaged in something more benign, so the necessary transition need not always be painful.

The point remains, though, that Reform alone—tweaks to the status quo—will not and cannot achieve this. In any case, reform in general is too slow. We don't have much time to play with.

Revolution

Beyond doubt, the world does need ***activism***—manifest at the time of writing in the protests in Hong Kong; Extinction Rebellion, Occupy, the young people's marches that were initiated by the Swedish teenager Greta Thunberg in 2018 to draw attention to climate change; Black Lives Matter; and many more, on all scales.

But we surely should avoid all-out Revolution if at all possible. Revolution may well be necessary here and there and from time to time but it is not going to happen worldwide—and if it did, it would surely be disastrous. Even if the revolutionaries agreed on what it was they were actually fighting *for* (a very big 'if') we can be sure that the outcome would not be as intended. Throughout this book I will emphasise the phenomenon of '***non-linearity***' which says that in real life there is no simple relationship between cause and effect. In nature, any small change may have enormous and multifarious consequences—the so-called 'butterfly effect.' Similarly, wars or revolutions may affect everything else that happens in the world forever after, but not necessarily or usually in ways that are predictable. We can be sure only that large-scale revolution would have a host of unseen and unintended consequences that have little or nothing to do with the initial intention. The Russian revolutionaries in the years that led up to 1917 were surely not seeking to create Stalin's USSR. The seemingly all-powerful Lenin himself was deeply suspicious of the young Stalin. All revolutions too that are not just storms in teacups lead sooner or later to violence which often smoulders on for decades and centuries—unpleasant, and certainly counter-productive.

Revolutions, too, whatever the good intentions of their initiators, tend in practice to be primarily destructive. The status quo is disabled or obliterated and people are urged or forced to jump ship—but, typically, with nowhere to jump to. The result, too often for comfort, is a power-vacuum, filled by whoever is quickest of the mark—which in Russia, as Lenin faded in the early 1920s, was Stalin; or else is chaos, like The Terror in France in the 1790s, the sad denouement of the French Revolution. Sometimes, after revolution, the country is transformed, albeit not necessarily in the way that was intended—as in Russia. Sometimes, after the convulsions have died down, or been put a stop to, the country reverts to the *status quo ante* or something very like it—as in France in the early 19th century, and most of North Africa after the Arab Spring of 2010.

Renaissance

In contrast, ***the whole point of Renaissance is to build the alternative*** before ***the status quo is destroyed; so that when people jump ship they do have somewhere to jump to.*** Agriculture again provides the prime example. Almost all countries—with just a few exceptions—could build agriculture *in situ* that would at least be able to keep the people in good fettle while the rest of what is needed is re-conceived and re-built. Farming really is qualitatively different from everything else that we do and if we farm well, then we can still keep going until better times even if everything else is failing. But if farming fails the whole society must collapse, however flashy the city's architecture and however many theoretical billions there are in the banks.

In short, the method of Renaissance is in effect as recommended—and acted upon—by Mahatma Gandhi in early 20th century India: simply start to create, *in situ*, the kind of world we want to see, and allow and sometimes actively encourage the status quo to wither on the vine.

To be sure, the change the world needs is ***radical***. In all areas we have to get down to the roots. But we need not assume from the outset that we need change everything. Often we can bring about radical change of the kind required just by re-invoking some past practice, or by re-combining established practices in new ways. Often—perhaps more often than not—we do need to push existing practices aside, and the institutions that support those practices, which may often require hands-on activism. But we need not *seek* confrontation. We should just get on with the things that need to be done and not have a fight with the status quo unless and until they come at us with real or metaphorical pressure-hoses. In short, ***Renaissance is revolutionary in the literal sense—that it turns things around—but it is not innately confrontational.***

So what does Renaissance entail?

An agenda for Renaissance

The task before us is huge and infinitely complex. We can never get to the end of it. It's a perpetual journey—though this is what makes it so interesting. The necessary thinking embraces all scholarship including or especially all science and religion and all the practicalities of living, from mega-engineering and IT to the crafts of pottery and gardening and cooking. Even more than that; it requires what the Greeks called ***metanoia***—a change of attitude, of mindset, of the way we look at the world. Yet the task before us—in reality an agenda, for all humanity for all times—can be summarized in a simple diagram (see next page).

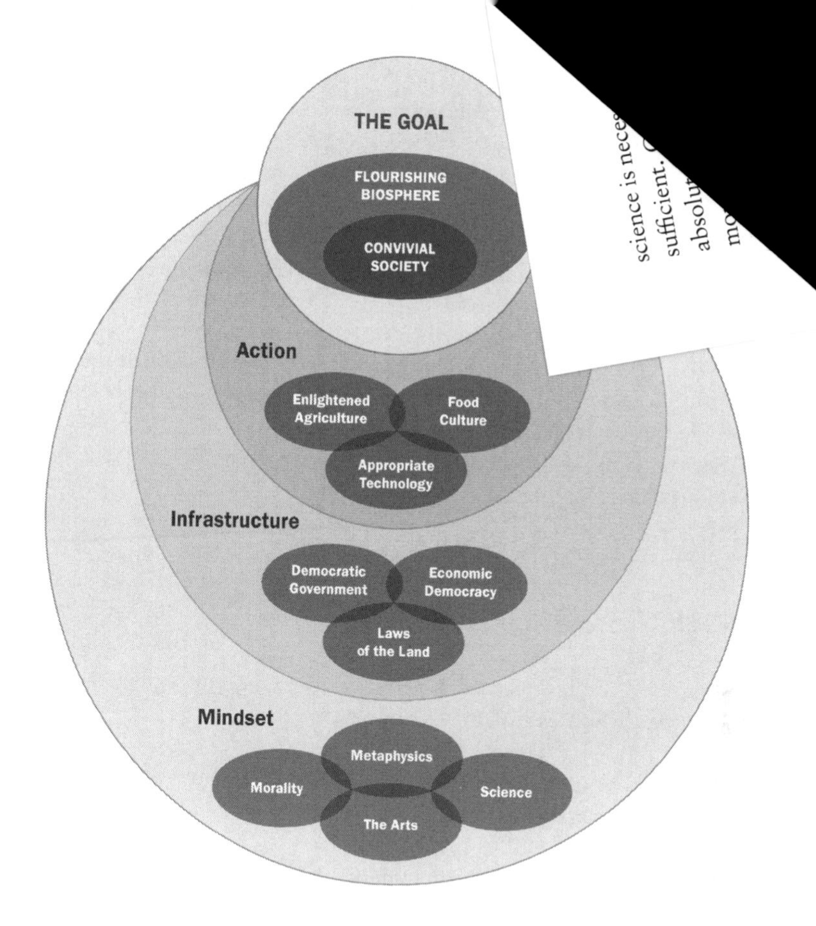

As you can see, there are 12 balloons in the diagram, arranged in four tiers. Each balloon represents a subject area—which on the whole correspond pretty well with the academic faculties in traditional universities. This makes life easier. We already have a structure to work with, even if much or most of the content needs to be changed.

Each and every subject—each balloon—needs to be re-thought from first principles. Even more to the point—***everything must be re-thought in the light of everything else.*** Science in particular is obviously one of the great shapers of the modern world and one of the greatest assets of humankind, yet as I shall argue in chapter 13, science should never be taught without specific reference to the philosophy of science, which shows above all that science is limited in what it can tell us; and nothing should be taught without reference to metaphysics (chapter 14). In short, ssary, and a vital component of human culture, but it is not Context is all. Similarly, or perhaps even more so, economics ely must not be taught in isolation, as if it was just a game of ney. Economics taught without reference to moral philosophy and to ecological reality is a disaster, and indeed is now threatening to kill us all (chapter 10). If we re-think each of the balloons separately then we finish up with a kaleidoscopic worldview: better perhaps than a monocular view, but basically a mess nonetheless. By re-thinking everything in the light of everything else we should wind up with a truly ***holistic*** worldview. Only then will we really have achieved ***coherence***—and coherence, right now, is what we lack.

For the purposes of discussion, however, we do we need to take the balloons one by one. Thus:

TIER I: THE GOAL

The top tier, **Tier I**, is marked **THE GOAL**: and the goal, I suggest—the point of this whole endeavour—should be to create:

> **Convivial Societies—with Personal Fulfilment—within a Flourishing Biosphere.**

The word 'convivial' ultimately derives from the Latin *con* meaning 'with' and *vivere* meaning 'to live.' I intend it to mean that human beings should strive to live together in harmony, with amity and mutual support, ***both to create true societies and also to ensure that each individual member of the society feels fulfilled.*** To achieve a balance between the two—the needs and reasonable aspirations of society on the one hand, and of the individuals within on the other—is perhaps the key task of politics, but alas the task is rarely spelled out formally—which is one good reason why conviviality on all but the smallest scale is rarely achieved. Some societies seem to demand that their citizens should behave like ants, sacrificing all to the common good, as in Mao's China. Others offer their citizens carte blanche—or at least the more aggressive or privileged citizens—and let the society as a whole take its chances; resulting among other things in what the Canadian economist John Kenneth Galbraith (1908-2006) called 'private wealth and public squalor.' The US is the global exemplar. Whether human beings are capable of long-term conviviality is discussed in the next chapter. To anticipate, I think the answer is 'Yes' (or there would be no point in this book). The tension between society and individuals and the political implications thereof are discussed in chapter 9.

The term '***biosphere***' is infinitely to be preferred to the usual word, 'environment.' 'Environment' simply means 'surroundings' and in practice tends to mean stage scenery—a nice view; or it means real estate, for a property with a nice view can fetch a higher price. Indeed the word 'environment,' in this context, should be banished to some *Index Expurgatorius*. The adjective that corresponds to the word 'biosphere' is not 'biospheric,' which sounds a bit odd, but 'ecological.'

The word 'biosphere' was coined in the late 19th century by an Austrian geologist, an expert on the Alps, **Eduard Suess** (1831-1914), and further elaborated in the early 20th century in particular by the French Jesuit palaeontologist **Teilhard de Chardin** (1881-1955). 'Biosphere' means 'the living world.' It does not, like 'environment,' imply that the world is our own personal cornucopia. It implies that we are part of the whole, like atoms in a molecule, or cells in an organism, or members of a family. The whole is our life support, and we are beholden to it. Other creatures, as St Francis is reported to have said, only in part metaphorically, are our brothers and sisters. Or we could simply say, as mystics from all traditions have often said, 'All life is one.' I very much like the term '***Gaia***,' after the Greek goddess of the Earth, which compares the whole world to an organism. Thanks mainly to the presence of living organisms, the Earth as a whole operates in ways that keep conditions constant (more or less) no matter what—and this is what is meant by ***homeostasis***, which is one of the defining features of living systems. The English scientist James Lovelock (born 1919) first thought of the concept in the 1960s although the name was suggested by his friend and neighbour, the novelist William Golding (1911-1993). More in chapter 4.

I have not market-tested the slogan 'convivial societies within a flourishing biosphere' or even submitted it to the referees of some learned journal but I have tried it out on quite a few people and most seem to agree that 'convivial societies within a flourishing biosphere' are indeed to be desired, and no-one has suggested anything significantly different, or better. So until they do, I will stick with it.

It strikes me that most modern governments do not spell out clearly what they are aiming for. They do produce manifestos; but manifestos on the whole are shallow documents, mostly responding *ad hoc* to the perceived problems of the day, with little or no discussion of the underlying moral or ecological principles (if indeed they have any principles of a coherent kind, as opposed to ideologies and a shopping list of intentions). The eight governments drawn from all the major parties that Britain has endured since Mrs Thatcher took over in 1979 have all focused above all on 'economic growth': year-by-year increase in 'gross domestic product' aka 'GDP.' GDP is at best a crude measure of material wealth and is a very poor measure indeed of wellbeing, either of people or of the biosphere. The headless chicken pursuit of 'economic growth' without moral or ecological guidance, and without a clear and generally acceptable goal in mind, won't do. Step one, then, is to define what *will* do—what really is desirable. Then we can gear our efforts and our institutions, including the economy, to that. But first we need to define our goals—what we are trying to achieve. 'Convivial societies (with personal fulfilment) in a flourishing biosphere' at least seems a reasonable first draft.

TIER II: ACTION

Then, **Tier II**, we need to consider what we actually have to do, day to day, to bring about a better or indeed a possible world: what is appropriate **ACTION**. 'Action' means everything we do: building, teaching, health and social care, farming, cooking, engineering in all its forms, energy, communications including IT, trade, transport. 'Action' thus includes all forms of technology. But it must be what E.F. ('Fritz') Schumacher in the 1970s called ***Appropriate Technology***. Specifically we need technologies that are geared to, or at least take proper account of, the need and desire both to promote conviviality and to look after the Earth. Many people are well aware of this. 'Green energy' and 'passive housing' (no extra heating needed!) and even green transport are already with us and could be the norm by now were it not for the inertia of, and the vested interest in, the status quo. More in chapter 5.

But I will focus specifically on farming and food—because these are the things we absolutely have to get right (and in many ways are getting most wrong). 'Modern,' city-based governments like Britain's don't take agriculture seriously (they spend a lot of time and our money on it but that's not the same thing at all) and yet it is at the heart of *all* the world's affairs, both human and non-human, affecting everything else and affected by everything else, and so it illustrates everything we need to talk about, from the science of ecology to the cogitations of metaphysics to all the practicalities of everyday life. Also, I have been looking seriously at food and farming for the past 50 years and am beginning to feel that I have some handle on them.

As discussed in chapter 6, we need agriculture that is specifically designed to provide us all with good food without wrecking the rest: what I have been calling ***Enlightened Agriculture***, sometimes shortened to ***Real Farming***. What we have, and governments like Britain's are very proud of, is agriculture that is designed to maximize and concentrate short-term wealth—'a business like any other,' as the slogan has it (I first heard it in the 1970s). Such farming is anomalously called 'conventional' although it should more accurately be termed **'Neoliberal-Industrial.'** Neoliberal-industrial farming is a loose cannon of mega-proportions that is threatening to kill us all. But it is what passes as progress. Enlightened Agriculture cannot flourish, however, without a matching ***Food Culture.*** Fortunately—and this is one of life's great serendipities!—enlightened agriculture is perfectly compatible both with sound nutrition and with the world's greatest cuisines. But it all needs re-thinking. Chapter 7.

TIER III: THE INFRASTRUCTURE

But—another key message of this book—nothing can be put right *ad hoc*. We cannot do the kinds of things we need to do—build in the ways we need to build, or farm in the ways we need to farm—unless with have an appropriate **INFRASTRUCTURE, Tier III.** Infrastructure in general is discussed in chapter 8. It is provided primarily through ***Governance,*** which need not imply govern*ment* but in practice usually does (chapter 9). Governments in turn make their policies felt via the ***Economy*** (chapter 10) and the ***Law*** (chapter 11). Alas, the policies and modus operandi of the three prime components of the infrastructure are geared only to a limited extent and often only tangentially to what I suggest should be our goal (convivial societies in a flourishing biosphere). In practice, often, they are leading us in quite the opposite direction. The economic model that now prevails, that of ***neoliberalism,*** is particularly destructive, morally and ecologically. Indeed, combined with the uncritical technophilia that is also fashionable, it is, I suggest, the greatest single threat to humanity and to the natural world. The phrase keeps recurring throughout this book, or at least in my head: 'No wonder the world is in a mess!'

TIER IV: MINDSET — TOWARDS THE PERENNIAL WISDOM

To achieve our goals, though, and as the basis for all further thought and action, we need **Tier IV**: an appropriate **MINDSET**. We need to explore all the attitudes and ideas—often unconscious, or at least unspoken and unexamined—that form the basis of all our understanding, and shape the way we think: what we think life and the universe are really *like*; what we think is true; what we feel really *matters*. Four approaches in particular help to shape our worldview: science, moral philosophy, metaphysics (which I take to be at the core of all religions, even if not explicitly recognized as such) and the arts.

Moral philosophy aspires to describe what is good, and why. It seems fashionable to argue that there can be no universally agreed morality—that everyone has their own point of view, and (some say) that all those points of view should be considered equal since, in the absence of a universally accepted God, there is no one with the authority to judge between them. In chapter 12, I argue that this is not so. Most people in all societies and cultures agree upon the same shortlist of virtues: ***compassion, humility,*** and ***a reverent attitude to nature***; and the greatest of these, it is widely agreed, is compassion. Compassion is conceived in various ways (Christians tend to speak of 'love') but it is at the moral core of all the great religions, even though some followers within almost all religions sometimes choose to behave otherwise. A world that is rooted in compassion, extended to all humanity and to all other creatures, would truly have a hope of a long-term, convivial future. It's the ultra-competitive, devil-take-the-hindmost, neoliberal *Zeitgeist* that now prevails that is threatening to kill us all—especially when yoked to gung-ho science and the technophilia that this gives rise to.

Science aspires to tell what the universe is made of and how it all works—but few these days formally address the philosophy of science, which asks what science really is and what it is not, and what it can really hope to tell us and what it cannot. Very few people—not even scientists who are seen as the guardians of science, and certainly not politicians who largely decide the direction of scientific research—truly have a *feel* for science, what it is and isn't, and what it can do and can't. So science is deployed very badly; not called upon when it could have useful things to contribute, but often relied upon when faith is not justified. So it is that science, which undoubtedly is one of the triumphs of humankind and should be one of our greatest assets, is often an accomplice to our destruction. More in chapter 13.

Both moral philosophy and science (and indeed all serious thought!) are rooted in **Metaphysics** which asks what are often called 'the ultimate questions': what is the Universe *really* like; what is truth, and how do we know what's true; where does 'good' come from (as opposed to 'what is it good to do?'); and—the great imponderable, though this should not stop us pondering it—How come? How come things are as they are? These are indeed key questions but as Professor Sayed Hossein Nasr of the George Washington University points out, metaphysics as an independent discipline has largely gone missing; and this, he suggests, is the greatest single cause of the disastrous state in which the world now finds itself. I think he is right. Chapter 14.

Finally, **The Arts** may be seen as the jokers in the pack—the bards, wild cards, court jesters. Jokers are vital players, drawing attention to what we might otherwise miss, questioning our assumptions, and generally shaping our attitudes—and attitude is all, or at least is the sine qua non. We look at the world differently through the eyes of Schubert, or Gerard Manley Hopkins, or Lennie Cohen. Chapter 15.

The elements in Tier IV, taken all together, bring us as close as we are liable to get to the idea of ***the Perennial Wisdom***; the grand and universal insights that are needed if we are ever to put the world on a firm and agreeable footing. The Perennial Wisdom as conceived by the ancients was entirely an exercise in metaphysics. Now, though, metaphysics needs to embrace the insights of modern science too. All in all, we could say that the task before us—the thrust of the whole agenda is

To apply the Perennial Wisdom to everyday life.

That, surely, is worth dedicating a lifetime to.

Finally, to get the ball rolling, chapter 16 asks (very briefly), what can be done? What can each of us do to help bring about the Renaissance? Who's doing what? And what are the chances of success?

Given the present state of the world, the perpetual strife, the loss of species, global warming and rising sea-levels, the inadequacy of governments, and the confusion or the disengagement of much or most of humanity, our chances of rescuing the world in a tolerable state seem slight. ***Yet there is still hope.*** Hope is not the same as optimism but, as St Paul declared in his first letter to the Corinthians (13:13), it is a necessary virtue. Despite the wrong-headedness in high places, and all the obstacles to good thinking and good action, and all the inducements to take short cuts and behave self-centredly, a lot of people worldwide are already doing the kinds of things that need to be done and so providing models for others to follow and so providing platforms on which to build. In this scattergun fashion the people-led Renaissance is already happening.

Part II

THE GOAL

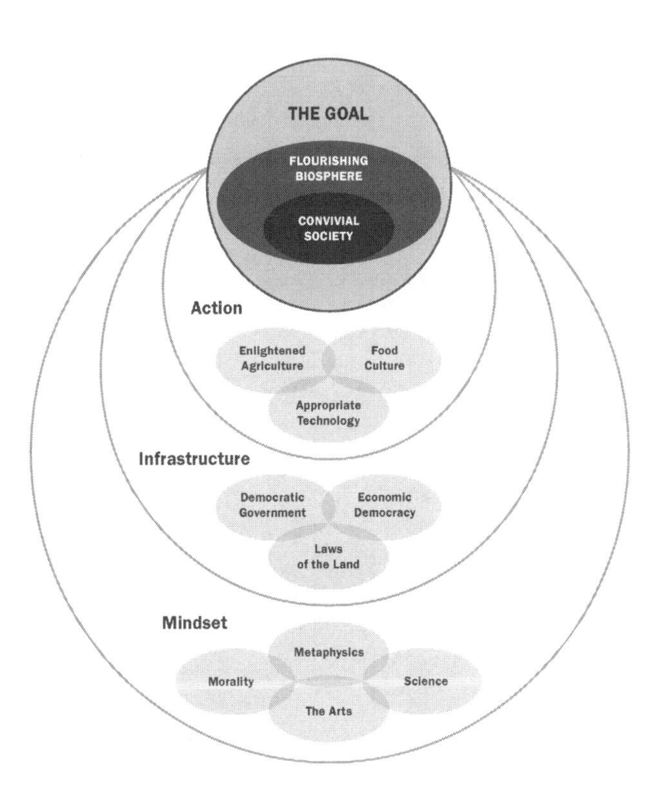

3

CAN HUMAN BEINGS REALLY BE CONVIVIAL?

I cannot but conclude the bulk of your natives to be the most pernicious race of little odious vermin that nature ever suffered to crawl upon the surface of the earth.

The King of Brobdingnag from Jonathan Swift's *Gulliver's Travels* (1726)

A STRONG THREAD OF SELF-LOATHING RUNS THROUGH western thinking, beginning it seems with the Fall, when Adam and Eve tasted the forbidden fruit in the Garden of Eden and were peremptorily booted out—after which successive prophets and preachers and especially St Augustine in the early 5th century have saddled us all with the couple's 'original sin.' Patricians and intellectuals at least from Plato in the 5th century BCE to Thomas Hobbes in the 17th century have generally agreed that human beings are a wayward and treacherous lot who need to be kept in check by the great and the good—or, more specifically, by patricians and intellectuals. Christian leaders of all persuasions, from the fiercely Catholic Torquemada to the fiercely Protestant John Knox, have queued up to warn us that unless we repent and mend our ways we will surely burn in Hell—although Knox, in the footsteps of John Calvin (and of Augustine), declared that most of us would probably burn anyway, even if we did mend our ways (for God is not to be bargained with and once He's made up his mind, your number's on it). Christianity seems always to have carried with it a huge burden of guilt and indeed of fear. A great pity. I take religion very seriously (chapter 14) and consider myself 'a friend of Christianity' but guilt and hellfire are not what it ought to be about.

Charles Darwin, kind and liberal gentleman that he was, didn't help. His defining work of 1859, *On the Origin of Species by means of Natural Selection* carries the subtitle, *Preservation of Favoured Races in the Struggle for Life*. In the book he also speaks of 'the struggle for existence.' Life, in short, he suggests, is inescapably competitive—one long punch-up, so some of his most influential successors have concluded, from conception to the grave—or even before conception, since sperms compete for access to the egg, and the potential eggs compete to be presented to the sperm. Each living entity seems obliged to treat all others as potential rivals who must be overcome, for those who do not must fall by the wayside. In life's struggle there can be no holds barred. We may find it convenient from time to time to form alliances but, as Niccolo Machiavelli argued in *The Prince* in the early 16th century, we must always be alert to the main chance, and be prepared to jump ship and change sides. If our chances of surviving and reproducing are enhanced by lying, deceiving, and betraying our erstwhile friends, then so be it. That's life. That's politics. That's reality. That is the principal theme of Shakespeare's history plays.

Small wonder that we have turned out so badly! Conviviality may seem a worthy goal but are human beings really up to it? Can we really be convivial, except now and again, when it suits us? Can we really be trusted? Can we trust each other? Aren't all of us liable to put the boot in as soon as it's advantageous to do so? Isn't it prudent always to be on our guard? Shouldn't we just have to accept that life's a bitch and, to misquote *Wall Street*'s Gordon Gekko, that niceness is for wimps, or at least must be reserved for our daughters and our Cocker Spaniel? Daughters can seem a little fickle as poor King Lear discovered but that's the price of parenthood. We can at least trust dogs because love is bred into them and hence is unconditional. Besides, if they become too uppity, we can always have them put down.

This edgy, ultra-suspicious, guarded and opportunist attitude to life—

just a step or two away from paranoia—is often blamed, or justified, by reference to Darwin and is sometimes called 'neodarwinian' or even 'ultradarwinian.' If life really is a non-stop 'struggle for existence,' then everyone must constantly be under threat, forever on the *qui vive* and forever on the lookout for the main chance. If that is the way things really are then of course it isn't safe to trust anyone. To compete successfully we must get our retaliation in first. General conviviality is too risky. The laws of biology, our inherited nature, militate against it.

But this surely is not what Darwin intended. What is commonly called 'neodarwinism' should more accurately be called ***metadarwinism***, meaning 'beyond Darwin'—for it is largely an invention of later commentators and would-be disciples.

As will discussed in chapter 10, this metadarwinian emphasis on competition has helped to give rise in recent decades to the ultra-materialist, ultra-competitive economic theory known as neoliberalism—complete reliance on the no-holds-barred, all-against-all global market. I suggest that the combination of ultra-competitive metadarwinism, and ultra-materialist, ultra-competitive neoliberalism, coupled with an apparently absolute faith in the sanctity and power of science and high technology (chapters 5 and 13)—is now the greatest threat to humankind and to all life on Earth, overriding the essential human qualities of conviviality and common sense. Yet this ultra-competitive, metadarwinian neoliberalism has become the political norm, taught in dedicated courses in some of the world's most prestigious centres of learning, and supported by some of the world's best-rewarded intellectuals. At the very least this is perverse.

To be sure, there is some truth in Thomas Hobbes's idea that societies need governments—but as argued in chapter 9, this is not, as Hobbes seemed to suggest, because we need the great and the good to tell us what to do. We need them simply to protect us against the minority who are not convivial, for whatever reason, and seek to do us down. As Steven Pinker points out too in *The Better Angels of Our Nature* (Viking Books, 2011), we also need some kind of quasi-independent power group to administer justice, so that we don't need to take the law into our own hands, which is difficult, and risky, and is likely if successful to start a vendetta, a feud, of the kind that has dogged many (most?) societies through most of history. Vendettas and feuds may smoulder on for generations, as with the fictional Montagues and Capulets in *Romeo and Juliet*, or for centuries, as with the Scottish clans of the MacDonalds and the Campbells, who I believe are real. Unfortunately, as argued in chapter 9, people who are not convivial and seek only to come out on top often do come out on top, and hence are over-represented in positions of power, so that *we* need to be protected against our putative protectors. As the Roman poet and satirist Juvenal asked in the 1st century CE, '*Quis custodiet ipsos custodes*?': 'Who will watch over the guardians?'

Here, though, I want to argue in absolute contrast to what has become the accepted truth that ***conviviality is our natural state.***

Why human beings, above all, are nice

Human beings are, undeniably, social creatures. More than that we are *eusocial* where 'eu' means 'good' in the sense of 'good-and-proper': really *really* social. Like ants, bees, termites, and naked mole rats, we simply cannot survive on our own, or not at least for very long. We depend on the skills and cooperation of others. Thus Robinson Crusoe in Daniel Defoe's eponymous novel, marooned on a desert island, could not have survived without the artefacts he rescued from the shipwreck—artefacts made by other people—and without the eventual company of Man Friday. As John Donne famously observed a few decades before Defoe, 'No man is an island,' and although his meaning is primarily spiritual it is also practical.

Beyond doubt, human societies work much better if the people within them feel well-disposed towards each other; that is, are truly convivial. Natural selection is concerned above all with survival. Animals undoubtedly benefit from living in societies in all kinds of ways. Therefore natural selection should favour sociality and sociality is surely reinforced by true feelings of conviviality. The Darwinian prediction is not, therefore, that the default position of human beings is to be at each other's throats, waiting for the chance to put the boot in. ***The Darwinian prediction is that conviviality should be built into us, honed by our evolution.***

So why doesn't it look that way? It is easy to see why politicians and clerics should tell us that we are bad—it gives them a plausible reason to seize the reins and justify their status. But how could some of the world's greatest thinkers, like Plato and Hobbes, have got it so wrong?

Well, for one thing, alas, conviviality is not our *only* natural state—for we, humans, are the ultimately protean beings, able in principle, largely by virtue of our enormous brains and the intelligence that should go with them, to behave in (almost) any way we want. We *can* be social and cooperative, meaning convivial, which is what most people would say is 'nice'; or we can be unsocial, self-centred, competitive, and aggressive (i.e. nasty). We are also, as ultra-social and indeed as eusocial beings, extremely susceptible to the ideas and criticisms of others—which means that our own personalities are to a very large extent shaped by the people around us. In short, most human beings are perfectly able to be nasty as well as nice, and most of us are nasty from time to time; and how nasty we are, and how consistently, depends partly on our inherited psyche and partly on the people we encounter as we go through life.

Yet for everyone who is not a psychopath or otherwise damaged, conviviality is always an option. It is in our psyche somewhere. Indeed for most of us (all who are not psychopaths) ***conviviality is our preferred option.*** Most of us would far rather be nice and are eminently capable of being so. For the most part we need only or primarily to live in circumstances that encourage us to be nice. A prime task of government, therefore, or indeed *the* prime task, is to create conditions that encourage niceness, which means to encourage sociality and the search for personal fulfilment. In contrast, present-day governments in line with the doctrine of neoliberalism generally urge us instead to compete for personal wealth and status. Those who advocate the competitive approach to life claim to take their lead from that pillar of the Scottish Establishment Adam Smith (1723-1790) but Smith, like Darwin—and like most great thinkers indeed: Jesus, Muhammad, Marx—has been horribly misrepresented by his would-be disciples. More in chapter 10.

Here, though, we encounter a very considerable serendipity (one of many serendipities that crop up throughout this book). For niceness is not just a human invention and the option of niceness does not, as we have so often been assured, require us heroically to override our underlying animal nature. As Adam Smith argued in his *Theory of Moral Sentiments* of 1759:

> *How selfish soever man may be supposed, there are evidently some principles in his nature, which interest him in the fortunes of others, and render their happiness necessary to him, though he derives nothing from it except the pleasure of seeing it.*

Darwin's idea of evolution by natural selection—what Spencer called 'survival of the fittest'—when properly understood reinforces Smith's argument. Indeed the theory of natural selection when properly construed *predicts* that niceness should be our natural state, and indeed should be our default position, when given a chance; and a great deal of modern biology, which is to say of science, adds weight to the theory.

The biology of conviviality

In practice, all creatures, however solitary they may seem, need to cooperate with their fellows to some extent. Truly social animals benefit in many different ways from the company and the efforts of others. In the perpetual search for food, two sets of eyes are better than one and a dozen or more sets are better still. Vultures collectively look out for corpses. Zebras and prairie dogs collectively watch out for predators. In many ways, more often than not, there is safety in numbers.

Social life requires social skill: the ability to give and take; manners. One of the very first things that lion and wolf cubs and baby chimpanzees must learn (on pain of death) is who in their group they can take liberties with and who they must treat with respect, or indeed avoid. Social living certainly has its drawbacks—commonly there is a hierarchy, sometimes called a pecking order, and those at the bottom often have a very rough time. Even so, an individual at the bottom of a social hierarchy, though harassed from pillar to post, is more likely to survive and even to reproduce than one who is cast out and condemned to live alone. Exile in ancient societies was one of the worst of punishments. Animals in places where food is scarce and communication is difficult are perforce adapted to the solitary life but even the most solipsist are obliged to cooperate for the purposes of sex. Sociality, in short, is not a luxury, a refinement, to be found as Plato supposed only in societies that like to think they are civilized, and it certainly does not require us to override our own biology. It is a very necessary survival tactic. Indeed I am inclined to suggest that ***the ability to rub along with others, particularly those of the same species, is the most universally effective survival tactic of all.***

Even this—just rubbing along, keeping clear of irascible males—makes huge behavioural demands. True sociality, potentially the most beneficial, requires give and take. It requires each individual to exercise at least some restraint. It may even, from time to time, require some measure of ***altruism***: individuals making some sacrifice, or putting themselves at risk, for the benefit of the rest. Thus social creatures from monkeys and prairie dogs to ducks and sparrows make 'alarm calls' when threatened which may draw attention to themselves but also alert the whole group to the danger. Honey bees sting invaders to protect the hive even though they die as a result. Some biologists and moralists—including Darwin's great friend and ally T.H. Huxley (known to Darwin's children as Uncle Henry)—have argued that bees are therefore great moralists, a lesson to us all, but most feel that self-sacrifice should not be considered truly 'moral' unless it is a conscious decision—and bees, most feel, just sting because that is the way they are programmed. Thus bees and many other animals—including most mothers in species that take care of their offspring, and some fathers too—are altruistic in the functional, biological sense though not necessarily in the sense that most moral philosophers mean by the term.

Truly to get the most benefit from social life, however, animals must actively ***cooperate***. So it is that lions and wolves hunting in groups have a far higher success rate than tigers or bears, which operate alone. Truly *eusocial* creatures like us are obliged to cooperate because no one individual can master all the necessary skills of living. Thus as Adam Smith emphasized in his other great book, *The Wealth of Nations* in 1776, human societies work most efficiently when they practice division of labour. Yet, as discussed elsewhere in this present book, too much specialization turns us into ants (as Adam Smith also pointed out). To be fully human, we must retain our flexibility and our ability to choose.

Human beings are able to cooperate to a far, far greater extent than any other animal—and this, rather than our individual braininess, is what makes us truly special; gives us a decisive ecological advantage over all other creatures, with clear daylight between us and the rest. Roughly as René Descartes suggested in the 17th century, our hyper-cooperativeness springs from our ability to capture and represent our thoughts and feelings in the form of words—and then to communicate those thoughts and feelings to others, quickly and precisely, through expression and body language but most importantly through speech. Again, other animals from vervet monkeys to prairie dogs express particular thoughts and feelings through sounds but for the most part their languages seem formulaic. They select from a menu of stock ideas: one sound for 'snake' and another for 'eagle' and so on. Human language is open-ended, infinitely flexible (or so it seems), able in principle to express anything at all, articulated through infinitely versatile speech. Other animals share information to a far greater extent than has generally been realized but no other animals can pool their thoughts as we are able to do. In principle, our whole species can operate as one. Insofar as the human brain is comparable to a computer, humanity as a whole is like billions of computers in parallel, and the whole is far greater than the sum of the components. ***Biologically we are apes but in our ability to think and feel collectively we are in effect a new life form.***

The politics of the whole world in effect forever has been based primarily on competitiveness and the prevailing, neoliberal economy is competitive to the nth degree. The ability and willingness to compete is now widely seen as one of humanity's greatest virtues, if not as *the* greatest virtue. Competition no doubt has its place—to some extent it is a spur to action, and to some extent that can be a good thing. But the urge and eagerness to compete all too often overrides cooperativeness. Instead of pooling their knowledge for the general good, industrial companies operate in secrecy, one from another. When companies do cooperate—as pharmaceutical companies and government scientists did in World War II to develop penicillin for general use—they race ahead in leaps and bounds. Thus politics and the modern economy sacrifice humanity's greatest asset. There is no coherent thinking behind them. Perverse.

Sex and sociality

Nothing requires cooperation more obviously than sex. I say 'sex' rather than 'sexual reproduction' because sex as a way of reproducing is somewhat inefficient. Reproduction with sex requires two parents with a great deal of hassle and sometimes a great deal of risk while asexual reproduction (achieved in various ways of which cloning is one) requires only one parent. ***The real biological function of sex is not to reproduce in the sense of multiply but to mix up the genes.*** It's the *recombination* of genes plus occasional, random mutation that produces variation in the population, and generation by generation. In nature, genetic variation is the chief defence against epidemic. If all the individuals are genetically identical then a parasite that can take hold in any one of them can take hold in them all. Hence the efforts of some high-tech agriculturalists to produce clones of 'elite' crops and livestock is intrinsically dangerous, not to say seriously misguided. Attempts are then made to ward off disease by introducing 'resistance genes' by genetic engineering which is considered very avant-garde and therefore progressive but it surely would be better (and a great deal cheaper and less socially disruptive) just to leave well alone, and not to produce the clones in the first place. As the generations pass, the variation brought about by recombination and mutation provides the variation without which natural selection cannot function. So it is that all creatures that are not evolutionary dead ends practise sex of a kind. Bacteria simply swap packets of DNA. Their wondrous promiscuity enables them to evolve to form new strains that can exploit new niches in the blink of an eye (or at least, commonly, within weeks or months).

Creatures like us (and mushrooms and oak trees) mix the genes of different individuals by producing specialized gametes, eggs and sperm—and to bring the two together requires a great deal of cooperation. Creatures like oak trees or orchids and barnacles which are rooted or otherwise stuck to the spot cannot move their whole selves one to another but they must at the very least coordinate the release of gametes—and then rely on wind or tides or some obliging vector, like bees or moths or hummingbirds, to carry the male's gametes to the female. Effective insect pollination requires close cooperation of flowers and insects. As Darwin noted, particular flowers and particular insects often evolve over time to become more and more interdependent; long-tubed orchids pollinated by night by moths with commensurately long proboscises; long-tubed clovers pollinated by bumble bees; a series of more or less exclusive clubs. We now know too that the apparent battle of the sperm to fertilize the egg is *not* just an all-out struggle. Spermatozoa also cooperate: many may work together to assist the one that finally succeeds.

Sexual congress of a kind that requires direct physical contact between the would-be parents requires especially high levels of cooperation. Each prospective partner must signal to the other their willingness or eagerness to mate—and each must recognize the other's signals. Otherwise the approach of one individual upon the other may look very like a threat. Then one or other would-be parent—usually the male!—finishes up dead; or at least, in modern human societies, up before the beak in a court of law. Sometimes, as in mantises, the male finishes up dead even if he does manage to mate successfully, treated by the female as a useful source of protein. Waste not, want not. In many species, for one or other of the sexes and sometimes for both, reproduction either sexual or asexual is the last fling. After it the participants die in short order. Some seem to trigger some internal mechanism of suicide; active self-destruction. Others just fade away, too enfeebled or disheartened to carry on.

But although sex seems innately cooperative, many modern biologists in ultradarwinian vein have chosen instead to stress its competitiveness. Men and women, they say, have different *agendas*. Thus a best-seller from a few years' back opined that *Men Are from Mars, Women are from Venus*. The rivalry, sometimes called 'the battle' between the sexes is again a prime theme of literature (not least in Shakespeare's *The Taming of the Shrew*).

The rivalry is explained, it's been argued, by the difference in basic biology. Men produce billions of sperm and go on producing them almost up to death—and each individual sperm could in principle (it seems) give rise to an offspring. Men therefore could in theory have millions of children. Women by contrast produce only about 100,000 eggs over their whole lifetime, and release only one a month, and usually run out altogether before they are 60 (since, throughout life, eggs that are not released steadily fade away). If one of the eggs is lucky enough to be fertilized then the woman is stuck with a nine-month pregnancy and then at least in a state of nature with the even greater physiological burden of lactation. So it is that women in traditional hunter-gathering tribes rarely manage to produce more than five children over a lifetime. Families of 10 or more are achievable only when a mother is on a very high plane of nutrition and/or the burden of lactation is taken over by wet-nurses or supplements of cow's milk and formulae.

The modern thesis of what Richard Dawkins called 'the selfish gene' argues that living organisms of all kinds are just vehicles for their genes and that genes have evolved to produce as many copies of themselves as possible, for those that do not maximize their progeny lose out to those who do. From this it seems to follow that the organisms that contain those genes should contrive to leave as many viable offspring as possible. Since men can produce a child with just a few seconds' effort (once they have procured a mate) it seems that they, like all males, can best do the bidding of their genes by fathering as many offspring as possible, from as many women as possible, and leave the child-rearing to the mothers. Men, on the face of things, are biologically impelled to be philanderers. Women, by contrast, would best serve the interests of their genes by finding a partner who will help to ensure that the infants survive by supporting her through pregnancy, and then help to bring up the child (given that human children take an unconscionably long time to mature).

Among animals at large we find both kinds of strategy. Stags, stallions, rams and bull elephants fight among themselves for the right to mate. The winner then takes all during a few riotous weeks of autumn (in the case of Red Deer stags) and then clears off (or is booted out), leaving the females to bring up the babies in peace (and sometimes cooperatively. Elephants in particular rely heavily on grandmothers and aunts). In most birds, by contrast, the males help with child-rearing too. A few, like swans, mate for life. It seems to be assumed that men must be more like stags than they are like male swans, possibly because men and stags are both mammals, while birds belong to a quite different lineage. Besides, stags on the whole are more impressive. Some mammals make good fathers too, however, including some primates, who are our closest relatives.

Yet in practice, men do *not* produce millions more offspring than women. Genghis Khan is said to have sired 1000 to 2000 children but the highest authenticated figure is 880, fathered by Ismael Ibn Sharif of Morocco (1672-1727). The most prolific woman on record was the wife of an 18th century Russian peasant, Feodor Vassilyev (b. 1707-c. 1782) whose 27 confinements produced 16 pairs of twins, seven set of triplets and four sets of quadruplets—totaling a somewhat astonishing 69. World records are not typical of course, by definition. But they make a point: that the most prolific men we know about, with wealth and slaves and a boundless supply of concubines, produced only about a dozen times more children than the most prolific woman. The total number of gametes that each produces seems hardly to be relevant.

For in reality, the best strategy for a man who seeks seriously to multiply his genes and found a dynasty, is not simply to light the blue touch paper and retire. He needs to ensure that his children thrive, and go on to have children of their own. Eastern potentates may be reasonably sure that their slaves and dependents will look after their progeny but ordinary men, the vast majority, are well advised even from a purely biological point of view to provide succour and protection for their children, and also therefore for the mother of their children who is best equipped and motivated to take care of them.

In short, the idea that men and women have different agendas is much exaggerated. Life is not that simple. Women are obliged by their biology to invest heavily in their children (pregnancy, lactation) but men must invest too, and in practice most men at least in modern societies do devote most of their energies to child-rearing even if their role is not so obvious. There does seem to be some 'rivalry' between the sexes one way or another but the roots of it are not as inescapably biological as it has been fashionable to suggest. This again is a prime theme of literature. In Jane Austen's *Emma* Emma Woodhouse and Mr Knightly circle each other until they (or in particular Emma) realize that they belong together. So too in *Pride and Prejudice,* where Elizabeth Bennet and Mr Darcy are at daggers drawn until they too realize where their true interests lie. The same is true up to a point even for Katherina and Petruchio in *The Taming of the Shrew*.

I do not want to pretend as some do these days that men and women are really just the same, and that the differences between them are just a matter of upbringing, because this is demonstrably untrue; and *vive la difference*. But the differences between the two are much less significant than the similarities. We might indeed suggest that ***women when you boil them down are just modified men—and men when you boil them down, even the hairiest and most macho, are just modified women.*** Each is a different version of humanity and the two together are entirely complementary. They are on the same side. Neither can claim to be the archetype. *Genesis* tells us that God created Eve from one of Adam's ribs but this does not seem literally to have been the case. Men still have twelve ribs, the standard mammalian quota.

Sociality and cooperation are the keys to intelligence

The idea that cooperativeness is linked to intelligence properly began, as is so often the case, with Darwin. In *The Origin,* in 1859, he said that he did not suppose that natural selection is the only driver of evolution—and in 1871 in *The Descent of Man, and Selection in Relation to Sex* he describes an alternative: sexual selection. Natural selection is about survival, while sexual selection alludes to life's second great problem—how to attract mates for the purposes of sexual reproduction. Often, Darwin perceived, sexual selection (which is about sex) and natural selection (which is about survival) are at odds—and so it is that the peacock's wondrous tail that the hens find so irresistible (provided it's bigger and brighter, with more eye-spots, than the rivals' tails) is also an encumbrance when it comes to avoiding the leopards with whom it shares the Indian forests. Later biologists pointed out that this is partly the point. The peacock is saying to the hen, 'Look at me! I can out-smart leopards even though I am carrying this enormous weight of feathers! Indeed, I can find enough food to provide the energy to grow them in the first place! What a truly splendid catch I must be!' This is called 'the handicap principle' which sounds counter-intuitive but seems to go a long way to explain the apparent extravagances of peafowl and other animals, including human animals—why, for example, the cavaliers of England's Charles I swaggered around in big feathery hats and wide-topped boots and generally bedecked in what the Chorus in Shakespeare's *Henry V* called 'silken dalliance.' They were saying to the world (including, consciously or subconsciously, potential mates) 'Look! I can beat these Puritan roughnecks even though I am kitted out like a stage-door Johnny!'

In order to compete for the attention of females—as they are obliged to do, if their lineage is to continue—males in general must find ways to stand out from the crowd. Brighter feathers and the *basso profundo* voices of Red Deer stags and male toads may take them a long way but intelligence and speed of thought are impressive too. So, at least according to some theory, males of many species including humans got cleverer and cleverer as successive generations competed to attract the most mates (for no-one denies that competition has *some* part to play!) and the females also grew cleverer and cleverer partly because they share most of the same genes that the males have but also because, over time, they became more and more discerning. So the two sexes are locked in *a positive feedback loop*: as the males grow smarter, the females become more critical and demand even greater displays of creative thinking—which in turn requires them to be more intelligent. Such a feedback mechanism was first proposed in the mid-20th century by the English statistician and evolutionist Ronald (R.A.) Fisher (1890-1962), and is known as 'Fisher's runaway.' Fisher's runaway—the two sexes egging each other on to ever greater heights—is a prime example of ***co-evolution.***

The Oxford primatologist Robin Dunbar has added a very significant twist to this line of thinking. He observes that in general, big, coherent groups of animals can out-compete smaller groups. But the larger the group, the more intense and various the social interactions will be. In short, to live successfully in a large group an animal has to have very finely tuned social skills—starting in infancy. So we encounter another positive feedback loop. The bigger and more various the group becomes, the more it becomes necessary to develop social skills—which requires intelligence; and the more socially adept the individuals become, the more they are able to adapt to the presence and the caprices of others, and the larger, more complex, and potentially more powerful the group can become.

There is more. Charles Darwin was a great field naturalist as well as a great theorist and he observed that animals and also other creatures not only cooperate but also, often, behave altruistically. This puzzled him because at first sight at least it is hard to see how natural selection could favour self-sacrifice. Natural selection, after all, favours survival.

A very plausible explanation was provided just over a century later by the idea of *gene-based selection* which Richard Dawkins explained very clearly in *The Selfish Gene*. The idea is that natural selection does not impact primarily upon individual creatures, as common sense suggests and Darwin supposed, but upon the individual genes that the creatures carry. Indeed, said Dawkins (though many feel that in this he went too far) individual creatures (including us) are just 'vehicles' for our genes.

So we see for example why mothers—or indeed fathers—might sacrifice their own life for their children. Each offspring contains copies of half the mother's genes, and half the father's genes. More to the point, this means that any one gene in the mother or the father has a 50% chance of being replicated in each of the offspring. Thus a parent who sacrifices her (or his) life to save two or more children enhances the survival chances of their individual genes (or replicas thereof) even though the parent(s) may be sacrificed.

This leads us to the phenomenon of ***kin selection***. The genes in any lineage of creatures 'seek' above all to be replicated; and it may be more beneficial to any one gene to encourage the individual in whom it resides to sacrifice his or her life on behalf of relatives, who are likely to carry copies of that gene, than to encourage that individual to cling to life at all costs. The genes do not, of course, think this out, as a matter of conscious strategy. It's just that genes that encourage their bearers to behave in particular ways are more likely to be replicated than those that do not. The Oxford biologist W.D. (Bill) Hamilton (1936-2000) coined the expression kin selection and it seems very neatly to explain why natural selection can indeed favour unselfishness, even to the point of self-sacrifice. Later biologists argued that altruism brings benefits not only when extended to kin, but also to non-relatives if the non-relatives seem likely to return the favour: so-called ***reciprocal altruism***. Dawkins' *Selfish Gene* explains all this admirably and it deserves to be a classic—but the title is most unfortunate. It seems to imply that our genes predispose us to selfishness where in truth, kin selection predicts that natural selection should often favour extreme *un*selfishness—which indeed is often what's observed. (I later wrote a book called *Why Genes are Not Selfish and People are Nice.* Possibly the most accurate title would be *Selfish Genes, Nice People*).

We come back to the idea, though, that intelligent creatures like us, as opposed, say, to ants and bees, have *choice.* Intelligent creatures more or less by definition can consider various options and weigh up the odds (to a greater or lesser extent depending on how bright they are). Thus human beings can choose at any one instant whether to be generous and share what they have, or to keep all the spoils for themselves: and they can choose, furthermore, who to share their goodies with. In the long term it may pay to be generous (helping small children who you may need to look after you in your old age, and generally building up friendships that may be useful in the future) but often there is no short-term pay-off and in general, immediate obvious benefits are of more use than hypothetical long-term reward. So why are people—and other intelligent animals too—often more generous and unselfish than the immediate situation seems to warrant? Why give tips to waiters or tell foreigners the way back to their hotel when you know you are very unlikely to see them again?

Again, we can easily answer this in theological terms—as in 'God requires us to be unselfish'—but biologists *qua* biologists feel obliged to ask, 'How could natural selection have favoured generosity even when there is no obvious advantage in being generous?'

One answer is that animals including us are *not* computers. We are not walking calculating machines. What we do at any one time is to some extent determined by the immediate circumstances, which is a matter of calculation, but is influenced too by our predisposition, our attitude, our mood. We are nice to strangers who we will probably never see again because we have evolved to be social animals and the most efficient, all-purpose way to function well in a society that is not itself dysfunctional is to be nice in a general kind of way; simply to be friendly unless there is very good reason to be otherwise. ***Niceness in short should be the default position.*** Niceness can of course be feigned. As Hamlet says *a propos* his murderous uncle Claudius

One may smile, and smile, and be a villain

—but villains tend to be caught out. It's hard to keep up the act. In truth the easiest way to be look friendly and trustworthy is to *be* friendly and trustworthy; and the easiest, most reliable way to be friendly is to *feel* friendly. In other words, since social living is advantageous, natural selection should not only favour social behaviour which includes generosity and altruism, but should also underpin such behaviour with an inbuilt predisposition of friendliness. We need in short *emotional intelligence* in addition to mere intellect. Or as Fyodor Dostoyevsky put the matter in *Crime and Punishment* (1866)

It takes something more than intelligence to act intelligently.

There is a further refinement. The emotionally-driven urge to cooperate leads on to *empathy*. Empathy is one significant step on from sympathy. Sympathy implies that we may feel sorry for someone else, and may (sometimes) choose to help them. Empathy implies that we not only feel sorry for some third party but actually feel their pain (or share their joy). More generally, it implies that we are able to identify with another person, or indeed with non-human creatures. Creatures that are capable of empathy are truly equipped to be social.

Again we find that this refined quality is not confined to humans. In *The Age of Empathy* the Dutch primatologist Frans de Waal describes chimpanzees in Tai National Park in Ivory Coast who helped their companions to recover from leopard attack. They licked and cleaned their fellows' wounds, warded off the flies, and slowed their pace when they travelled so that the injured ones could keep up. Similarly, as de Waal also relates, Jane Goodall tells the story of a chimp called Fifi and her two sons, Freud and Frodo. When Freud hurt his foot Fifi powered on ahead, content to let him make his own way as best he could. But Frodo stayed with Freud and whimpered, drawing Fifi's attention. When she did finally pull up, Frodo gazed at his brother's injured foot as if to communicate the problem. If it was a human doing this, we would not hesitate to say that Frodo appreciated Freud's pain and empathized with it. The western mindset says that we should not anthropomorphize—attribute human attributes to non-humans—but in truth there is no good reason in a case like this why we should not. Only prejudice and dogma prevent us from believing what our intuition tells us must be the case. Jane Goodall, with her close-up studies of wild chimpanzees, beginning in the 1960s in Tanzania, has probably done more than anyone to change human attitudes to animals in general and to begin to bury the idea, commonly though somewhat unfairly ascribed to René Descartes in the 17th century, that animals are just machines. As de Waal commented in a later essay

> *After decades of systematic underestimation of animal mental capacities, a period with some risk of overestimation could not hurt.*

The willingness to act altruistically, and the capacity for empathy, are the stuff of *compassion*: and compassion, as discussed in chapter 12, is widely acknowledged as the queen of all virtues, and is at the heart of all religions. Thus we cross the perceived boundary between biology and moral philosophy, and moral philosophy and metaphysics.

In July 1944, as the 15-year-old Anne Frank and her family hid from the Nazis and hence from the concentration camp she wrote in her diary:

> *It's really a wonder that I haven't dropped my ideals, because they seem so absurd and impossible to carry out. Yet I keep them, because in spite of everything I still believe people are really good at heart.*
>
> (Quoted by Thom Hartmann in *Unequal Protection,* Rodale Press, 2004, p. 1).

Surely, she hit the nail on the head.

In short, the metadarwinian idea that we and our fellow creatures are locked in unremitting struggle is obviously highly destructive, and is also inaccurate. Competition is of course a fact of life. But so too is cooperativeness, which in intelligent creatures gives rise to compassion; and ***cooperativeness and compassion are the prime ingredients of conviviality: the three cs.*** Indeed, as argued later, in life as a whole and indeed in the universe as a whole cooperation must out-weigh competition, for if it were not so then nothing would cohere. Atoms are coalitions of fundamental particles and are the stuff of the whole physical universe. The cells of which creatures like us (and mushrooms and oak trees) are composed are coalitions of specialist organelles, mitochondria and chloroplasts and all the rest, bound by a reticulum of membranes. Furthermore, each organelle evolved separately. Each is derived from some prokaryote (bacterial) ancestor. Each individual eukaryotic cell is a coalition of organisms that once were entirely separate. Each cell is a master class in cooperativeness. Indeed I am inclined to suggest that ***competition is***

a fact of life but cooperation is the essence; and cooperation in human beings is secured by a general ambience of conviviality. Overall, for all the drama and perceived conflict, life and the universe as a whole are in harmony—a harmony that the Buddhists in particular call the ***dharma.*** In the concept of the dharma biology, morality, and metaphysics come together. They need not be in conflict.

All this has very obvious political implications.

The politics of conviviality

If conviviality is truly our natural, preferred, and most advantageous state then it follows that the prime task of government is not to keep our supposedly innate viciousness in check, as Plato and Hobbes suggested. It is to enable our innate niceness to come to the fore. Since humanity as a whole benefits most from being social it follows that we should be aiming above all to build strong societies. Politics that focuses on society is properly called *socialism*. That at least is what a great many people including me and including the founder of Britain's Labour Party, the Scottish former miner Keir Hardie (1856-1915) take socialism to mean. Socialism need not and should not be doctrinaire. It does not have to yoke itself to any particular economic system. Still less should socialist systems be despotic and ride rough-shod over individuals. True socialism can (and I suggest must) be rooted in compassion.

It is perverse in the extreme to adopt systems of politics and an economy that make a prime virtue of competitiveness and indeed of ruthlessness that have helped to lead us to our present parlous state, and to override the emotional mindset and reject political systems that would, if properly construed and acted upon, answer all our needs. Alas, it seems that a minority of human beings *are* ultra-competitive, and because they are so focused on power and wealth, and so determined to achieve them, they force their way to 'the top' and then set the tone of the whole society; and the majority, who just want to get on with their lives, content to live in a state of peace (and indeed of conviviality), offer far too little resistance. Thus nice people are dominated by nasty or at least by seriously misguided people who give a false impression of what humanity is really like, and is capable of. This, I suggest, is the central dilemma and the tragedy of human existence. More in chapter 9.

4

A FLOURISHING BIOSPHERE: MORALITY, ECOLOGY, AND A SENSE OF THE SACRED

A man is truly ethical only when he obeys the compulsion to help all life which he is able to assist, and shrinks from injuring anything that lives. ... Life as such is sacred to him ... Ethics are responsibility without limit towards all that lives.

Albert Schweitzer, from *The Philosophy of Civilization*, Amherst: Prometheus Books, 1987 (first published in German and in English, 1923), pp. 310-11

The good man is the friend of all living things.

Mahatma Gandhi

THE STATS ARE HORRIFYING: A 60% DECLINE in the abundance of all the world's wild species in the past 40 years; not simply within my lifetime but within my children's lifetime. In South and Central

America there's been an 89% decline in overall abundance while freshwater fish the world over have dwindled by 83%. Half of the world's coral reefs have died in the past 30 years and the rest could follow if the oceans continue to grow warmer, deeper, and more acid. All this is recorded in the 2018 *Living Planet Report* from the WWF (World Wide Fund for Nature).

Also alarming is the *tone* of the WWF report—which, alas, reflects the crudely materialistic, anthropocentric mindset of the modern world. For it tells us, quite rightly, that if we give a damn about the natural world (and, by implication, about the future of humanity) then we cannot continue with 'business as usual.' But then, as is the norm these days, the report seems to take it more or less for granted that business as usual is what we are stuck with. The very first paragraph of the Executive Summary tells us that that the natural world is of 'incalculable importance to our health, wealth, food and security'—which is fair enough as far as it goes. But then it goes on to say: 'All economic activity ultimately depends on services provided by nature—estimated to be worth around USD125 trillion a year.' Well, USD125 trillion is an awful lot of money but it's not what really *matters* and if we focus our thinking and our strategies on money as is now deemed to be 'realistic' then we and our fellow creatures will have had our chips. (Just to quibble, too, why are summaries in modern reports always called *Executive* summaries? Why do their authors assume that they must appeal above all to people who sit behind big desks?)

Sheer, physical loss of habitat is the main cause of the general decline. A third of all the world's land is now down to agriculture which, for the most part, is more and more hostile to wildlife. Agricultural land includes *most* of the world's most fertile land, where a great many of the world's wild creatures would prefer to live, if they had the chance. The world's national parks are mostly in semi-desert or in uplands. As Isabella Tree records in *Wilding* (Picador 2018), England has only 94,400 hectares of *dedicated* wildlife reserve—less than one per cent of the total land area—while France, say, has 2.75 *million* ha. England's ten national parks 'all have large areas of intensively grazed sheep' and/or are managed as grouse moor, with commensurate slaughter of native predators—and, because the grouse moors are deforested, there is an added risk of flooding in the surrounding lowlands. Many of the 4000 SSSIs (Sites of Special Scientific Interest) are 'eroded, neglected, and sometimes completely forgotten about' and the rules that are supposed to protect them are routinely 'overruled by roads and building projects.'

One of Britain's recent fly-by-night Secretaries of State for 'the environment,' Angela Leadsom, declared that 'The lowlands are for farming and the uplands are for butterflies'—but most butterflies don't live in the uplands and Golden Eagles and Scottish Wild Cats live in the wild and woolly hills of the north not because they like fresh air but because they have long since been kicked out of everywhere else. Edwin Landseer's somewhat louche *Monarch of the Glen* is an icon both of wilderness and of British imperial power—but upland deer on average are one-third smaller than those in the gentler, southerly woods of Windsor Great Park. The Glen is not their favourite habitat. Neither Ms Leadsom nor most of her governmental predecessors apparently thought it necessary to find out what the matters they are in charge of—farming and the biosphere—are actually about, partly because this is not really their thing and partly because they don't have time to look seriously at the issues thrust into their care, crucial though they are for all life on Earth, both human and non-human. Besides, Ms Leadsom had her eye on bigger things—including, for some time, the premiership. To governments in urbanized countries like Britain, agriculture is just a rather irritating corner of the economy that seems to be necessary but has a job to pay its way. Golf is more profitable. So, for that matter, in terms of return per unit of capital invested, is hairdressing. The biosphere—still conventionally known as 'the environment'—is just another resource, nowadays modishly called 'natural capital'; or else is seen merely as an encumbrance.

The habitat that does remain to us is largely ***degraded***—a third of all the world's agricultural soils according to the FAO—and/or is ***polluted***, with heavy metals, complex industrial molecules that wild bacteria are not equipped to deal with (the wondrous Bayou swamps of the southern US with their swamp cypresses and 'Spanish moss' have been used as a chemical dump), and by agricultural run-off. Generous doses of nitrogen (N) and phosphorus (P) marvellously boost the yield of crops that are bred to respond to them, at least in the short term. But they play havoc with wild plants which on the whole prefer low fertility; the ones that do well on high inputs of nutrient, like nettles and docks, are the ones we call 'weeds.' Wild algae in ponds, lakes, and even in the oceans run riot when plied with extra N and P, flushed from the world's industrial farms, much to the detriment of everything else.

Every year, too, nearly 13 million tonnes of plastic—a truckload every minute according to Greenpeace—are dumped in the oceans. When the plastic is still fresh it chokes fish and seabirds and when it has broken up the particles choke the filter feeders of the plankton, on which the whole marine ecosystem depends. 'Biodegradable' plastic doesn't necessarily break down seamlessly into things that are completely innocuous. Indeed it does not necessarily degrade at all in the way the manufacturers intend, for *nothing* degrades unless conditions are right. What breaks down in days in a compost heap may endure forever in an acid bog—or in some anoxic niche in the ocean. Starch-based plastics do seem to degrade innocuously if conditions are right but to make enough of them requires an awful lot of starch—which is mostly grown in the form of highly fertilized maize in the US. Maize is a major food crop, or should be, and the US is a major grower, but up to a third of US maize is now used for plastic or is simply burnt, as 'biofuel,' producing only marginally more energy than the oil that was used for fertilizer to grow them in the first place. But it's all very profitable for the time being and that is all that really counts. Like most technologies designed ostensibly to stop the rot, biodegradable plastics are not really 'sustainable' at all. They are merely less conspicuously unsustainable.

Even the world's governments are beginning to notice and to feel that something must be done but plastics are embedded in the modern economy and business is business. Perhaps we should focus instead on plastics that are absolutely *not* degradable and use them when their job is done like gravel, for building, as is already done to some extent. Indeed, these days, a great many of the pebbles on the world's beaches are worn-down lumps of consolidated plastic. (Could non-degradable plastic suitably compacted and kept out of harm's way be a significant carbon sink?) Right now there don't seem to be any totally convincing solutions to the plastics problem, short of a more or less total ban, at least on plastic packaging.

The ***global warming*** that is already so obvious is mostly caused by gases from human industries—and industrial farming is a big contributor. CO2, methane, and compounds of nitrogen billow from modern fields and intensive herds. All these gases are 'natural'—they are key players in various ecosystems—but they also act as 'greenhouse gases' (GHGs). As recorded in chapter 1, the atmosphere now contains more than 400 ppm of CO2.

To be sure, in the very long-term global warming could almost be an asset. Two hundred million years ago the atmosphere contained an estimated 550 ppm CO2—and this was the time the first big dinosaurs flourished; a hugely rich assemblage of creatures, including the biggest that ever lived on land. In the Eocene epoch, from 55 to about 24 million years ago, CO2 levels were above 600 ppm and it was even hotter—and this is when the modern orders of mammals truly got into their stride. As the present world grows warmer vast areas that are now all-but uninhabitable, at least to human beings, will become positively pleasant: Siberia; northern Canada; Greenland; even Antarctica.

But the long term is too far away for human beings and for most of today's creatures. Warming right now is reducing habitable land as the glaciers and ice-shelves melt and sea-levels rise. Polar bears are the modern symbols of disaster as the Arctic ice on which they hunt for seals, is now too thin and fragile or fails to form at all. Hundreds of islands worldwide could soon disappear, some with thriving human societies and many or most with their quotas of unique species. If the coastal plains and the river valleys are flooded as is certainly on the cards then we would lose much of the world's most farmable land (including Britain's East Anglia) and almost all the world's greatest cities: London, Paris, New York, Prague, Amsterdam, and so on. Most animals these days cannot migrate as they please—big mammals in particular are confined to reserves—and will die where they stand as the habitat changes around them. For the foreseeable future, indeed, global warming caused by GHG pollution threatens to make nonsense of all our aspirations.

Yet still there are people in high places who deny global warming and refuse to consider that humanity is largely or entirely to blame for it—for as Noam Chomsky observed,

> *Even the simplest, the most obvious, the most crucial facts are invisible if they do not accord with the needs of power.*
>
> ('Beware Americans talking stability,' in *New Internationalist*, April 2011, p. 46.)

High on the list too of threats to wildlife the world over are ***'exotic' species*** or ***'invasive' species***, introduced from foreign lands by human beings, usually inadvertently but often deliberately. Britain now has around 2000 invasive species. Most of them are innocuous or indeed are assets but some—an estimated 15%—we could definitely do without. Many of Britain's most conspicuous mammals are imports: rabbits; brown and black rats; the house mouse; Sitka deer, Chinese water deer, and muntjacs; mink—astonishingly efficient, semiaquatic predators; plus various birds including the ubiquitous Canada Goose and the Ringed-necked Parakeets now flourishing in SE England; and terrapins, frogs, various fish including the Zander and indeed the Rainbow Trout and a growing shortlist of invertebrates including American crayfish and lady-birds and Chinese mitten crabs in the Thames, escaped from Chinese restaurants. Hawaii has suffered mightily from immigrant ants (it has no native ants of its own). California is full of Mediterranean plants while the Mediterranean is stuffed with American plants including prickly pear cacti and agaves; and both are bestrewn with eucalypts, from Australia. Australia in turn is plagued by rabbits, foxes, domestic cats from Europe and the Hawaiian Cane Toad (brought in to control rats in the sugar-cane fields of Queensland). New Zealand in turn is beleaguered by Australian possums, which among other things eat birds' eggs and carry TB. New Zealand does have some native mammals—bats, seals, and sealions—but it has no native *terrestrial* mammals. The possums were imported for their fur. I am writing these paragraphs in Portugal (I'd like to say I walked here in the manner of St Paul or Gandhi but alas it wouldn't be true) and have in view a patch of Bermuda Buttercup. In truth it's a wood sorrel (*Oxalis pes-caprae* in the family Oxalidaceae) from South Africa but either way it is highly invasive and very difficult to get rid of by acceptable means, since it propagates asexually by small bulbs which break off and stay in the ground when the plant is uprooted. In Portugal it is taking over entire habitats. In the bit of the Algarve where we are staying it is often hard to find a single wildflower that is not imported. It is all very depressing.

The damage done by exotics is sometimes obvious—Australia's imported foxes and feral cats are laying waste the native marsupials—but it is often more cryptic. European wasps in New Zealand rob whole chains of native species of their sustenance by pinching the gum from the native conifers. Imported trees and timber bring disease—the most spectacular being the American Chestnut blight, brought over with big-seeded Asian Chestnuts at the end of the 19th century in a misguided attempt to cross them with the native types. American Chestnuts once sustained entire nations of Native Americans in what is now the Eastern US. They were so abundant, it was said, that a squirrel could hop from chestnut tree to chestnut tree all the way from Georgia to Massachusetts without coming to ground. The blight fungus wiped out almost the entire species in a few decades in the early 20th century. Attempts to impede the spread of the disease by clear-felling may have made things worse, by removing that putative minority of trees that may have had some resistance. The near wipe-out of Common Elm from much of Britain and Western Europe in the late 20th century by a beetle-borne fungus is immeasurably sad but almost minor by comparison.

Despite the best and often heroic efforts of wildlife organizations (including WWF) and their wardens, the ***illegal traffic in endangered species***—for trophies, pets, and Chinese medicine—compares in scale with the illegal trades in arms, drugs, or human trafficking. Worse: the biggest, most spectacular, and/or rarest species are the most targeted. *All* the 'charismatic mega-vertebrates'—big cats, great apes, and all the five extant species of rhino—have been taken to the brink, or beyond, largely by hunting, and although elephant numbers may look reasonable on paper (for the time being, relatively speaking) their decline is such that all could be gone from the wild in a few decades or less. The many species of Europe's birds that migrate north to south with the seasons are hugely depleted by hunters, mainly in Malta, Cyprus, Egypt, Lebanon, and Syria who, according to Birdlife International, shoot about 25 million a year.

Many animals, too, are still hunted for ***bushmeat***—however meagre the pickings, and however rare the creatures may be: from Hyacinthine Macaws in South America to bushbabies in Africa, almost certainly including some species that are not yet known to science. This is almost excusable—the hunters for the most part are desperate, with families to feed—but it is no less regrettable and is surely preventable. If the people weren't so poor and/or had access to farmland they would not need to hunt to feed their families. I know there is more to it than that but the fact remains that there are benign solutions to all the world's problems which to a large extent are simply not tried because they would upset the *status quo*. It is easier to write off the wildlife or to shoot the poachers than it would be to create a more equitable economy.

There is no excuse at all for the wholesale devastation of sea-life by the world's ***industrial fisheries***. Whaling once was even worse—most of the more commercially desirable types were brought virtually to extinction by the 1950s. Then, mercifully, it was largely put a stop to by international law—but now (late 2018) the Japanese are planning to start commercial whaling again (as opposed to the kind ostensibly carried out for scientific purposes which they practice already). The usual pious excuses are given: 'human rights'; 'cultural heritage'; and, of course, the clincher—'economic growth.' Fishing communities have a right to make a living too no doubt but traditional, artisanal fishing did little or no long-term harm and employed far more people than the high-tech newcomers who are pushing them aside. Free market zealots are wont to claim that commercial fishing or whaling are self-limiting because, as the prey becomes rarer, it is no longer cost-effective to catch them. But this is simply not true, although it is the kind of falsehood that is seized upon in high places, eager to maintain the *status quo*. Whalers and fishers can and do pick off rare species in passing while making a living from commoner ones, and populations of wild creatures may become inviable even when numbers may still seem quite high. Blue Whales, the largest animals that have ever lived, were almost gone by the 1950s and although they are now protected, some biologists still fear that they may never recover. There may already be too few, in too large a space, to form viable, breeding populations. For any species, to judge what kind of yields are truly 'sustainable' requires very careful science over long periods—and the science, however well it is done, is bound still to be inexact. The idea that economists, applying a simplistic piece of economic dogma (as discussed in chapter 10), can make predictions of an ecological kind and so determine the fate of species and ecosystems, is absurd. But then the world as now run, and the pompous and lens-focused people who preside over it, *are* absurd. Instead of seeking to placate the powers-that-be in the name of 'realism,' scientists should be pointing out their absurdity—but those who do so do not generally get the top jobs.

Modern commercial fishing does enormous damage—***collateral damage***—to non-target species: to seabirds, corals, deep-sea habitats that are hardly yet known at all, and nursery grounds of all species on the seabed and in reefs and mangroves. As every schoolchild used to know, too, salmon live mainly in the sea but breed in rivers and suffer when the rivers are polluted or made inaccessible, while European eels breed in the Sargasso Sea in the Caribbean and feed in European wetlands and in Britain at least are endangered as wetlands are polluted and drained. This illustrates a grand principle: that ***many animals lead complex lives and need different habitats at different stages***. Many migrate huge distances, including those who seem too fragile for the task, including baby eels and hummingbirds and many a warbler, and Painted Lady butterflies, and all the components of their habitats—whether it's a friendly foodplant in the next field or a swamp in another continent—need to be in place if they are to survive. Typically, too, it takes years or centuries of dedicated natural history to work out what all the different creatures *do* need. (The necessary studies these days are aided by wondrous high technologies, from radio-tracking, night-vision cameras and drones to molecular biology—individual animals and groups are tracked by their DNA. Sometimes high tech *can* be highly 'appropriate' (chapter 5)).

Frightening, too, is the ***rate*** at which even the commonest species can disappear when the tide turns against them. In the last 100 or so years the Passenger Pigeon in the US, once so common that they sometimes broke the branches of big trees as they landed en masse, disappeared in a few decades (along with the American Chestnut). So too the Kakapo. The giant flightless parrot of New Zealand was once there for the taking (and was duly taken) but is now the subject of heroic rescue. The Black Rhinos of Africa were almost common even when I was a boy but are now reduced to a few hundred in the wild. In Britain, country people of my generation and indeed much younger describe the gentle call of the Turtle Dove as the sound of their childhood (just as it was of Shakespeare's and of Chaucer's). Now they are rare: a plunge from 250,000 in the 1960s to fewer than 5000 today, and the prospect of total wipe-out. With the probable exceptions of Brown Rats and cockroaches and other tough and versatile cashers-in on human detritus, nothing can be considered safe.

What, though, are we trying to achieve? And how can we judge improvement?

What does it mean to say that the biosphere is flourishing?

The health, wellbeing, or status of the biosphere can be judged in many different ways. Is the life ***abundant***—a high biomass per unit area? Is it ***productive***, producing a great biomass in a short time? Is the ecosystem ***stable***—able to stay more or less the same for many years, or millennia, at a stretch? Is it ***resilient***, able to bounce back after a set-back, or resist change, or change direction when it becomes impossible to adapt? Is it ***diverse***, with all that that implies: diversity of taxa—kingdoms, phyla, classes, families, species; genetic variation within each species; variety of ecotypes (ways of life); diversity of habitats—for different creatures, and for any one species at different phases of its life?

In practice, too, conservationists tend to ask, is the status quo ***natural?*** 'Natural' is an elusive concept which many philosophers have wrestled with, although usually to little avail. Some suggest that everything that exists is 'natural' since very obviously it is part of this world—but this implies that Heathrow airport is just as natural as a desert island, which seems simply to rob the word 'natural' of all meaning. In practice a 'natural' habitat is one that resembles the pristine state—what the landscape would be like if human beings didn't try deliberately to change it. This is a rough and ready definition but it hits the spot. In truth, for most purposes, rough and ready definitions often work best. Common sense fills in the gaps.

Yet none of these criteria of wellbeing, taken alone, is quite satisfactory. The vast boreal forests of Siberia or Canada have a huge biomass but their rate of growth—their ***productivity***—is low. Intensive feedlots produce an enormous amount of animal flesh in a very short time but they are hardly model ecosystems. In some ways, they are the precise antithesis. A desert landscape may be extremely ***stable*** precisely because there is very little in it to change. Nowhere is more stable than the moon. In general, the most diverse ecosystems tend to be the most stable—but some ecosystems are extremely stable and yet are almost monocultural, like the great bogs of sphagnum moss that form peat when they die, as in Ireland, Siberia, and Finland. Contrariwise, when one or a few 'keynote' species are removed from a diverse ecosystem hundreds more may follow in its wake—and precipitate loss of a whole cascade of species is not what is normally meant by stability.

Resilience is a better measure of wellbeing—but again, by itself, it is not enough. A eucalyptus forest may recover very quickly after fire (because eucalypts are beautifully adapted to resist fire) but eucalyptus forests tend to contain very little life apart from more eucalyptus, plus a few specialist feeders like the koala. They are not ideal models. ***Diversity*** is a good measure of wellbeing—but again it is not quite enough, taken alone. Suburbs can be extremely diverse precisely because they are so heterogeneous, with niches for cliff-dwellers like martens and peregrines, and for woodland and heathland species like foxes and butterflies. But not all species do adapt to suburbs by any means and all the suburbs in any one region tend to contain the same varied but nonetheless restricted suite of species and if any one country was *all* suburb, as increasing areas of Britain already are, a great many species would be lost. Then again, a zoo or a botanic garden may be extremely diverse. But the different creatures in a zoo or garden do not interact, or very little—and what really matters in a true ecosystem is or are the interactions. Wondrous though each may be, individual animals or plants are just the actors in the global theatre and as Hamlet observed, the play's the thing.

In truth, the quality that really matters in an ecosystem is life itself—in short, its ***dynamism***—or, better still, its ***vitality***. A flourishing ecosystem has the qualities of rich music. It has melody—the comings and goings of the creatures within it. It has harmony—the interactions of the whole. It has rhythm—day and night, winter-summer, dry season and rainy season. There is counterpoint—many different themes interweaving. There is variety of tone, amplitude, and intensity: sometimes non-stop action, sometimes tranquillity. Ecosystems, though, so far as is known, follow no precise, prescriptive score, like a symphony. They are more like jazz, not so much a composition as a meta-composition: basic rules, but with endless scope for improvisation, the outcome depending on the caprice and genius of the players. Whether it's Beethoven or Brubeck, the quality of music cannot be judged purely by the intellect and neither can anything else that really matters, including the wellbeing of ecosystems and of human societies. Quality can be analysed and may be quantified but above all it must be *felt*. Knowledge must be increased and analyses must be sharpened but above all, feelings must be cultivated.

Right now the biosphere is suffering on all counts—rapidly losing diversity, abundance, and vibrancy. So:

What do we really need to do to put things right?

Always we need to ask the three basic questions as listed in chapters 1 and 2:

WHAT IS IT GOOD TO DO?

WHAT IS NECESSARY?

WHAT IS POSSIBLE?

Always we find that if we *really* want to create convivial societies (with personal fulfilment) and take due care of our fellow creatures and the fabric of the Earth then we need to operate within the guidelines of morality and ecology. Always we find that nothing can be put to rights ad hoc. Everything we do and believe has to be re-thought from first principles—and this process must be repeated even when, or especially when, we think we have already got things right. And everything must be re-thought in the light of everything else.

When we apply these ideas to the particular issue of wildlife conservation we find we need to think along four main lines, each in concert with all the others:

1: Ecology

2: Land management

3: Economics

4: Attitude

All are vital. Briefly:

1: Ecology

Ecology is a matter both of attitude and of science. As England's Sir Humphry Davy (1778-1829) pointed out, we cannot hope to understand nature unless we approach it with

... an attitude of admiration, love and worship...

But Davy is best known as a scientist—one-time president of the Royal Society, an outstanding chemist and inventor of the miners' Davy lamp—and would surely have acknowledged that good intentions alone are not enough. We also need to know what we are doing insofar as this is possible—and for this we need good science.

The science that aspires to get to grips with the living world is that of ***ecology***, a term coined in the 1860s by the German biologist Ernst

Haeckel (1834-1919) from the Greek *oikos* meaning household—which also gives us the word 'economy.' The word 'ecology' caught on while 'biosphere,' coined a few years later apparently did not. A pity. Ecology is commonly perceived in academic circles and by grant-giving bodies to be an inferior pursuit, less taxing and therefore less worthy than, say, molecular biology. In truth it should be seen as the queen of the sciences because it deals most directly with life as it is—and life as it really is, is infinitely complex. The relationships between its infinite components are decidedly non-linear (cause and effect are never simple) and the whole pursuit is shot through with unknowns, and also as Donald Rumsfeld famously observed in another context with 'unknown unknowns,' and with unknowables—all of which means that the conclusions of ecology must always be uncertain. *All* science of course is uncertain (chapter 13) but ecology is uncertain in spades. Modern ecologists are good scientists, as well as naturalists, proposing testable hypotheses and applying intricate maths. But in the end, like physicians, they must act without perfect knowledge and rely even more than most scientists must on their own human judgement.

A few examples will illustrate the difficulties.

How much can we ever hope to understand?

First there's the problem of sheer ***numbers***. No one knows even to within an order of magnitude, how many species there are in the world. About 1.7 million have been formally described but that is clearly only a fraction of the whole. Some entire regions, often in places that are most likely to be species-rich, are as yet unexplored, and the places we may think have been studied to exhaustion—including Britain and the US—still produce surprises. With more intensive field studies and DNA analyses we can see that many groups of creatures we have identified and think of as single species in fact include several—or many. Simon Bearder of Oxford Brookes University reckons that there could be as many as 30 different species of bushbaby in West and Central Africa although only five or six have been formally described. Joel Cracraft of the New York Museum of Natural History, now suggests that there may be twice as many distinct species of birds as are formally recognized so far: not around 11,000, but 20,000-plus. Yet birds are probably the most thoroughly studied (and easiest to observe) of all animals. Sober calculations suggest that there could be as many as 30 million discrete (or more or less discrete) species of living creatures worldwide but in truth there could be many more than that. When DNA is isolated from the wild (as, remarkably, is almost easy to do these days) we find that most of it is from prokaryotes (bacteria and archaeans) and usually only a small fraction of what's found can be ascribed to any known species, meaning that the vast majority of wild prokaryotes are so far unidentified. On the grandest scale, it was only in the 1970s that Carl Woese, at the University of Illinois, perceived that the creatures that were then called Bacteria in fact include two distinct groups of organisms—the Bacteria proper and what he called the Archaea: so different that they should, said Woese, be placed in separate 'domains.' The body cells of creatures like us and oak trees are coalitions formed by combinations of at least one ancient archaean and various bacteria. Creatures that have these complex cells, including people and oak trees, are classed in third domain, the Eukaryota. The eukaryotes in short, and particularly big creatures like us with trillions of cells, are master-classes in cooperation. The point keeps recurring: ***competition is an escapable fact of nature but cooperation is the norm.***

For the time being, erring well on the side of conservatism, taxonomists are wont to suggest that there could be around 8 million species in all—of which we have identified less than a quarter. Since it can take a very long time to discover and describe even one species, we would never have a complete inventory even if all humanity was focused on the task, which it isn't. Taxonomy these days is a much neglected pursuit. Besides, new species are appearing all the time—not least through hybridization, which at least in plants has proved to be far more frequent than was ever supposed; and although many hybrids are infertile (as mules generally are), hybrid plants in particular may become fertile through a variety of somewhat recondite mechanisms. It is impossible to know, too, how many species are present and operating within any one habitat but—when we add in the inconspicuous types, like the fungi and single-celled 'protists' and the prokaryotes, as we surely should—it must almost always run into thousands. In short, we don't even know what's out there, and never can.

Then there's the issue of ***complexity.*** What matters is or are the interactions between the players—and the number of possible interactions is, literally, infinite; and although the relationships are to a significant extent competitive, overall they are ***synergistic*** or—a better term—***mutualist***, meaning beneficial to both or all (or at least some) of the players.

One example can serve to illustrate complexity—and mutualism: that of the Almendro tree (*Andira inermis*), which I was introduced to in Panama; a beautiful umbrella-shaped leguminous tree, meaning it's related to the laburnum (and gorse and peas and beans). It produces festoons of pink flowers after the rains in April, each succeeded, when duly pollenated, by pods, each with a single seed. The pods are woody, but each pod is coated with a green and tasty pulp.

Monkeys and many other species come to feast on the almendro pods and most do the tree very little good at all—like the monkeys that mostly crunch the pods in situ and eat the seeds, although they do drop a few. The banqueteers who are truly useful to the tree are the fruit bats (similar to Old World flying foxes though a separate lineage) which carry away the pods—because if they stayed to feed on the tree they would be picked off by owls, among the mortal enemies of bats. The fruit bats fly off with the pods to somewhere safe—and so disperse the heavy seeds.

But bats can't crunch the pods. They simply eat the pulp around the outside, and let the pods fall to the ground. So far so good—but the seeds remain trapped in their wooden casks. Enter the agoutis, large relatives of the guinea pig. They break open the pods and eat the seeds—but they don't eat all of them. They bury some for later, like European squirrels burying nuts (and many other rodents too). So the seeds are not only dispersed, but planted.

Still the story is not ended. If the agouti comes back later and digs up the buried seeds then that is still bad news for the tree; and if the agoutis forget a few of them and allow them to germinate, they come along later and polish off the shoots. So we come to the final player—the ocelot; those beautiful, middle-sized spotted cats. They eat a fair proportion of the agoutis—and so it is that many of the buried seeds, or the shoots, do not get eaten. So the next generation of almendros is planted, and their future is assured.

Except that it isn't. For the final, final player is not the ocelot. As always, it is us, human beings. For hunters trap ocelots—their fur is too tempting. So more agoutis survive than nature intended. For good measure, we have also messed up the climate so the spring rains are not as emphatic as once they were and unless there are short, sharp downpours, the almendros do not bloom so readily. No flowers, no seeds. Our own ways of life are very good for some creatures (like rats and cockroaches) but on the whole we can see once again that our impact is negative in ways we just could not have anticipated.

Note how complex this story is—and how counter-intuitive. Who could have guessed that the fate of a tree depends on a spotted cat, whose only interest in trees, one might suppose, is as a hunting ground or a look-out post? In fact it took decades to work out the intricacies—by a very accomplished field scientist, Egbert Leigh, of the Smithsonian Institution, which has a field station in Panama. Note, too, that seed dispersal is only one aspect of the almendro's life. Leguminous trees in general, by fixing nitrogen and increasing soil fertility significantly but not too much, are key players in tropical forest ecology as a whole; and of course they interact with the mycorrhizas that underpin all wild ecosystems; and with goodness knows how many insects and arachnids and birds and fungi and all the rest that live and feed among their branches.

Yet, it's been calculated, there could be 30,000 or so different species of trees in the neotropics (from the north of Mexico down to northern Argentina and Chile). Their lives, we may presume, are not all as complex as the almendro but some are more so—like the world's 800 or so species of figs (key players in all tropical forests), each of which is pollinated by its own specialist species of wasp (see my own *The Secret Life of Trees* (2005).) In short: it would take more time than is left in the life of the Earth itself to describe all that is going on in a tropical forest even if all the biologists in the world worked all their lives at it.

Right now, though, the deadly combination of conventional governments and big business are sweeping the complexity aside to make way for neoliberal agriculture which, for the most part, is not needed (chapter 6). We could say, as Jesus did, 'Forgive them for they know not what they do,' but I can't help feeling that this would be taking forbearance too far. Even Jesus had his breaking point. All four gospels tell us how he turned over the money-changers' tables in the temple and this is surely a comparable case, writ even larger. In any case, people in high places really should know what they are doing, or at least try to.

The almendro story shows how ***cryptic*** the wiles of nature may be and how hard it is to work out what's really going wrong when species and ecosystems start to languish: and it shows too the damage that human beings can do even in passing (by killing spotted cats we also kill trees) and at long range (for we all contribute to climate change).

The decline of puffins on many of the islands around northern Britain and in Iceland provides another example. In spring when they flocked to off-shore islands to breed in burrows, puffins were thick on the ground (literally) but just in the past few years numbers on at least some of the islands have sadly declined. Is this because local people harvest the birds and their eggs for food? Probably not. They have been doing this for centuries without serious impact. Is it because commercial fishermen harvest the sand-eels which are the birds' principal food (not to sell but as bait for bigger fish)? They certainly have an impact.

But again the prime cause may be global warming. For the sand-eels that feed the puffins in turn feed on planktonic crustaceans known as copepods. There are still plenty of copepods around Scotland and Iceland but as the sea has warmed, albeit by only half a degree, the northern species of copepods have been increasingly displaced by species from the south. The southern copepods are less fatty than the northern ones—the fat is for cold-resistance, and the warmer the sea the less it is needed. So the southern types are less calorific and hence less nourishing than the northern types—so the sand-eels are undernourished. So there are fewer. So the puffins suffer. That at least is one highly plausible hypothesis.

The puffin story illustrates too the key issue of ***non-linearity***. There is no simple relationship in nature between cause and effect—and this means too that we, human beings, cannot predict with more than broad-brush accuracy how things may turn out. There are always unforeseen and to some extent unforeseeable consequences which virtually always include collateral damage. Advocates of modern-day, high-tech agriculture—that is: governments, big business, and their chosen advisers—take it to be obvious that they do know what they are doing, and how things will turn out. They are, after all, informed by science, and science is precise, is it not? 'Precision farming' is now a favourite buzz-word. But farming should be an exercise in applied ecology and true ecologists know that we can never know in detail where any of our actions will lead; and philosophers of science have been pointing out for centuries—Nicholas of Oresme (1320-1382) made the point well enough in the 14th century—that science itself must *always* deal in uncertainties (chapter 13). Always in our dealings with nature we must exercise the ***precautionary principle***. But modern governments and industries are gung-ho and thus fall foul of what for the Ancient Greeks was the mother of all sins, which is hubris: presuming to usurp the powers of the gods. The result, commonly, is disastrous.

The tale of the *Partula* snails in French Polynesia shows what disasters may ensue when people (agriculturalists, scientists, politicians, captains of commerce) seek to manipulate nature even with the best of intentions. Thus in the 1800s the giant African land snail *Achatina* was introduced to islands in the Pacific as a food source: mega-escargots. But the *Achatinas* bred like mad and became a major pest, eating everything in sight. Gardeners easily could harvest a wheelbarrow-full in the early morning as the sun came up and then do the same the next day. So in 1955 French agriculturalists introduced a predatory snail from Florida, *Euglandina rosea,* into French Polynesia, to destroy the *Achatina*. Snails seem unlikely predators but *Euglandina* kills other snails by tracking their slime trails then climbing on top and boring through their shells with their *radula*, an organ unique to gastropods which they wield like a file. Then they can gorge at leisure on the soft flesh within. Whelks operate in much the same way.

But *Achatinas* have thick shells. Easier by far were the small, local snails of the genus *Partula*. In Tahiti and the nearby islands rampaging *Euglandinas* polished off 64 of the native partula species within a decade. The IUCN's Red List of Threatened species for 2009 tells us that of the 80-odd known species of partulas 51 are totally extinct, 11 are extinct in the wild, and another 13 are critically endangered. The introduction of *Euglandina* was an exercise in biological pest control—the attempt to control unwanted invaders without recourse to industrial chemistry. This seems commendable enough but it can go horribly wrong and often has done because we simply don't know enough about wild ecosystems and how they react to intervention. *Euglandina* apparently were introduced to French Polynesia without proper trials—though even the best-laid trials don't always tell us what we need to know. Far be it from me to point fingers but the French do seem to be especially gung-ho their dealings with the biosphere, particularly in their colonies, far from their own doorstep. In similar vein, between 1966 and 1996 they carried out no fewer than 193 nuclear tests in French Polynesia. But no society is innocent. All meddle well beyond their competence.

All this may sound like a recipe for despair. For if we simply carry on with business as usual, taking what we need from the biosphere and allowing the rest to take potluck, then surely the decline will continue. On the other hand we don't know enough, and never can know enough, to take matters in hand with any surety of success.

Yet we need not give up. There are some huge serendipities. In particular, nature often proves remarkably resilient—far more so than we might dare to have hoped. Thus the American bison has recovered from a seriously low base at the end of the 19th century to relative security today, mainly just by being left alone. Britain's RSPB (the Royal Society for the Protection of Birds) has brought Marsh Harriers back to its reserve at Minsmere, Suffolk, not by reintroducing them but simply by creating suitable habitat—in this case reedbeds—whereupon they flew in from mainland Europe. The Channel is no obstacle, and it is remarkable how quickly the buzz gets round among wild birds of all species that there's new habitat on offer. Other species, though, like the Red Kite and the beaver have been actively reintroduced into Britain (beavers were once common). Some species the world over, like the Mauritius Kestrel, have been helped back to relative security by active intervention which may include breeding in captivity or at least in sheltered reserves (as outlined in my book of 1991, *Last Animals at the Zoo*). And although we cannot and never will be able to control and direct the wilderness with precision (which we surely should be glad about), we have identified a few basic principles, a combination of hard, quantified science and common sense, that seem to apply well enough in most circumstances. For example:

A few key principles

James Lovelock's concept of *Gaia*, mentioned in passing in chapter 2, is of key importance. Ecology in general leads us to perceive that all creatures directly or indirectly interact with all others. Gaia goes one step further: it tells us that ***living creatures together profoundly affect the structure, the chemistry, and therefore the behaviour of the fabric of the Earth itself.*** Soil bacteria turn clay into loam. Even more dramatically, there would be little (virtually zero) free oxygen in the atmosphere if it weren't for all the creatures—cyanobacteria, diatoms and other 'protists,' seaweeds, and of course plants—that practice photosynthesis, and release free oxygen gas in such vast quantities. Oxygen in turn oxidizes rocks: all those red rocks found all over the world and feature so prominently in the brooding landscapes of western movies are red because the iron within them has been oxidized by free oxygen, produced by green organisms. Oxygen also provides the ozone layer in the stratosphere that filters out cosmic rays which, in all but the most minute doses, are lethal to all Earthly creatures. Limestone rocks and cliffs, and flints, are the fossilised skeletons of various marine protists. The salt concentration of the sea remains steady at around 3.4 per cent because some of those protists, including the diatoms, foramens, and radiolarians, extract calcium and silicon to build their skeletons and this upsets the ionic balance and causes sodium and chloride in particular to precipitate out and form salt-beds. Since the salt in the sea is washed off from the land and since the oceans are about 3.5 billion years old the sea would be saturated in salt by now if it were not for this precipitation. If the sea was saturated then, like the Dead Sea, set between Israel and Jordan, it would be populated at best only by extremely salt-tolerant microbes.

This, plus the convenient provision of the ozone layer and the moderation of ocean chemistry and much else besides illustrate the second great significance of Gaia: that ***living organisms not only influence, profoundly, the nature of the Earth's fabric, but also tend overall, collectively, to keep the Earth in a state that is hospitable to life.*** In other words the biosphere as a whole, the Earth and all its creatures, acts like a giant organism. All the individual parts interact with, and are dependent upon, all the other parts—which is one conception of the term 'organic' (albeit not what chemists mean by it). Furthermore, the collective as a whole tends to keep itself in a steady state—a state that favours its own survival—which is the phenomenon of ***homeostasis***: which is a key characteristic of living organisms. Lovelock does not say that the Earth with its biosphere *is* a living organism; merely that it is analogous to a living organism. That in itself is a very strong statement, however—for no sane person would dream of taking liberties with a living creature of the kind that we take routinely with the Earth—not if they wanted the creature to live. No one would dig great chunks out of an animal and remove its vital organs and expect the rest to carry on as normal, in the way that we, for example, now mine the earth and obliterate rainforests. Thus the idea of Earth-as-organism is most salutary, did we but care to heed its implications. Gaia is at least a very powerful metaphor: and all human understanding in the end is metaphor (as discussed further in chapters 13 and 14).

Population size is of huge importance. We might assume, commonsensically, that creatures with vast populations are safe from extinction—but the stories of the Passenger Pigeon, the American chestnut, and the English elm (though it still hangs on in hedgerows) show that this just is not so. It is true though for all kinds of reasons that if any population falls below a certain critical number—which can be quite a high number—extinction becomes more or less inevitable. The Noah's Ark approach—one breeding pair per species—will not do. Genetic diversity is needed and if there are too few breeding animals then diversity is quickly lost—for each parent passes on only half of its genes and if only a few are breeding at any one time then some genetic variants won't get passed on at all and so the diversity dwindles rapidly with each generation. This is called ***genetic drift.*** Creatures whose numbers were depleted in the past but have now (partially) recovered still show the effects of this—as in cheetahs, African wild dogs, and elephant seals, which genetically are far too uniform for comfort. There's a huge threat too in small populations from ***demographic stochasticity.*** Populations ideally are 50% male and 50% female but this is only an average. Because of random variation it has sometimes happened that all the new babies in a small population are of the same sex—or that the only remaining male or female is infertile, or gets run over, or some such. Put accident, drift, stochasticity and other possible setbacks together and we find that as a rule of thumb, wild populations smaller than about 500 are extremely vulnerable. Many, nowadays, are below that threshold or right on the edge.

Habitats too need to be as large as possible. Five hundred tigers, for example, need an awful lot of territory. In addition, habitats that are too small suffer from ***edge effects:*** incursion of the outside world. The Great Bustard, one variant of which is the world's heaviest flying bird, suffers greatly from edge effects because it does not feel secure and will not breed unless it can keep well away from perceived threats, including the threat of human beings. Fragmented habitats can sometimes be linked by ***wildlife corridors,*** but corridors have a downside too—if, for example, they allow damaging predators or vigorous rivals to invade. Nothing is simple.

As mentioned too, the habitats of many animals are highly heterogeneous and ***all the different components need to be in place.*** Migrating geese, for example, commonly need to feed *en route* and if some marsh where they stop for refreshment has been drained and turned into a casino or an intensive cattle unit (or, like one I encountered in Panama, as a place to store surplus containers), they are sunk. Thus the whole world needs to be integrated—as acknowledged by the Ramsar Convention of 1971 which established rules for international cooperation. Sanity does prevail sometimes, though not often enough.

Then, somewhat counter-intuitively, it has become apparent in recent years that the traditional idea of 'trophic level' needs to be re-assessed. That is, ecologists took it for granted that in any given climate soil-type sets the tone of all ecosystems since the soil determines what plants can grow and the plants in turn determine what herbivores will be able to thrive, and the herbivores in turn determine what predators can evolve and flourish. The predators, in short, have commonly been thought of as dependents.

But in the 1960s the American ecologist Robert T. Paine (1933-2016) turned this apparently self-evident thesis on its head. He began his studies in rockpools. Unpolluted rockpools the world over are complex ecosystems with many different species doing many different things—photosynthesizers, grazers, predators, detritus feeders. The top predators, commonly, are starfish—so the commonsense theory suggests that if the starfish were removed, the rest should flourish. So in a spirit of inquiry Paine did remove the starfish from rockpools—and found that, contrary to expectation, the other species died off, until very little remained. The starfish, he said, act as ***keystone species***. Take them out and the whole ecosystem collapses. In short: the chain of influence in an ecosystem runs both ways. The top predators influence all the other creatures and ultimately the vegetation itself just as the vegetation influences the predators. More generally, an ecosystem with the predators in place is likely to be far more diverse and abundant than one without.

Now it's been shown the world over that languishing ecosystems of all kinds can often be restored and even raised to undreamt heights by reintroducing particular species, especially predators, that had previously been misguidedly removed to protect the rest. Yellowstone national park has been vastly improved by reintroducing wolves. For the wolves hang around near rivers where they know the deer must come to drink—and so the deer steer clear of the rivers unless and until their thirst really gets the better of them. Thus the riverside vegetation including trees is allowed to grow, which it cannot if deer are constantly nibbling. The roots of the plants stabilize the riverbanks which would otherwise erode—to the advantage of bankside creatures and of fish and all other aquatic species.

I suggest, as others have too, that the concept needs to be extended somewhat. Instead of individual keystone species, we should rather think of ***keystone core groups***: shortlists of creatures which between them set the tone of the whole. Thus the kelp forests off the coast of California operate as a trio. The kelp itself is essential of course—no kelp, no ecosystem. But sea urchins are essential too—they eat the kelp and keep it in order. The third essential player is, as always, the top predator—in this case the sea otter, for whom sea urchins are the staple diet. Without otters, the sea urchins run riot. Take any one of the three away and the whole system collapses.

I reckon that this principle—key core groups—is or could be of huge relevance to the practice of ***agroecology.*** As discussed in chapter 6, the idea of agroecology is to treat all farms as ecosystems and agriculture as a whole as a positive contributor to the biosphere (insofar as that is possible). The general idea is to create landscapes that on the one hand provide crops and livestock that people need and want (which is the 'agro' bit) but which also are as wildlife friendly and diverse as possible, and as close to the putatively pristine ('natural') state. At present there is much debate in Britain and indeed the world as to whether or not agroecological systems should include livestock—cattle, sheep, goats, pigs, chickens, ducks—and if so, how many. The ever-more vociferous vegans insist that landscapes would be far more productive—better both for people and for wild species—if they contained no livestock at all. Yet common observation and the principle of the keystone core group suggest that landscapes can be far *richer* if they include a range of herbivores (though of course not too many), which could be wild deer or could just as well be domestic cattle and sheep, plus top predators. On farms, as opposed to national parks, human beings stand in for wolves and lions.

More broadly, it becomes increasingly clear that many wild ecosystems that we think of as 'natural' are in truth languishing, far less diverse and abundant than they could be—because, in the past, insouciant farmers or well-meaning but misguided conservationists have removed particular predators or herbivores to encourage the others and in practice have undermined the whole system. Many present-day landscapes from the hillsides of Wales to the Serengeti to the North American prairie operate far below their potential just because we intervene too much, or have done so in the past. In general both in farming and in conservation we need to be more relaxed, less authoritative, because we don't know as much as we think we do. Go with the *Dao,* as the Chinese have it. But we have to have some conception of what we should be trying to achieve, and how to make it happen. This is where the science comes in.

2: How to manage land: land spared and land shared

Any one piece of land can be organized and used in an infinite number of ways but among the myriad options we can discern two main strategies: ***land sparing*** and ***land sharing.***

Neoliberal governments which nowadays include all of the most powerful ones favour land-sparing. Some land is ear-marked for cities, airports, roads, etc; some for agriculture; some for forestry; some for 'leisure'; and whatever is left over, which usually means whatever is less suitable for more profitable purposes, may be left alone (up to a point) or managed as 'wilderness,' sometimes officially categorized as a wildlife reserve or, if it is big enough, granted the status of national park.

Advocates of land-sparing claim that it is the most 'efficient' strategy. In particular, agriculture of the intensive, industrial kind—monocultural arable and plantations, and intensive animal feedlots that culminate in the CAFO ('concentrated animal feeding operation')—do indeed produce huge amounts of food per hectare, which in theory at least should leave far more for wilderness. Intensive industrial farming can also be highly profitable, at least as long as oil is affordable, which it will be as long as it lasts because the price is carefully manipulated to make sure that it is. So it all sounds good—at least to neoliberal governments for whom 'efficiency' and 'profit' are the key desiderata, and in practice are taken to mean the same thing.

Closer inspection, however, reveals that all is not so simple. Intensive livestock units may house a million pigs (literally) or chickens, or thousands or even tens of thousands of cattle, in a few hectares. This looks like fabulous efficiency. But the captive beasts are fed on cereal and soya that has been grown on many thousands of hectares, commonly in some far-flung place and generally at the expense of forest, wildlife, and local farming, plied with mega-tonnes of oil-based fertilizer, herbicide, fungicide, bactericide, and pesticide. A big pig unit can produce as much ordure as a major city although often, or usually, without comparable sewage disposal. The local river commonly must bear the load. The produce—meat or milk—is then transported hundreds or thousands of miles by oil-powered trucks and container ships. There is no true synergy between the livestock and their feed crops, as there always should be between plants and animals. The whole operation may seem efficient in terms of cash, at least within the present economy, but in terms of fuel energy expended per unit of food energy produced it is grotesque. Vast quantities of fresh water too are expended to grow the feed crops—irrigation for agriculture is by far the main drain on this most precious resource. The overall collateral damage is huge and if it was properly costed—'whole-cost accountancy'—such farming would be shown to be very expensive indeed.

The idea, too, that the land that is theoretically 'spared' by hyper-intensive farming is thereby released for wildlife is largely fictional. Instead, every effort is made to maximize production—and then to increase consumption to match; and this is then said to be meeting 'demand.' The myth is perpetrated that the world needs more and more food whereas in truth, as outlined in chapter 6, the world already produces about twice what we really need. But money rules and profit is maximized if farmers produce as much as possible. ***Agricultural strategy today is designed in large part to dispose of arable surpluses, mainly by feeding about half of what's produced to livestock and then encouraging meat consumption and if the surplus meat can't be sold then the surplus grains are burnt and called 'biofuel.'*** Indeed, global agricultural strategy as it stands, if 'strategy' is the right word, is to a large extent a scam, based on misconception and or indeed on lies.

Land sharing, on the other hand, seeks to combine land-uses: to use any one piece of land as far as possible for many different purposes. The ideal, as I see things, is a combination of sparing and sharing—but with the accent very much on sharing. That is: some areas *should* be used exclusively for human purposes, with no other species admitted. The intensive care unit is the prime example. Microbes are always present (they live in super-abundance in the gut) but they are not allowed to roam free in an ICU and everything that can be kept out, is kept out.

We also need enough wilderness (or as near to wilderness as possible) to maintain viable—meaning large—populations of truly wild animals—which means we need all the wilderness we can provide. Overall, right now, wildlife reserves are islands in a sea of human habitation whereas, if the world as a whole is truly to be resilient, we need things to be the other way around: islands of human activity in a matrix of wilderness.

But at least in the urbanized world by far the majority of land should be as mixed-use as possible. Agriculture *can* be wildlife-friendly and yet provide all the food that people need—and indeed provide much better food than has become usual, supporting all the world's greatest cuisines (chapter 7). The present shortfalls in supply and the collateral damage result overwhelmingly from bad strategy; destructive economics and inappropriate science. In general, small mixed farms should be the norm, with many more farmers—perhaps 10 times as many as is now the norm in countries like Britain. Much of Britain's countryside in the past was far more populous than it is now—the remains of half-forgotten, largely buried villages are everywhere—and yet had many times more wild creatures. I remember when skylarks were common and lapwings and curlews flew and settled in great flocks—and now over most of the country they are rare. Even 50 years ago the dawn chorus could be all-but deafening (and the Turtle Dove was heard throughout the countryside).

In truth, though, at the time of writing (Spring 2020) no-one can properly judge whether agriculture would be best served by land-sparing or land-sharing because land-sharing in a modern form has not yet been tried on a large enough scale or in a sufficient variety of conditions. I am pretty sure however that land-sharing should be the default strategy—what should be done unless there is *very* good reason to do something else.

Cities can be remarkably wildlife-friendly too. In industrialized, urbanized countries like Britain the suburbs can be the most biodiverse habitats of all, because they provide so many various niches. In Britain, foxes are now more common in cities than in the country—and far friendlier. The total species list of London is astonishing. I was in Old Delhi in the 1980s when it still contained the greatest concentration and diversity of birds of prey of any place on Earth. In some roads there were vultures and eagles in every tree. They didn't bother the people and the people didn't bother them. Peregrine falcons are now almost commonplace in some of the world's greatest cities from Chicago to Prague and Berlin. They control the feral pigeons (up to a point). In the late 1990s I came across the biggest heronry I have ever encountered—in the middle of Istanbul. In St Lucia, South Africa, hippopotamuses come into the town to graze on the manicured lawns (they prefer short grass) and although hippos in Africa kill more people than any other large animal the people and hippo of St Lucia seem to get along well enough, each respecting the others' space. Hippos, it seems, like most (all?) intelligent animals are not vicious. Mostly they are just nervous, and easily confused, and tend to hit out. Today the world's greatest concentration of leopards is in Mumbai. They live mainly on feral pigs. This surely is not ideal but it does show that wild creatures (Great Bustards aside) can be remarkably adaptable and that human beings and even the most potentially dangerous of creatures can rub along if they give each other a chance. The world's great cities—London, Chicago, Prague, Istanbul, Delhi—were not designed with wildlife in mind, but they were designed with *people* in mind, with variety and space. They were *not* built expressly to maximize profit, as cramped as possible, with every square inch costed. When and if the planners do take proper account of wildlife (as is beginning to happen here and there—one of the few convincing reasons for hope) the results can be wondrous. Bitterns booming from the reeds are symbols of wilderness and secretiveness but now they are living in a newly-created wetland in South-West London. Wildlife-friendly cities surely cannot make up for the wholesale loss of truly wild spaces but they can certainly make a difference.

But we cannot have wildlife-friendly farming and wildlife-friendly cities so long as the economy is single-mindedly dedicated to short-term profit. We need a quite different economy: different structure, different ideals.

3: A wildlife-friendly economy

John Maynard Keynes was among many economists who pointed out that the economy should serve *us*, human beings. We should not tailor our lives to suit the economy. Alas, only a few economists have argued so far that the economy should be 'green'—that it should serve our fellow creatures as well as ourselves. The present economy, though—the neoliberal kind—is not designed for either. It is designed to maximize wealth—and, in practice, to concentrate that wealth in fewer and fewer hands. The focus is on 'economic growth.' The excuse for this—based on an over-interpreted comment of Adam Smith in the 18th century—is that if we simply seek to maximize wealth then everything else will fall into place.

The trouble is that it won't, and doesn't. So long as the world's leaders continue in the belief that 'growth' is the *sine qua non*, not to say the panacea, and that it can be continued indefinitely, then the biosphere is sunk—and we with it. We need to turn economics on its head and to re-position economists in the social-intellectual hierarchy. As Keynes said:

If economists could manage to get themselves thought of as humble, competent people on a level with dentists, that would be splendid.

Ecologists and moralists should be setting the tone, with economists employed as executives and operatives. We need them together to provide us with 'Green Economic Democracy,' as discussed further in chapters 9 and 10.

Nothing worthwhile can be achieved, though, or not at least on any robust basis, unless we give a damn. Truly to put the biosphere on to a secure footing (and ourselves) we need the right *attitude*.

4: A matter of attitude

Human beings individually and collectively have exhibited a broad spectrum of attitudes towards nature, from fear and downright hostility—forest has often been seen to be uncivilized, or a sign of backwardness, or in any case a matter of shame—to the respect and deference of the Jains, who may brush the ground in front of them as they walk for fear of treading on insects. The principal division is between those who feel that the world was created (or in any case exists) for the express benefit of human beings, or indeed of their particular selves—an attitude that is ***anthropocentric*** or indeed ***egocentric***; and those who feel that we, human beings, should see ourselves as part of the whole biosphere, humbly beholden to it—a viewpoint that is ***biocentric*** (or ***ecocentric*** or indeed ***gaiacentric***).

Some of those in the anthropocentric camp take their lead from The Bible which in Genesis 1: 26 (King James version) says:

And God said, Let us make man in our image, after our likeness: and let them have dominion over the fish of the sea, and over the fowl of the air, and over the cattle, and over all the earth, and over every creeping thing that creepeth upon the earth.

Some insist that 'dominion' implies stewardship while others have all too readily taken it to mean that the world is ours to dispose of as we will; our very own cornucopia, or 'natural resource,' as the modern jargon has it. Both interpretations at least take it for granted that human beings are special; that there is an 'us' and a 'them.'

This is taken to be the 'rational' point of view and ever since the Enlightenment it has increasingly been accepted that 'rationality' must triumph over mere sentiment or intuition; and ever since the 18th century in particular, rationality has been equated with material gain. Yet if our attitude to nature is wholly materialistic, then the biosphere will collapse, and we with it, which doesn't seem 'rational' at all. In truth, we *need* to live in harmony with the rest of nature and to do this we need a change not simply of policy but of mindset. ***Above all, we need in some form or other to restore a sense of the sacred.***

More in chapter 14.

Part III

ACTION

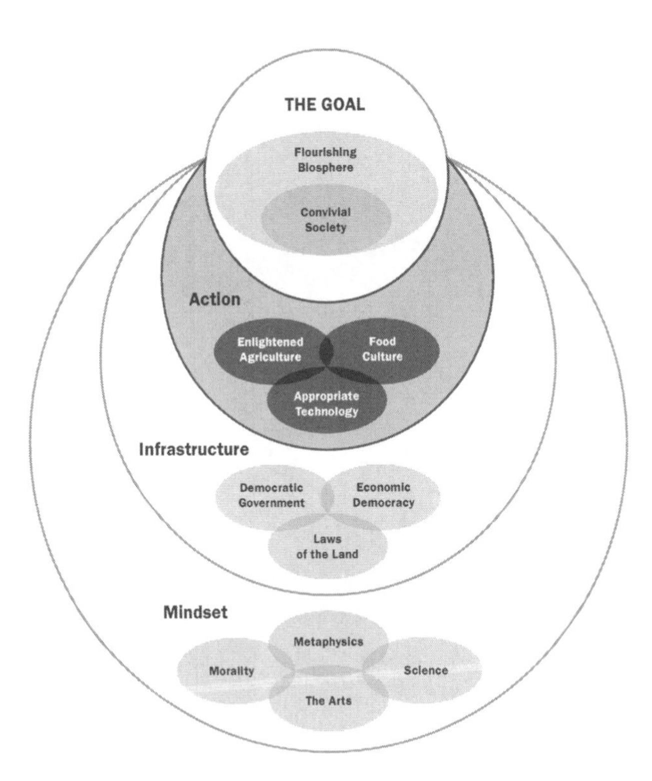

5

JOBS, CRAFTS, AND ROBOTS

The advance of science and technology means a human future of change so rapid and of such kinds, of tests and challenges so unprecedented, of decisions and possible non-decisions so momentous and insidious in their consequences, that mankind—that is surely clear—will need to be in full possession of its full humanity.

F.R. Leavis (1895-1978). From Two Cultures? The Significance of C.P. Snow (1962)

WHETHER OUR DESCENDANTS AND OUR FELLOW CREATURES will enjoy the sunlit uplands for the next million years (and then some), or will hit the buffers in a few decades' time, depends in the end on phenomena and events over which we have little or no control, like volcanoes and errant asteroids—or even, perhaps, some runaway virus. But the future depends too on what we, human beings, actually *do*; and that, in turn, depends on what technologies we come up with and put our weight and our money behind.

At the moment, despite the claims of some sincere optimists and a great many opportunist mountebanks, we are certainly not heading for the uplands. The buffers beckon, more urgently with each passing day. If we really want to create convivial societies and promote personal fulfilment and take proper care of the biosphere—if we feel that this might be rather a good idea—then we need technologies that are expressly geared to those ends, guided as ever by the bedrock principles of morality and ecology.

As things are, though, the neoliberal mindset prevails and the goal of modern technology is for the most part hedonistic and strictly materialist: more leisure, less work, with ever-increasing piles of wealth concentrated in fewer and fewer hands—mainly those of the superpowers and transnational corporates. Yet, very obviously, hedonism does not necessarily lead to happiness and happiness that is rooted in hedonism is not necessarily or usually fulfilling. We want our work to be agreeable and very few of us like to work all the time ('workaholism' is surely pathological) but all of us as human beings *need* work. Nothing is more erosive than forced unemployment. Furthermore, all too obviously, our modern, powerful technologies are trashing the natural world more rapidly and profoundly than ever before.

As always, to put things right, we need to think again from first principles—beginning, as always, with the most basic questions. Such as:

I: WHAT *IS* TECHNOLOGY?

Technology includes all the things that help us to get to grips with the material world and make our own lives easier, and all the tools and techniques by which we produce those things. Under this broad umbrella come textiles, ceramics, furniture, tools, musical instruments, sewing machines, the saddle and the bridle, kayaks, sailing ships and ocean liners, motor cars, trains, and jumbo jets, the telephone, lasers, computers, plus buildings and roads and sewers and all the rest which are the stuff of cities—which is to say are the stuff of civilization. For although the word 'civilization' *ought* to have connotations of good manners and humane governance it literally just means 'citification' from the Latin *civis* meaning 'city.' Cities, and hence 'civilization' in general, like all the products of technology, or indeed like everything that we do, can be either good or bad or, as is usual, both at the same time.

It used to be thought that only human beings use tools—and then it became clear that a lot of other animals do too, including macaques which may use rocks to break the shells of clams and thrushes that smash snails by bashing them against big stones (and so it now transpires do some fish!). So then anthropologists said that human beings are the only creatures that *make* tools ('Man the toolmaker' was the standard phrase, and one of the oldest human fossils from around two million years ago was called *Homo habilis*—'handy man'). But this turned out to be untrue too. For instance, chimps modify twigs with which to dig out grubs and termites and New Caledonian crows in the laboratory bend bits of wire to make hooks for similar purposes, and presumably in the wild do something similar with twigs. So then it was suggested that human beings are the only animals that use tools to make better tools—and so it was that a silversmith cousin of mine (Timothy Selwood of Clerkenwell) told me he spent more time making tools for fashioning silver than he did on the silver itself. All in all it is probably best to acknowledge as Charles Darwin said that most of what we do has some precedent in other creatures. But only we, the ultimately versatile and indeed protean creatures, combine all the skills in one—with the help of our tools.

Richard Dawkins felicitously coined the expression ***extended phenotype*** to describe the sum of the unassisted creature *plus* all the things that it uses and makes (where 'phenotype' is the sum of the animal's physical structure, physiology, and behaviour). Technology enables us to realize our full potential—or as the English-American physicist and all-round intellectual Freeman Dyson (1923-2020) put the matter:

> *Technology is a gift of God. After the gift of life it is perhaps the greatest of God's gifts. It is the mother of civilizations, of arts and of sciences.*

Indeed we might suggest in similarly metaphysical vein that our technologies are what enable us (or chimpanzees or New Caledonian crows) fully to be the creatures that God intended us to be. In this respect technology (like science, and the arts, and all scholarship) can be seen as a godly pursuit.

From stone hammers to IT

We can usefully identify three grades of technology:

Primitive

Artisanal/ traditional, including all bona fide **crafts**

And:

High tech

Primitive technologies are of the kind that chimps and crows (and some fish) might also adopt: stone tools and bent twigs and the rest.

Artisanal or *traditional* technologies, including all *crafts,* form the bulk of all human technologies. At least until the 19th century *all* technology was artisanal and most of what we take for granted today still is, albeit often modified by science. Artisanal technologies include needles and nails and chisels and saws, and the baskets and textiles that were built with their aid; ceramics; clocks and watches; spades and ploughs; temples and cathedrals; the world's great wooden ships and all their intricate accoutrements, powered by sail and human muscle; and weapons of war from spears of horn and basalt and bronze to Samurai swords of the finest steel, to cannons and muskets. All should properly be called 'traditional,' or 'artisanal' (from 'artisan') because they were brought to a very high level of perfection not with the aid of formal science but simply by *craft*, which is a combination of skill, common sense, traditional knowledge, and that mysterious quality known as 'feel,' which at its best is artistry. Craft engages the whole self, in short. Craft as a whole really is mysterious.

Artisanal technologies are sometimes called 'low' technologies—not because they are inferior but because they do not require formal science and hence, by definition, are not 'high.'

'High tech' is technology that could not have come about except through the insights of science. It is in effect 'applied science.' High tech thus defined did not start to make a significant impact until about 1800, when the industrial revolution was getting properly into its stride. To be

sure, the earliest machines of the industrial revolution that transformed the textile industry—the ones we learnt about at school, like (John) Kay's flying shuttle and (James) Hargreaves' spinning jenny (don't ask)—were really of the traditional kind: skill and knowledge were needed to make them, but not formal science. Among the earliest devices that really did involve formal science—knowledge rooted in tested hypotheses (chapter 14) —were the Davy lamp, invented in 1815 by Humphry Davy (1778-1829) to provide light for coal miners from a burning wick without blowing up the mine; and the steam engine. Both, though, had been taken to a very workable level by engineers of an artisanal kind before scientists (properly defined) came on board. In both these cases science served primarily to refine an existing idea. Both are examples of ***science assisted craft***—which, I suggest, is a key concept. In other cases—like the laser, which plays so many roles in modern life—the essential science came first, born of the most recondite theory. Lasers are high tech through and through.

Beyond doubt, high tech has transformed the world these past 200 years or so and the comforts of modern life are inconceivable without it. Modern obstetrics alone is enough to justify all medical science. ***Modern IT can be seen as the ultimate extended phenotype***—for in principle it enables us to share our thoughts *instantly* with everyone on Earth, and it is our ability to share our thoughts so freely and thoroughly that gives us such an edge and has made us the dominant species. This fact alone, it seems to me, is enough to demonstrate that our default position should be to cooperate, to increase our ability to work together, rather than to compete. It makes no sense to base our economy and our politics, indeed our whole mindset, on competition, as the neoliberal, metadarwinian zeitgeist urges us to do. With modern IT we can be ultra-cooperative. In the words of Tim Berners-Lee (b. 1955), inventor of the World Wide Web:

> *Hope in life comes from all the interconnections among all the people in the world.... The experience of seeing the Web take off by the grassroots effort of thousands gives me tremendous hope that if we have the individual will, we can collectively make of our world what we want.*

Incidentally, Tim Berners-Lee and the saintly, poetical Humphry Davy both opted *not* to patent their creations. They intended them for the general benefit of all humankind. And so they have proved.

More broadly, the United Nations predicts that the human population could reach as much as 10 billion before it starts to level out (chapter 1) and we cannot hope to sustain such numbers for more than a few years without high tech. But we also need perhaps above all to contain our own ingenuity and to ensure that the good things that we do are not hijacked by minorities for their own more-or-less-exclusive benefit. Specifically, ***we need to ensure that hi-tech is not expropriated by corporates for the exclusive benefit of shareholders,*** which is what happens now.

II: WHAT IS 'APPROPRIATE'?

Technology in principle if not necessarily in practice can help us to create any kind of world, and any way of life, that we want to achieve. The kind of technologies that help to achieve what we want and need are called, appropriately enough, 'appropriate.' But we need to define much more carefully than we do the kind of society and the kind of world that really *are* desirable. The central conceit of this book is that we should be trying to create 'convivial societies (with personal fulfilment) in a flourishing biosphere.' Yet it seems that the dominant oligarchy (corporates, financiers, and governments like Britain's plus their selected advisers) is aiming instead, primarily, to create as much wealth as possible and to maintain the hierarchical *status quo*—because they take it to be self-evident that the world *should* be ruled by oligarchs, like themselves.

The two kinds of ambition are at odds—in some ways absolutely so. As summarized by Barrett Hazeltine and Christopher Bull in *Appropriate Technology: Tools, Choices, and Implications*. Academic Press, Orlando, 1998) the technologies that really could lead us towards the kind of world we really need and most people want are

> *small-scale, decentralized, labour-intensive, energy-efficient, environmentally sound, and locally autonomous.*

In absolute contrast, the kind that maximize short-term wealth and concentrate power seek to minimize human labour (with fully automated factories and farms) and are carried out on the largest possible scale, often with enormous and largely irreversible damage to the biosphere. We could still rescue vast landscapes and ecosystems but there can be no going back from the mass extinction that is now in train. In other words, the kind of technologies that the powers-that-be are developing most zealously and in the end with our money ***are in large part the complete opposite*** of the kind that really could pull us out of the mire.

Already there is a comparably vast assemblage of technologies out there that *could,* if only we put our weight and some of our wealth behind them, solve *all* the world's material problems forever more. The next two chapters look more closely at the twin technologies that matter most of all—those of farming and food, which we really need to get right and in practice are getting most wrong. Here I will just look briefly at three familiar but contrasting technologies that illustrate some of the main generalizations: the bicycle, GMOs, and IT.

The one that gets it right: the bicycle

The bicycle shows us what *should* happen. Bikes are for everyone. Everyone *ought* to be able to afford a bike.

The first 'bicycle' of all was the 'dandy horse' (aka 'running machine') of 1818. It had no pedals—it was really just a scooter with a seat—a typical piece of artisanal engineering which a blacksmith could knock up. The dandy horse was useful on smooth roads (it didn't have tyres or springs) which in practice meant the pavement, but was not much good for much else. Modern bikes of the kind that enable the seriously fit to whizz up the Pyrenees, or help normal people to get to work and do the shopping have synthetic rubber tyres and a host of alloys and carbon fibres and all the rest, all put together with the aid of computers and wind-tunnels and ergonomic theory; still conceptually simple but in practice endlessly intricate, very definitely high tech. In short, the modern bicycle is science-assisted craft *par excellence* and is also among the most unequivocally appropriate technologies of all; liberating and, with due care, more or less non-polluting.

Huge potential but definitely threatening: IT

As outlined in chapter 3, the quality that sets human beings apart from all other creatures is not simply our ability to think more broadly and deeply than the rest seem able to do. It is our ability, through word-based language with a syntactical base, to share and hence to pool our thoughts and thus to operate collectively as one great unified mind. Perhaps the most significant of all technologies, therefore, are the ones that enabled us to record our thoughts and feelings—the stylus, the pen, the typewriter—and then to communicate those thoughts and feelings more widely—the printing press, then the telephone, radio, and TV. Now we have modern Information Technology, aka IT.

IT should, as Tim Berners-Lee envisaged, bring huge benefits—and clearly, it already does. It is sometimes assumed that the only technologies suitable for poor countries (what Gandhi was happy to call 'the Third World' and is now commonly called 'the majority world') must be of the artisanal kind—which, indeed, often hit the spot. Yet the internet and the mobile phone are a huge and increasingly essential boon for people living close to nature in remote places. All too clearly, though, IT can also be a threat. It is creating forms of virtual reality that can seem more real than the real world itself and threatens to reduce the complexities of the world to sound-bites—with what effect on human judgement? In other guises IT seems to be priming the world for a new form of 'cyberwar' that has already perverted elections and caused financial crashes and could easily lead to real war. IT allows what Abraham Lincoln called 'the better angels of our nature' to make their voices heard but it also unleashes the demons.

Even worse—and this could be the greatest threat of all—computers in one form or another are now encroaching on all the professions; and computers in mobile form—robots—will encroach more and more on the trades and skills that provide employment for most of humankind. This is all very well if computers merely provide the professionals with an aide-memoire, or do the routine calculations, leaving the doctor or the teacher or the high-street bank manager free to think and behave like a human being. Already, though, robots and other smart machines are threatening not simply to help but to usurp. Worse: however smart they become, computers in the end are stupid. They can do only what they are programmed to do—or at least, they can operate only within the rules that the programmer lays down for them (although they do occasionally behave in ways that the programmer did not intend and could not have predicted).

Even worse: as the American philosopher John Searle predicted would be the case back in the 1970s, latest research on IT suggests that the thought processes of computers are *qualitatively* different from our own.

In particular, as Professor Rosalind Picard of the Massachusetts Institute of Technology has of late been pointing out (some of her excellent lectures are on the web), computers lack *emotional intelligence*, which means they lack the essential quality of empathy; the quality that enables us truly to care for each other and live convivially, and to do so as a matter of choice. As outlined in chapter 14, various straws in the wind suggest that consciousness is not generated inside our own heads, as seems to us to be the case, but is a property of the universe itself. We do not create consciousness. We partake of what is already out there, like a radio receiver—or a receiver and transmitter combined; each individual brain is a relay station. But computers do not partake. As John Searle said, computers merely *simulate* the human mind. They do not replicate the human mind. Robots, however 'android' can never be more than simulacra.

Without empathy, teaching or banking by computer tends to be inflexible, not to say formulaic. The more the formulae become the norm the more difficult it becomes to change direction—and this means that whatever the present generation of programmers feed into present-day computers is liable to become the norm forever more. Yet as Edmund Burke pointed out in the 18th century, it is very dangerous for any one generation to impose its will forever on the generations that follow. That really does mean an end to progress—or progress at least of the intellectual and moral kind, which is what is really needed. A computer-run world looks flashy and ultra-modern but in reality it could trap us in the present *Zeitgeist* forever, neoliberal and technophilic—or at least until we hit the buffers. In short, this smart and flashy tech looks 'progressive' but in truth it could bring real progress—progress of heart and mind—to a halt.

Increasingly, too, smart computers are being linked to wonderfully versatile machines to create a new generation of robots that can perform an ever-increasing range of manual skills—down to and including all trades and crafts and even, for example, some of the intricate skills of surgery. Again this is fine so long as the robots merely help people who really know what they are doing to do their job more easily and free them from too much grunt-work. But increasingly they are pushing human beings aside altogether. Thus ***we are organizing our own redundancy as a species***, relegating humanity itself to the sidelines. Most normal human beings—all but the few who thrill to the new machines and/or are growing rich by them—would surely agree that this is not a sensible ambition; especially as we, human beings, are infinitely more subtle than any machine is ever liable to be. Or we would be if we did not lock ourselves in to silly ideas.

Brilliant science misdirected: GMOs

GMOs—'Genetically modified organisms,' which in practice means crops and livestock tailored by genetic engineering—illustrate all the big issues. In *some* conditions (though by no means all) GMOs do yield more heavily than traditional crops, and may be more pest resistant (for a time), and may contain particular nutrients in greater amounts, and may look better on a supermarket shelf (or at least bigger and shinier); and although GMOs cannot legally be grown in Europe for commercial purposes (which at the time of writing still includes Britain), senior politicians in governments like Britain's, and the Royal Society, the world's most prestigious assemblage of scientists, seem to regard them as a Godsend, or at least like the US cavalry arriving in the nick of time, with bugles a-blare, to save us all from certain death (or a fate worse than). This is what Britain's then Secretary of State Owen Paterson told the Oxford Farming Conference in his keynote address in January 2014:

> *Britain is a world leader in science, technology and innovation.... We need to not only embrace new techniques and technologies, but also to apply new thinking to our policy-making and business models. Farming contributes over £9 billion a year to the UK economy. I firmly believe there is room for further growth ... You have great opportunities to grow thanks to your well-deserved, world-wide reputation ... Just one example of the potential for exports is the lucrative Chinese pork market, which we opened up in 2012. It grew from £5 million in the first nine months to £14 million for the same period last year.*
>
> *In July we published the first ever Agri-Tech Strategy. It sets out the need to improve our ability to translate our world class research into practical applications that will make us world leaders not only in agriculture but also in the science and technology that supports it. We have committed £160 million of which £70 million will help to commercialize new agricultural technologies ... There will be an Agri-Tech Business Ambassador to drive forward exports in agricultural technologies.*

This is an exciting time. New technologies and markets present farming with unprecedented opportunities to grow.

Incidentally, Britain's agricultural supremos are no longer called Minister or Secretary of State for Agriculture, as was traditional, for Britain no longer has a Ministry of Agriculture. Now we have Defra: the Department for the Environment and Rural Affairs. Similarly, the erstwhile AFRC, the Agricultural and Food Research Council, has been replaced by the BBSRC, the Biotechnology and Biological Sciences Research Council. Thus the word 'agriculture,' the most important human pursuit of all, has been airbrushed out of the top echelons of Britain's government. Farming in Britain now is just another 'rural affair.' to rank alongside golf, shooting, and tourism; and intellectually it is perceived as a branch of biotech.

Mr Paterson emerges from his keynote speech as a prime example of an uncritical ***technophile***: a person with unswerving faith in the present or potential power of technology to solve all our problems and indeed in the fullness to time to make us omnipotent. Technophilia is the conceptual counterpart of ***scientism***—the belief that science tells us or soon will tell us all that is worth knowing, and indeed will one day make us omniscient, if only we spend enough on it. Both are huge and obvious mistakes (see chapters 13 and 14) but alas, some professional technologists are technophiles and some scientists preach scientism. Yet the most dangerous technophiles of all are those politicians in positions of influence. Mr Paterson, to be fair, did grow up on a farm but like most out-and-out political technophiles, including Britain's Tony Blair and Dick (Lord) Taverne or the highly influential Michael Gove, Paterson discovered science and technology late in life and sees them as a source of magic bullets.

The greatest threat of all, though, is that research in science and technology like everything else is now driven primarily by the market, in line with the ideology of neoliberalism. In other words both are geared more and more to the perceived need to maximize short-term profit, and this is called 'realistic.' Governments warn us to beware of terrorists and communists and religious extremists but the greatest threat by far to the future of the world is the deadly combination of uncritical technophilia and neoliberalism, as espoused by the world's most powerful governments and particularly, it seems, by Britain.

But to return to the thread: it is indeed the case that GMOs may sometimes seem to offer advantages but they emphatically do *not*, on the whole, improve significantly on traditional practice, at least under real, field conditions. Indeed they can and sometimes do a great deal of harm both ecological and sociological (and conceivably in health terms too, although the evidence is confusing, not least because it seems that what evidence there is is actively suppressed, and the research is put a stop to). In the world as a whole, more than 70% of the world's farms are family holdings of less than one hectare—and yet, according to FAO (the Food and Agriculture Organization of the United Nations), these small holdings between them produce at least 70% of the world's food. (See Professor Michel Pimbert of Coventry University in *Economic and Political Weekly* (Vol. 53, Issue No. 41, 13 October 2018.) Professor E.R. ('Bob') Orskov, previously from the Macaulay Institute, Aberdeen, dedicated most of his professional life to the world's small farms and farmers and reckoned that most of them could easily double their output, if necessary, *not* by piling on more fancy western technology but simply with a few logistic tweaks—including simple technologies and better access to markets. I once asked small dairy farmers in an Indian village why they did not produce more milk to sell to the local town, which it seemed they could easily do, and they pointed out (with commendable forbearance) that their cows could not lactate except in the rainy season when there was fresh grazing to be had—but in the rainy season, the roads were impassable. They didn't need modern, high-yielding Holstein cattle (which usually languish in less than ideal conditions) and still less did they need GM super-cattle. They just needed better roads.

The zeal for GMOs has now given rise to the commensurate zeal for 'gene editing'—altering the genomes of crop plants or livestock not by adding genes from other organisms but by altering or rearranging the genes that are already there. We are assured with the same confidence that once attended GMOs, and in some circles still does, that nothing can possibly go wrong. In truth the only real difference between GMO technology and gene editing is that we have had nearly 40 years to see that GMOs *can* go wrong (the first GM crops were produced in the 1980s) and not enough time to see what can go wrong with gene-edited plants. But there are at least good theoretical reasons at least for proceeding with caution and already there are signs that all may not run smoothly.

The money spent on GMOs and gene editing—or even a tenth of that money—would surely do far more good if it was spent on helping small farmers to realize their potential, often with simple inputs like rubber tyres for their carts (and better banking and marketing and so on). Besides, as outlined in the next chapter, the world doesn't actually *need* more food. Food security and quality are what really matter—best achieved by growing local crops locally. Furthermore, agriculture is by far the world's biggest employer (an estimated two billion people) and in a finite world with finite resources there is nothing useful apart from farming that such vast numbers of people could conceivably do. Small farmers and their families pushed aside by high-tech industrial farming merely swell the ranks of the one billion who now, according to the UN, live in urban slums (though I was assured by a senior member of the European Bank that the slums are really quite jolly. So that's alright then).

Given that the world's small farms do most to 'feed the world,' and provide the world's people with employment which means with income and dignity, the industrial high-tech monocultures that are now sweeping them aside are clearly not 'appropriate'—not, that is, if we truly care about the future of humanity and of the biosphere. (And if we do not, then what do we care about?).

If we developed and deployed technologies that really are appropriate to the world's real needs we could start to solve all the world's material problems right now; and as the material problems are solved, many of our political, social, and spiritual problems would disappear as well. There is always room for improvement of course, and we surely should not ease up on R&D. But on the technical front we already seem to know enough to turn things around. That we continue to tolerate and even to vote for the kind of governance and the kind of economy that are clearly on the wrong tack, morally, socially, ecologically, and technically is, frankly, absurd.

III: HOW CAN WE GET IT RIGHT? A MATTER OF ATTITUDE

As always, ***attitude*** is key: how we *feel* about things; what we feel our priorities should be—what we should be trying to do and why; whether we want truly to promote conviviality—whether we want to cooperate and so create harmony, or to compete and so come out on top; whether we truly regard ourselves as a part of the biosphere or feel that the biosphere is ours to fashion as we will; and indeed, how we feel about technology itself, and the science that may underpin technology. Are we technophiles, who equate smartness and power with progress? Do we subscribe to scientism—the belief that science is the prime source of wisdom, and should always be given priority? Contrariwise, do we see tech and science as threats to our beliefs and the status quo or to our cosy ways of life? Or are we prepared to respect great technology for its brilliance and style and acknowledge science as an intellectual and indeed as a spiritual triumph but nonetheless recognize their limitations and shortcomings? Or do we perhaps feel that science and tech are in the wrong hands (in the hands, that is, of neoliberal technophiles) and are leading us in seriously unfortunate directions, and need to be reined in—truly to be focused on the need, not to make rich people richer and powerful institutions more powerful, but to improve the general weal, both of humanity and of our fellow creatures? This last approach—one of common sense and common morality—is surely the one we really need; as always, ***a proper balance of reason and intuition.*** This roughly speaking is the theme of Pope John Paul II's encyclical of 1998, *Faith and Reason*. Wise though it is, though, Pope John Paul II's view of life is not what prevails.

Plato, in the 5th century BCE, was among the first that we know about to sound a warning. Too much ploughing and overgrazing erode the soil and clog the rivers with silt, he said—and, although the clock is ticking ever more insistently, we continue to do precisely the things that he said we should not, as is plain to see in Wyoming, Brazil, Berkshire, Australia, Africa, India, and China—wherever you look, in fact. In the 16th century some warned that the fast-flowing millstreams dug to power the new flour mills were destroying the natural waterways. But debates about the merits and demerits of technology truly began in earnest with the rise of the industrial revolution the late 18th and early 19th centuries when big, noisy and often noisome industries began to become part of everyday life.

There were heavyweights on both sides. Broadly welcoming (though far form uncritical!) were the members of the Lunar Society who met in Birmingham by the light of the full moon (how else would they have found their way?) between 1765 and 1813 to discuss the new ideas and possibilities. Regulars included the biologist and poet Erasmus Darwin (grandfather of Charles); the potteries magnate Joseph Wedgwood; James Watt, pioneer of steam power; Matthew Boulton, the business partner of Watt; the writer Thomas Day who urged the abolition of slavery and was a fan of Rousseau (of whom more later); and the chemist and theologian

Joseph Priestley. And while William Blake wrote of the 'dark satanic mills,' some of his artist contemporaries and successors revelled in the new sights and sounds. Joseph Wright of Derby and James Ward loved to paint the fire and toil, and some of the most famous paintings of J.M.W. Turner were celebrations of steam.

But others sounded serious notes of caution. In 1811 a movement of discontented textile workers known as the Luddites set about smashing the weaving machines in the newly established factories in the English Midlands, Lancashire, and Yorkshire. The term 'Luddite' is often used as a term of abuse—a symbol of obduracy, ignorance, and general pig-headedness. In reality the Luddite protests were broadly based—for working people in general were suffering horribly at that time and the new machines were often adding to the misery. Neither were the Luddites crudely anti-'progress.' Rather they saw very clearly as many in positions of influence still fail to see that new technologies insouciantly or too zealously introduced shove human beings to the sidelines, and wreck the biosphere in passing. Kevin Binfield, who edited *Writings of the Luddites* (2004), concludes that the Luddites 'were totally fine with machines.' They attacked only the ones whose owners used them in 'a fraudulent and deceitful manner' to replace skilled tradespeople with poorly-paid machine-minders. Says Binfield:

> *They just wanted machines that made high-quality goods, and they wanted these machines to be run by workers who had gone through an apprenticeship and got paid decent wages. Those were their only concerns.*

(From 'What the Luddites Really Fought Against,'
Smithsonian Magazine, March 2011).

But the government and the industrialists did not heed the subtext. They chose to see only the damage that the Luddites caused, and put a stop to the movement in 1813 with draconian punishments that included at least 15 executions.

In the modern world, as Paul Mason (b. 1960) comments in *PostCapitalism* (2015), we can observe unfolding before us a somewhat grisly economic cycle. Machines are introduced to replace workers until the unemployed workers are prepared to work for so little money that it is cheaper to employ them than it is to build machines—so then we are back to what in effect is serfdom. So it is that in Britain at least in recent years teams of (mainly) East Europeans with buckets and sponges have largely replaced the drive-in car washes that were all the rage a few years ago. Indeed, we might cynically observe as some indeed have done that the great social and economic reforms of the past 200 years, ostensibly brought about by various workers' movements like the Luddites, and later by the trade unions, and abetted by enlightened intellectuals like Robert Owen and William Wilberforce and Karl Marx, did not result as is ostensibly the case from a very necessary moral shift. They have been concessions, granted to working people by the powers-that-be in those historical periods when human labour and artisanal skill is particularly necessary. As soon as it ceases to be necessary—as is increasingly the case as smart machines take over—then people can again be reduced to what have often been derogatorily referred to as 'coolies.' In the end, the Renaissance we need can only be brought about, and put on a robust footing, by a radical shift in *attitude*. Has the *attitude* of people to people, or of people to other species, really changed since the 18th century?

Always of course the question arises—'Why make something by hand that a machine could make more or less flawlessly with far less effort, a hundred times more quickly and a tenth of the price?' The reformer and aesthete John Ruskin (1819-1900) provided at least part of the answer. He pointed out, quite simply, that craft is a human pursuit, while machines are just machines. He loved real, Mediaeval Gothic architecture because we can still see the chisel marks and the gargoyles and misericords and all the rest reflect the thoughts and feelings of their creators as no factory-made facsimile can do. More generally, he said:

> *We want one man to be always thinking, and another to be always working, and we call one a gentleman, and the other an operative; whereas the workman ought often to be thinking, and the thinker often to be working, and both should be gentlemen, in the best sense. As it is, we make both ungentle, the one envying, the other despising, his brother; and the mass of society is made up of morbid thinkers and miserable workers. Now it is only by labour that thought can be made healthy, and only by thought that labour can be made happy, and the two cannot be separated with impunity.*
>
> From: 'The Nature of Gothic' in volume 2 of *The Seven Lamps of Architecture* (1849).

This perfectly describes the balance of farming—or indeed of all crafts.

William Morris (1834-1896), key player in the Arts and Crafts movement, owed a great deal to Ruskin—but he also wrote:

> *I do not [believe] we should aim at abolishing all machinery; I would do some things with machinery which are now done by hand, and other things by hand which are now done by machinery; in short, we would be the masters of our machines and not their slaves, as we are now. It is not this or that...machine which we want to get rid of, but the great intangible machine of commercial tyranny which oppresses the lives of all of us.*
>
> From: 'Art and Its Producers,' 1881. Quoted in Issue 196 of *Socialist Review,* April 1996.

This seems to me like eminent good sense. Nowadays, craft is often seen as 'elitist' since only the relatively well-off can afford hand-made clothes and pots and whatever. But in a rich country like Britain we should be asking why this is so: why so many people can't afford the good or even the basic things of life—not just hand-made pots but also good fresh food; and the answer, as discussed in chapters 9 and 10, lies not with lack of overall wealth but with huge economic inequality. In a country like Britain everyone could afford at least a few hand-made things if they wanted them, and could certainly afford good food (chapters 6 and 7), if only we installed an economy that spread the wealth more evenly.

It is not true, however, as Morris himself clearly recognized, that hand-made goods are necessarily superior. Hand-made crockery tends to be heavy and doesn't always stand up to punishment while factory-made crocks can last forever and the best of them, like those made by Wedgwood and the other great midland potteries, were and are among the finest of all artefacts. They demonstrate human craft and machine in harmony. Morris was right in this as in most things—it's the balance that matters; that and the underlying intent—either to make life better for all or to make rich people richer. Then again, most of us who are reasonably above the breadline have far more *stuff* than we actually need. It can be better in all kinds of ways to spend a lot of money (relatively speaking) on a few things that are beautifully and lovingly made than on a load of junk that is designed to be thrown away. Craft in short is a key player in the minimalist economy (chapter 10).

Tolstoy learnt a lot from Morris and for example in *Anna Karenina* he describes the exploits of his alter ego Levin who, though an aristocrat like himself, likes nothing better than a day spent scything with the peasants. Tolstoy admired peasants more than anyone (and the scythe in modern form—made of the finest lightweight steel—is making a serious come-back). Tolstoy in turn corresponded with Ghandi until his (Tolstoy's) death in 1910 and Gandhi applied his way of thinking to his own peaceful uprising against the British—in which, in particular, with echoes of the Luddites, he emphasized the value of the spinning wheel; a route to autonomy and hence to dignity.

In *Tools for Conviviality* (published 1973) the Croatian-Austrian philosopher and Catholic priest Ivan Illich (1926-2002) similarly emphasised the need for personal and social autonomy. The technologies he called 'convivial' were those that make us more autonomous. He singled out the bicycle and the telephone, which allows one-to-one, two-way communication. Broadcasting, he felt, was non-convivial since—at least in those days! —the flow of information was all one way, from the centre to people at large. He surely would have a different attitude to modern IT. Autonomy is the core idea of anarchism—which, as outlined in chapter 9, does not simply mean lawlessness. At its best it implies societies of people who each are self-reliant and make their own decisions but *choose* of their own volition to devote a significant part of their efforts (whatever is needed) to the wellbeing of the whole group and preferably too to the wellbeing of the biosphere (which is 'green anarchism'). Peasants are autonomous par excellence and peasants in countries like Russia have been and are a very strong political force; anarchism features very strongly in the Russian politics of the late 19th century. The philosopher and writer Peter Kropotkin (1842-1921) was a powerful advocate of anarchism and Tolstoy was a great admirer. Peasants are the most autonomous people of all—and the Russian communists of the early 20th century found it very hard to bring them into the fold. Only in over-urbanized countries like Britain, where most people are far removed from the land and hence from what might be called the realities of life, would 'peasant' be used as a term of abuse. In essence, all traditional farmers are peasants and as Adam Smith (1723-1790) commented in *The Wealth of Nations* (Book 1 XI Part III):

> *The ... ploughman, though generally regarded as the pattern of stupidity and ignorance, is seldom defective in this judgement and*

discretion ... He is less accustomed, indeed, to social intercourse than the mechanic who lives in a town ... His understanding, however, being accustomed to consider a greater variety of objects, is generally much superior.

England's traditional 'yeoman farmers' were essentially peasants although as they grew wealthy they tended to aspire to be gentry. Alas!—nowadays the wealthiest farmers tend to see themselves as businesspeople, seeing farming as 'a business like any other' and happy to plug themselves into the neoliberal economy and take their place in the House of Lords. The technology of farming both reflects and drives the different attitudes. Traditionalists favour small-scale machinery (which can be very high-tech, as bicycles can be) while agri-businesspeople favour 500 horsepower tractors and CAFOs ('Concentrated Animal Feeding Operations'; see chapter 6) and combine harvesters as big as a small cottage. Thus we see how technologies and economies and therefore ways of life and the fate of humanity and the world are intertwined (a point that Karl Marx emphasized).

Perhaps, though, the most influential of all 'philosophers of technology' (as they might be called) was and is the German-born and Oxford-educated E.F. ('Fritz') Schumacher (1911-1977). Schumacher helped to re-build the German economy after World War II and then for 20 years was Chief Economic Adviser to Britain's National Coal Board. In 1973 in *Small is Beautiful: A Study of Economics as if People Mattered* he argued what in effect is the main thesis of this chapter: that we cannot use technology simply to solve technical problems *ad hoc*, and/or simply to generate wealth. Technology is appropriate only if it meets the reasonable social and personal aspirations of humanity, and if it looks after the biosphere (what was, and usually still is, called 'the environment'). In other words, ***the purpose of technology and all that feeds into it (including these days a great deal of modern science) is to contribute to 'convivial societies in a flourishing biosphere.'*** All the rest, however flashy and lucrative, is diversion and/or is downright irresponsible.

Schumacher tells us much of what we need to know. He was very practical—primarily an economist, strongly influenced by John Maynard Keynes; was technically savvy; and acknowledged more and more the absolute importance of a moral and metaphysical underpinning to all serious thinking—an admirer or the Buddha and of Gandhi and increasingly drawn into the Catholic Church. A network of centres worldwide keeps his philosophy very much alive (not the least being Schumacher College in Devon, England).

In short, these past 200 years, as a whole swatch of technologies have taken humanity and the Earth itself into a whole new epoch, a succession of great thinkers from Ruskin to Schumacher (and many more) have urged us not to be too impressed by technical brilliance or flashiness and still less by money, and a great many craftspeople (potters, carpenters, weavers, small farmers, and so on and so on) have continued to show what really can be achieved. What matters most is the *effect* that our technologies have on ourselves—our ways of life, our politics, our relationships, our health, our psyche—and on our fellow creatures and on the Earth. All of this is illustrated most cogently in the set of technologies that is the most important of all—and also perhaps the most crudely managed: agriculture.

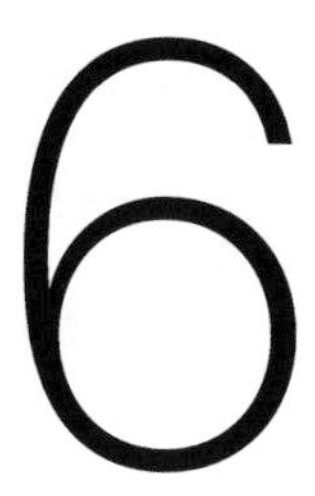

THE ABSOLUTE IMPORTANCE OF ENLIGHTENED AGRICULTURE

After what are called the fine arts, and the liberal professions ... there is perhaps no trade that requires so great a variety of knowledge and experience.

Adam Smith on farming. *The Wealth of Nations*, Book I Chapter X Part I

AGRICULTURE VERY OBVIOUSLY IS OUR CHIEF SOURCE OF FOOD—by far. Less obviously, it is the world's biggest single employer—by far. It occupies a third of all the land on Earth including *most* of the most fertile land. All in all therefore it is right at the heart of all the world's affairs, both human and non-human, affecting everything else and affected by everything else. It is in short the thing we absolutely have to get right—but alas, in practice, to a large extent, are getting most wrong. If we do get it right then the dream—convivial societies with personal fulfilment within a flourishing biosphere, starting with the next million years—will be within our grasp. If we continue to get it wrong then we really will be heading for the buffers. You might suppose, therefore, that the oligarchs who dominate the world, led (we might hope) by democratically elected governments that have our best interests at heart, would take it very seriously indeed.

This is not how it seems, however. In practice the world's most powerful governments are committed to the neoliberal ideal of 'economic growth'—to ever-increasing wealth achieved by competing head-to-head in the global market to maximise profits and 'market share' and to concentrate the growing wealth in fewer and fewer hands (for in any competition there are more losers than winners). So long as the oil still flows and the world's economies are still geared to it the easiest way to maximize and concentrate agricultural wealth is to install bigger and bigger and smarter technologies that maximize outputs and minimize labour—for human workers are difficult to deal with and prefer to be paid even when they are not working and even, indeed, when they are off sick. Human muscle and horsepower have long been replaced by tractors that nowadays have the power to tow a battleship and by combines as big as a small cottage, all of which can be driven by remote control. Soon, if the trend continues, the state of the farm will be monitored from the sky and all the chores will be carried out by robots. All animals will live indoors, fed on artificial diets minutely adjusted to their body chemistry—until whole beasts are replaced by factories of cultured flesh, with ersatz flavours to which our descendants will no doubt become accustomed. And so on and so on.

This, for many in high places, is the dream. They call it progress. Humans will be obsolete and the rest of life will be reduced to raw material to be traded as commodities. In short, the world's agricultural strategies as framed by the world's most powerful governments, in concert with corporates, financiers, and their chosen advisers, are driven, like everything else, by neoliberal economics and uncritical technophilia. Life will be kept at arm's length. Agriculture will be conceived—as indeed it already is in avant-garde circles—not as the life support and the principal occupation of the human species but as 'a business like any other'; and business has been re-conceived not as the natural underpinning of democratic societies but simply as the means to generate wealth.

In general, and most unfortunately, the methods that are now being developed in pursuit of ever-increasing wealth and de-humanization, and the strategy and mindset that favours those methods, are ***the very opposite of what is required to foster conviviality and to keep the natural***

world in good heart. The partnership of neoliberalism and gung-ho technophilia is damaging in all contexts but as always, its worst and most immediate effects are seen in agriculture.

The forms and grades of farming

Agriculture is the attempt to control wild nature so that it provides more food and other desirables (fibres, drugs, pigments) than it would if left to itself. Primarily this is a human endeavour—although as usual, there are precedents in nature. Ants protect aphids to fleece them of their honeydew, and some fish protect favoured patches of weed and thereby influence their genetics—and these are the rudiments of farming.

Farming of the humankind falls into three broad categories: ***horticulture*** (from the Latin *hortus*, meaning garden) —the care and cultivation of individual plants; ***pastoral*** or ***livestock*** farming; and ***arable***—cultivation on the field scale. The 'staple crops'—the ones that provide us with the bulk of our food energy and protein—are mostly grown on the arable scale. Cereals are the main staples, followed by pulses (peas, beans etc), a miscellany of other seeds (such as buckwheat), and tubers, notably potatoes. Many non-staples are now grown on the field scale too down to and including flowers and herbs. There are also hybrid forms of farming such as ***agroforestry***, which combines any form of growing or of husbandry with trees; and ***aquaculture***, incorporating ponds and lakes (not to be confused with the artificial high-tech offshoot known as aquaponics).

Each of these kinds of farming takes many millions—literally!—of forms simply because no two farms are alike (although as high-tech takes over the different forms are increasingly uniform). But I suggest that all the many and various forms of farming can broadly be classed either as ***pre-scientific agriculture,*** or as ***science-assisted agriculture.*** Emphatically, I am *not* equating 'science' with 'high-tech.' As outlined in chapter 13, science as properly conceived is the sum of all the insights that can be attained by framing formal hypotheses and testing them. Science thus defined does include metallurgy and mechanics and electronics and other 'hard' sciences that have given rise to high tech. But it also includes physiology and psychology (in some forms) and modern genetics and—perhaps most importantly of all, as is only now being properly appreciated!—***ecology***. All these basic sciences are intended to show us how the world really works, partly for the pleasure of knowing things and partly so that we can operate more effectively and—we might hope!—safely and benignly.

The pre-scientific and the science-based (or science-assisted) kinds of farming can each be subdivided into three grades to give six in all. Thus:

PRE-SCIENTIFIC AGRICULTURE:

Proto-

Primitive

Artisanal

SCIENCE-ASSISTED AGRICULTURE:

Science-assisted artisanal

Neoliberal-Industrial

Enlightened Agriculture

Each grade takes many forms and the different grades overlap but this rough classification is useful nonetheless. In slightly more detail:

Pre-scientific agriculture

Proto-farming includes all early attempts—conscious and unconscious—to influence the landscape so as to make it more amenable. A prime example is the 'fire-stick farming' of Australia—a term coined by the Welsh-Australian archaeologist Rhys Jones in the 1960s. The aboriginal people set fire to the dried-out vegetation of the bush to encourage new growth—then trap the animals that come to feed.

Primitive farming is one step up: encouraging favoured wild plants; discouraging weeds and predators; luring and then trapping wild animals; and generally pushing the whole environment in the desired directions (in this context the term 'environment' really is appropriate). These are the first steps towards true domestication, profoundly influencing the genetics and behaviour of the local plants and animals as the generations pass. People provide protection for individual plants that are less thorny and more succulent, and various animals establish a mutually beneficial relationship with the people who seek to exploit them (dogs and pigs for example come to scavenge—and then are eaten). The first stirrings of such farming could well date from 100,000 years ago or more. Dogs were probably the first of our mammalian domesticates—serving as scavengers and general cleaners-up, guards, body-warmers, and hunting companions, while those that were surplus to requirements were doubtless eaten.

Artisanal farming is farming as craft—or rather as a spectrum of crafts; the word 'artisanal' derives from 'artisan,' meaning 'skilled worker,' or 'craftsperson.' Artisanal farming can also properly be called 'traditional'; it is what most bona fide farmers have practiced possibly for 40,000 years or so—and still do. The whole process is very conscious: the farmers know what they are doing. Plants are not simply protected. They are deliberately planted and sown. Animals are corralled. All the way along the line the farmers select the ones that suit them best—the plants that are least thorny, or fibrous, or toxic, and have the biggest seeds, and the animals that are most tractable and productive—and so as the decades and centuries passed wild plant and animals were transformed into recognizable crops, and skittish and often dangerous wild animals gave rise to (fairly) compliant livestock. Arable farming—needing soil preparation and sowing—was surely the last form to get into its stride. The 'Neolithic Revolution' of around 10,000 years ago (after the last Ice Age) was not the beginning of agriculture in the broad sense. It was, though, the beginnings of arable farming on a large enough scale to show up in the archaeological record.

By Old Testament times all the basic elements of modern farming were in place: horticulture, livestock, and arable, with crops and livestock that are significantly different from their wild ancestors. In *Genesis*, written about 2500 years ago but referring to events much earlier, Cain was the arablist, the tiller of the ground, and Abel was the pastoralist, the keeper of sheep (God preferred the pastoralist, let it be noted!). Modern agricultural scientists often claim the credit for 'feeding the world' but the biggest hurdles were overcome well before the time of Christ. We could almost say that it was all over bar the shouting: that all the advances since those times, including the wonders of modern science, were and are the icing on the cake—and, like icing, can definitely be over-elaborated. Artisanal farming—farming as craft—is still the global norm.

Science assisted agriculture

Science-assisted artisanal farming has two strands to it—as indeed does science itself. First, 'pure' science provides insights of many kinds that help traditional farmers and breeders to do all that they do with greater understanding and more hope of success.

Secondly, 'applied' science provides high tech which can sometimes sweep traditional practices aside but may also be deployed to enhance the various crafts. For instance, modern (small) tractors are high tech and are definitely useful and the mobile phone is a definite boon, especially for small farmers in remote places. Indigenous farmers can benefit as much as anyone from carefully chosen high tech—without unduly compromising the ancient ways of life and beliefs that are so precious.

High tech first came properly on board in the early 19th century when Justus von Liebig in Germany and John Bennet Lawes in England first showed that plants need both phosphorus and nitrogen, and began the development of artificial fertilizers. In the 20th century, science-assisted artisanal farming—fertilizers, herbicides, pesticides, mechanical power and breeding based on the science of genetics—became the norm in the western world and is commonly called 'conventional.'

Neoliberal-industrial agriculture is science-assisted farming taken to the nth degree, operating within the diktats of the neoliberal economy (chapter 10). It treats all crops and livestock as commodities to be produced in maximum amounts, commonly for further processing to 'add value' and maximize profits; and farms are conceived as production lines, with the different 'products' (crops and livestock) each produced in separate, ***monocultural*** units. Labour is cut to the bone (zero labour is preferred) which is said to increase 'efficiency'—which it does by definition since efficiency is commonly *defined* as goods and/or money produced per employee. NI agriculture is wonderfully successful in its own terms—yields, total output, and the wealth that can be generated, are fabulous. Wealth and power are concentrated too: each stage of the food chain 'from field to fork' is now dominated by a few handfuls of 'transnational' corporates. To a large extent too the different stages are 'vertically integrated' so that Bayer—having gobbled up Monsanto in 2018—is now a major player both in agrochemistry and in plant breeding (with heavy emphasis on genetic engineering). Most farmers the world over are poor but the captains of the food and agro-industries are generally very rich indeed. 'Twas ever thus, in all fields. Those who do stay poor while those who control those who do, grow rich.

But while NI agriculture with all its razzmatazz extends its reach a billion people remain undernourished and the collateral damage to societies and to the biosphere is horrendous. Indeed, NI agriculture emerges as a prime and sometimes the sole cause of *all* the world's present disasters, from social unrest and conflict and mass under-employment and depression to pollution and climate change to mass extinction. Unfortunately the world's most powerful people equate wealth and high tech with progress and see NI agriculture as the way ahead. So the NI approach is rapidly becoming the norm and nowadays indeed is anomalously called 'conventional' as if it was simply an extension of the kind of agriculture that was practiced in the middle years of the 20th century—artisanal farming with add-ons. But it is not. It is a quite different beast.

Enlightened Agriculture (EA) is rooted firmly in artisanal farming, which is to say in traditional practice, but in its modern forms it is very much informed by many kinds of science: geology, soil chemistry, meteorology, and biology in all its forms with special emphasis these days on ***microbiology*** and—above all—on ***ecology***. Indeed EA provides a foretaste of our whole future, if we aspire to survive in tolerable form for more than another few decades, for it is moving us out of the age of industrial chemistry that is not sustainable, and into an age of ecology which certainly can be. Truly enlightened agriculture is still a minor player and the most powerful governments and big business see it therefore to be 'niche'—if indeed they are aware of it at all. Yet it is the kind of farming that the world needs above all. So what does it entail?

The nuts and bolts of Enlightened Agriculture

EA is informally but adequately defined as

> **Farming that is expressly designed to provide everyone, everywhere, with food of the highest standards, in terms both of nutrition and of gastronomy, without cruelty or injustice and without wrecking the rest of the world**

This should be eminently achievable. Of course we need more research on all fronts, particularly but not only in science, technology, and economics. But we already know enough to get the world on track.

The expression 'Enlightened Agriculture,' sometimes rendered as 'Real Farming,' is novel: I claim to be the first to coin it, about a decade ago. In practice, though, EA is compounded of two big ideas that other people thought up and are already widely acknowledged. They are:

Agroecology *and*

Food Sovereignty

The economic structure that would best support EA is that of ***Green Economic Democracy,*** (of which more in chapter 10); and always, in all fields, whatever we try to do, we should respect ***Traditional Knowledge.*** It is a huge mistake—hubris writ large—to take it as a premise that we can always improve on what was there before, and, still worse, to assume that improvement must mean high tech. More in chapters 13 and 14.

In more detail:

Agroecology

Like all forms of farming agroecological systems must be:

Productive

Sustainable

Resilient

Agriculture that does not meet these fundamental requirements will leave us hungry and/or obese and diabetic, with the biosphere in a tail-spin—which, to an uncomfortable extent, describes the status quo.

When it is done well, agroecological farming meets all these basic needs triumphantly—and in the end is the only form of farming that can do so. NI farming, presented with lashings of commercial rhetoric has given the illusion of success, at least to the satisfaction of governments like Britain's, but the underlying folly is ever more apparent.

Of course we need farming to be **productive**—10 billion mouths to feed in a few decades' time is a lot. But above all—***we need to acknowledge that enough's enough!*** As outlined below, the present output of food worldwide is enough for 14 billion people—40% more than we should ever need—and the continuing demand from on high to produce 50% more by 2050 (or twice as much by the end of the century) has nothing to do with need or even with 'demand'—not when 'demand' is properly defined. Focus now should shift from mere quantity, to quality and wellbeing—of human beings, domestic animals, and the biosphere. Focus must shift too from the ludicrous and futile attempt to gear agricultural strategy to the short-term vagaries of the market, to true concern for the long-term future.

'**Sustainable**' does not mean that we should go on doing precisely the things that we do now, for ever and ever. It does mean that we should retain the ability to continue farming of some kind for ever and ever, starting with the next million years. This is at least theoretically possible if all inputs are renewable and all deficits are replaced.

'Resilient' means that we must continue to farm productively even though conditions change—which they will, and especially the all-important climate. This means either that our farming systems must be able to bounce back rapidly after setbacks *or*, if the setbacks are too great, that we must be able to change direction rapidly. In short, the key to resilience is flexibility.

Clearly, there is tension between the three demands—production, sustainability, and resilience. In general, the more we employ NI methods to maximize short-term production (monocultures, big machines, industrial chemistry, all on the biggest possible scale) the less sustainable our agriculture will be, and the less resilient. Big single-purpose monocultures are intrinsically inflexible. Even if big industrial farmers want to change direction—and I know from many conversations that many of them do—they find they cannot because they have sunk all their capital in their industrial enterprise, with a lot of debt on top of that; and along the way have probably compromised the soil so that the land needs several years' work (at least) before it is fit for proper farming again. For such farmers in the short term it is not 'realistic' to change direction even though humanity and the biosphere require them to do so with all possible urgency.

But agroecology is what's needed. The general approach is to ***treat each farm as an ecosystem, and to treat agriculture as a whole, worldwide, as a key component of the biosphere.*** In truth, agriculture will always compromise the pristine biosphere to some extent but its intrusion must be as non-destructive as possible. Where possible, agriculture should make a *positive* contribution to the global ecosphere, creating new, species-rich habitats. Overall, agroecology seeks to ***emulate nature.***

Nature is not maximally productive but, as we saw in chapter 1, we don't need to maximize production. If we grow the right things in the right ways we don't need to raise fertility to outlandish levels with mega-doses of industrial fertilizer; and we don't need to breed wheat that will give 15 tonnes per hectare or cows that produce 15,000 litres of milk (both of which have already been achieved). Such feats are flashy and are the subject of hyped-up conferences in prestige venues but they are unnecessary and they simply lead to more problems—biological, social, and indeed economic. But then, as Richard Nixon was wont to point out, technology advances largely by correcting (up to a point) the problems created by previous technologies—and if the original technology and the ones that are intended to make good the damage both make money, what's the problem?

Nature too is obviously supremely ***sustainable***—it has sustained many millions of species in great abundance for the past four billion years. A few million more—a thousandth of the time that has passed so far—will be more than enough to be going on with. Indeed, planet Earth will probably not be habitable for another four billion years for cosmological reasons over which we have no control so we cannot hope to live on this Earth forever whatever we do. If there is such a thing as eternity then it must be on another plane. Another few million though is perfectly feasible—provided we change direction, fast.

Clearly, too, Nature is wonderfully ***resilient***—for in the billions of years of life on Earth conditions have changed spectacularly. At times the whole world has been more or less tropical and at other times has been weighed down by ice almost from pole to pole. The Eocene epoch, from about 55 to about 35 million years ago, was extremely warm: northern Canada, Alaska, Siberia, Greenland, and indeed Antarctica were all perfectly habitable, and were duly inhabited by an astonishing variety of mammals. Yet in the Pleistocene Ice Ages, which ended (for the time being) only about 10,000 years ago, there were glaciers half a mile thick over much of Britain. The snow that now sits permanently on the top of Ben Nevis is a vestige, a reminder of what once was. The Flow Country of Sutherland and Caithness is a remnant of Ice Age tundra. During the long history of life on Earth, too, the continents themselves have been positively athletic—racing around the surface of the globe from the poles to the Equator and sometimes back again, spinning on their axes, joining up into super-continents then splitting apart, leaving the ocean currents, the bearers of heat and cold, to sort themselves out as best they could.

Yet through all of this, life has come smiling through. True, along the way the biosphere has suffered five mass extinctions—but has always sprung back over the following few million years, each time producing evolutionary and ecological novelties, suites of animals and plants that in sheer technical ability often far surpassed what was there before. Our own species with our unique ability to philosophise is one such novelty, which almost certainly would not have come about if the dinosaurs had not been wiped out by the Cretaceous/Tertiary (K/T) extinction of around 65 million years ago. The resilience of nature as a whole is very much in line with the concept of Gaia: the Earth as a whole perceived as a quasi-organism, the arch-exponent of homeostasis.

Of course we cannot and should not seek to emulate everything that nature does. Nature after all can be horrendously destructive (tsunamis, volcanoes, asteroid strikes, and all the rest). But we can and should ask how nature achieves the things that we would like—and need—to achieve: more than adequate productivity; sustainability; and resilience.

The keys to Nature's successes

Productivity, sustainability, and resilience all reflect nature's underlying ***biological efficiency***. In a nutshell, ***nature sustains a lot of life with minimum input and minimum waste***. In fact, because of this biological efficiency, natural ecosystems tend to become *richer* over time (see chapter 4). In contrast, modern industrial farms commonly degenerate over time, sometimes to the point of virtual sterility. Soil becomes what American mid-western farmers all too accurately call 'dirt.' So why the difference?

Well, industrial farmers aspire to be 'efficient' too—all commercial enterprises strive for efficiency!—*but they have a very different perception of what efficiency means*. Commercial efficiency is quite different from biological efficiency, and is achieved by quite different methods. Biological efficiency *promotes* and underpins sustainability and resilience while crude market-driven commercial efficiency is the antithesis of both.

Key here is the concept of ***redundancy***—duplication of input and effort which at least in conventional commercial circles is deemed to be superfluous. Commercial producers whether of wheat or cotton or motor-cars are given to understand that they absolutely should not employ two people where one could do the job (at least to some minimum standard). Farms these days tend to be contracted to supermarkets that demand regular consignments of perfectly predictable produce delivered 'just in time,' to save the supermarket the trouble and expense of storing it. Thus, in general, commercial enterprises of all kinds including farms tend to be stripped to the bone (apart from the potted plants in the foyer for PR purposes, and a walnut desk for the boss and BMWs for the board). So there is no wriggle-room in super-efficient enterprises. If one link in the network fails the whole lot goes down. A shortage of fuel as might be caused by all kinds of political and natural hiccups brings the delivery trucks to a halt and then the whole caboodle seizes up.

But in a well-established ecosystem almost every niche is occupied by more than one kind of creature. So it is that farmers and non-farmers alike are especially alarmed by the decline of honey-bees. So we should be—but in truth if we lost honey-bees altogether, it need make very little difference. Solitary bees which live in holes rather than in hives are often better pollinators than honey-bees and Britain alone has more than 260 species of them. Flies, too, are good pollinators, at least of some plants. Natural ecosystems, in short, have 'redundancy' built into them. For every one creature doing a particular job there may be half a dozen or even hundreds on standby, waiting to fill the niche if the most conspicuous species fails. This isn't always so—many plants rely on *particular* pollinators and many animals including many kinds of butterfly and moth larvae will feed *only* on particular plants and some species known as 'keystone species' support a whole entourage of others who are in trouble if the keystone disappears. Even so, most players in the world's ecosystems have understudies that a logistics expert would feel are superfluous. In general, too, the older and better-established the ecosystem becomes, the greater the 'redundancy.' But it's precisely because of this apparent redundancy that the ecosystem as a whole is so resilient, shock-resistant, and, over time, sustainable.

In short, ***'efficiency' conceived in crude commercial terms—as an absence of redundancy—is absolutely at odds with the ideals of resilience and sustainability***. Whatever technical gimmicks are introduced, a system of food production and distribution that is driven by the perceived need to maximize commercial efficiency will always be highly precarious. Once again we see that if we really care about the long-term future, we cannot allow ourselves and the world to be guided by the principles of modern commerce. We need a new mindset—one based on moral principle and ecological reality. We also need people in positions of influence who understand those principles, and share the mindset. Just to hammer the point; again we see that what is now considered normal (commercial) practice is the precise opposite of what the world really needs.

Biological efficiency really does matter—and in nature is achieved in four main ways. First, as outlined in chapter 3, nature is astonishingly ***diverse***. Secondly, the different creatures interact in an infinity of different ways—which often are antagonistic but overall are ***synergistic***: the different species benefit from the activities of the others. Thirdly (despite the essential redundancy) nature is supremely ***economical***, not to say parsimonious. This economy is manifest in two main ways. Thus, with a few special exceptions (such as estuaries) natural ecosystems are ***low-input***. All ecosystems borrow from other ecosystems (the oxygen I am breathing now was probably produced in large part by photosynthesizing plankton somewhere out in the Atlantic) but on the whole they make do with what is close at hand. Secondly, the overall economy of nature is ***circular*** or ***cyclic***. What one species rejects, others treat as a prime source of nutrient. Detritivores (consumers of detritus, like a lot of flies) and saprobes (digesters of dead matter, like many fungi) are supremely important—and in turn are food for predators. In nature, the same atoms of oxygen, hydrogen, nitrogen, phosphorus, sulphur, iron, magnesium, and all the other elements that are the stuff of living creatures go round and round and round. The carbon in carbon dioxide may one day form part of the atmosphere; the next day part of a plant; the next day part of a cow; the next day poo; the next day part of a fly; the next day part of a bird—and so on and so on for billions of years (literally).

Finally, although soil may be disturbed from time to time—for example by landslides or herds of migrating ungulates, or indeed by natural diggers like pigs—on the whole ***nature does not cultivate***. The soil is left undisturbed year on year, and often century on century, enabling the ecology of the soil itself to become richer and richer as organic matter is added and the myriad inhabitants of the soil—bacteria, archaeans, fungi, protists, and animals of all phyla—combine to create an ecosystem that may be as diverse and intricate as a forest or a coral reef. Biologists are only now beginning to appreciate the absolute importance of the soil microbes, particularly the bacteria, and of the mycorrhizal fungi, which live symbiotically within and around the roots of *most* wild plants and hugely extend their range and versatility. The soil biota is seriously damaged and may eventually be destroyed by ploughing in particular and by too much artificial fertilizer, pesticide, and herbicide. (Nutritionists too have cottoned on to microbes as outlined in the next chapter.)

So how can these ecological principles be translated into farming practice?

Farms as ecosystems

Diversity leads us to ***polyculture***: ***the mixed farm*** (combinations of different crops and animals sharing the same space) ***with genetic variation within each breed or variety***. In short: ***avoid monocultures***.

Clones are monocultures supreme. In a population of clones, whether of crops, livestock, or in the wild, all the individuals are genetically identical. Some crops are naturally clones, including potatoes, reproduced asexually from tubers; and fruit trees are clones, multiplied from cuttings. But it is ecologically desirable to mix up the genotypes as much as possible. If we must grow clones (which for some crops is essential) then they should at least be mixed with other species and varieties.

Synergy implies that the different enterprises on the farm should be ***integrated***. On traditional mixed farms, for instance, whey from cheese-making is a valuable feed for pigs, and straw from cereals provides both feed and bedding and in either case it finishes up as manure to fertilize the fields. Mixed farms par excellence are still to be found in South-East Asia: arable and aquaculture combined in the paddy fields; horticulture on all the higher ground; water buffalo, pigs, chickens, ducks, and carp. I have seen this at first hand and it can be wondrous: biologically, aesthetically, socially.

Minimization of inputs and particularly of oil-based fertilizers and pesticides leads us to embrace ***organic farming***. Organic should at least be seen as the default position: what all farmers and growers should do as a matter of course unless there is a very good reason to do otherwise. That high-input farming based on agrochemistry is now considered 'conventional' is, frankly, weird. Agriculture must be conceived as an exercise in biology and alas, many if not most modern agriculturalists and policy-makers are not biologists. Real biologists, who actually like whole animals and plants (and all the rest) are becoming thin on the ground. ***Biodynamic*** farming and ***permaculture*** are variations on the organic theme that deserve to be taken very seriously.

Reduction of cultivation leads us to ***minimum tillage*** or 'min-till,' or indeed ***zero tillage***. Weeds, the immediate enemies, are controlled not with the aid of herbicides but wherever possible by the various guiles of organic farming, including permaculture, with its thick mulches. Modern, short-stemmed, varieties of 'semi-dwarf' wheat gives marvellous yields for a time when suitably fertilized but they need lashings of selective herbicide too or they are liable to be swamped by fast-growing weeds. More traditional varieties are tall (as shown in the paintings of Breughel). They do not yield as heavily as modern varieties because they put a lot of their energy into straw rather than seeds—but if they are planted at the right time they do out-grow the weeds (and wheat straw is very valuable in its own right, not least for thatching).

The principle of agroecology is also made manifest in various particular enterprises that have often been pushed aside by industrial agriculture.

Thus, worldwide (though less so in high-tech Britain than in many other countries) there is increasing interest in ***agroforestry***. One example—as pioneered at Wakelyns Farm in Suffolk by Martin Wolfe—is ***alley cropping***: crops of any kind—arable or horticulture—raised between rows of trees of many kinds (including fruit trees). In some years, as part of a rotation, livestock can be raised in the rows instead of crops. Convention has it that trees and crops don't mix—but they certainly can, to the advantage of both. For example, the trees bring up nutrients from deep in the ground—a fine example of re-cycling. They also provide 'beetle banks'—reservoirs of predatory insects and spiders that demonstrably reduce the pests in the neighbouring crops. Traditional hedgerows separating traditionally small fields are agroforestry of a kind. The key concept is that of ***land equivalent ratio***. A field with trees and crops raised together in well-tempered synergy yield more and/or is worth more than the same field would be if it contained trees with no crops or crops with no trees.

There's increasing interest too in ***pasture-fed livestock***—cattle and sheep (and pigs and poultry too to a surprising extent!) especially the kind raised not on custom-bred and heavily fertilized high-energy, high-protein, monocultural grass but on natural pasture (insofar as any pasture can ever be said to be 'natural') with a variety of grass species and a host of other herbs as well, many of which have special nutritional and therapeutic value (as outlined in chapter 7). Pasture-feeding goes hand in hand with the small but significant rise in ***micro-dairies***. Dairy farmers who are plugged in to the modern industrial food chain find it hard to make a living unless they have hundreds of high-yielding Holsteins (and hybrids) with all the gear that goes with them, fed on custom-bred ryegrass fertilized to the hilt, with cereal and soya supplements—but a few farmers even in Britain have unplugged themselves from the high-tech commercial chain and make an acceptable living by direct selling of fresh, high-quality, unhomogenized milk from twenty or even fewer cows of traditional breeds such as Ayrshires and Dairy Shorthorns. It can be done, and it is certainly worth doing. Small dairy farms run on agroecological lines should be serious players in future food and farming strategy.

Enlightened, agroecological farms that incorporate some or all of these elements are also wildlife friendly—and, as remarked in chapter 4, the whole cause of wildlife conservation is seriously compromised, not to say dead in the water, unless farming is wildlife friendly.

All this has enormous economic, social, and hence political implications. For farms that are maximally mixed and integrated and basically organic are bound to be ***complex***—they are designed to be. So the husbandry must be intricate—which means they must be ***skills-intensive***: not with armies of slaves or serfs to do the work of tractors, but with a great many skilled, hands-on farmers and growers. ***Britain could probably do with eight or ten times as many farmers as it has now.*** When enterprises are complex and skills-intensive there is little or no advantage in scale-up, so the agroecological farms that the world really needs should in general be ***small to medium-sized*** (though there is plenty of scope for small units to form various kinds of cooperative).

The wiles and wonders of agroecology could and should occupy a fair slice of humanity for all the time our species lasts—but alas we must leave it there. What of the other components of Enlightened Agriculture? Briefly:

Food Sovereignty, Green Economic Democracy, and Traditional Knowledge

The expression ***Food Sovereignty*** was first coined in the 1990s by the world peasant movement, *La Via Campesina*. It proposes that all people, everywhere, should have control of their own food supply. At the national level this seems to me to imply ***national self-reliance***. At the more personal level it implies ***subsidiarity***—the idea that all decisions should be made at the lowest level possible, meaning that food and farming should wherever practical be organized by communities. Via Campesina, incidentally, is surely the biggest organized social movement in the world, with 200 million followers. It seems, though, that very few people in the western world have heard of it. Ho hum.

Self-reliance does *not* mean total self-sufficiency. It would be absurd for Britain, say, to try to grow coffee or bananas, although the Brits have a huge appetite for both. Self-reliance does mean that all countries should contrive always to produce enough of the kinds of foods it *can* grow readily to keep all the people in good fettle even if supplies from abroad are interrupted. ***Most countries in the world could be self-reliant, if they set out to be so,*** and most would be far better off if they were—including almost all the countries of Africa who now appear regularly on national TV news as economic basket-cases, constantly threatened by famine.

Emphatically, self-reliance does not mean an end to trade. Thus Britain should continue to buy coffee and bananas from the people who are better able to grow them—*provided* the trade is fair and ecologically acceptable. The farmers themselves should be properly rewarded for their efforts (which typically has not been the case) and crops should not be grown for export at the expense of local farmers or—as is commonly and perhaps generally the case these days—if the crops are grown in ways and in quantities that wreck the local biosphere. Then again, some crops and other produce are far easier to export than others. In general, dry or fermented produce, like grain, spices, or (some) wines travels well, but anything wet needs special protection, often involving elaborate packaging and/or dubious industrial chemistry to keep predators and agents of decay at bay.

In short, ***a general global strategy of national self-reliance*** organized as far as possible by communities, supplemented by ecologically and socially sound ***fair trade***, seems the right way to go. The global, labyrinthine food network that we now have, dominated as always by the world's superpowers and a couple of handfuls of mega-corporates and financiers, is, once again, the precise opposite of what's really needed.

Green Economic Democracy is discussed in chapter 9. 'Economic democracy' in general implies a mixed economy—meaning as outlined in chapter 9 the ***tripartite mixed economy***: a synergy of public (government) ownership, private ownership, and community ownership. Even more to the point, ***all commercial endeavours of all kinds should be conceived as social enterprises and operate in accord with the absolute principles of morality and ecology, controlled as far as possible by people at large.*** If this was indeed the norm the world's problems of all kinds really could be solved. (More in chapters 9 and 10).

More and more intellectuals in high places are beginning to appreciate the absolute importance of ***Traditional Knowledge***—as represented by artisanal farming and reflected in folk wisdom. Thus as Professor Michel Pimbert, the director of the Centre for Agroecology and Water Resilience (CAWR) at Coventry University has been arguing for some years, all attempts to improve agriculture in traditional societies *must* be planned and carried out in close collaboration, from the outset, with the local people—including or especially the accompanying programmes of scientific research. The local, often indigenous people are the most affected—and they also understand best what the local problems really are, and often have the best solutions, which outsiders often don't realise. As argued too in chapter 7, modern nutritional theory to a very large extent—and, I am inclined to say, at its best—is reinventing folk wisdom. If we cooked like our great-grandmothers we would not go far wrong.

Alas, however: western intellectuals in particular often seem to have taken it for granted that traditional peoples including peasant farmers are 'ignorant,' and so must be 'educated' or swept aside. In the same kind of spirit, the world's most powerful governments, from the West, the East, and the Middle East, tend to treat the terrain of less affluent countries as a *tabula rasa*, virgin territory, and ignore all that was there before. Old-style imperialism that required expensive armies and a dedicated civil service has given way to land-grabbing that can be done at long range through the now conventional mechanisms of commerce, tempered as always with a little sharp practice. The great empires of the past have largely disappeared but the imperial spirit lives on. Again we see that what is needed perhaps most of all, or at least is the *sine qua non*, is a change not simply of method or even of economic structure but of *mindset*. As stressed in the chapters of Part V, a little humility would not go amiss.

One last question: if present methods are so destructive, and the alternative is so obvious and well-tried, why do we, or rather the ruling oligarchy, persist with the status quo?

Two reasons, I suggest. First, as outlined in Part IV, the oligarch-dominated world is locked in a positive feedback loop. The approach that the oligarchs favour is the one that favours the oligarchs.

Secondly, the oligarchs have chosen to believe and to promulgate a whole list of assumptions that are simply untrue.

Misconceptions and just plain lies: the six great untruths that are threatening to kill us all

More or less everything that we are told about food and farming by the oligarchs who dominate our lives—the government, the corporates, big finance, and large but mercifully not all sections of academe—is untrue, or at least is seriously misleading. Thus we are told that:

1: *We must produce more and more food to keep up with rising population and rising demand—especially the demand for more meat.*

The present population stands at 7.8 billion and is still rising—but the UN demographers tell us that the percentage *rate* of growth is falling and should be down to zero sometime after 2050, which means that numbers should stabilise. Then the world population will at most reach 10 billion and could be a lot less (see chapter 2). This of course is a great many—but the world already produces enough for 14-15 billion people, as you can check for yourself with statistics available on the web. Thus the world currently produces 2.5 billion tonnes of cereals a year, and one tonne provides enough food energy and protein to support three people for a year—so cereals alone provide enough macronutrient for 7.5 billion people; and cereals provide only half the world's energy and protein—the rest comes from pulses, tubers, fruit and vegetables, meat, dairy, and fish.

The idea that we need more, and more, and still more has little to do with real need and everything to do with commerce. We should be focused on food quality and eco- and people-friendliness rather than sheer bulk.

2: *As people grow richer, they 'demand' more meat.*

As societies are 'lifted out of poverty' meat consumption rises. In particular the US became hooked on steaks and burgers after World War II and the economic depression that preceded it; and Beijing and other big Chinese cities now bristle with burgers and fried chicken.

Yet, though most people do seem to like meat, there is very little evidence for any active 'demand.' The evidence, when looked at objectively, is that people eat what's available and what—for whatever reason—is fashionable. As outlined in chapter 7, all the world's greatest cuisines from Italy to China via the Middle East and India make only sparing use of meat—as garnish, stock, and for occasional feasts. We can easily produce enough meat for truly great gastronomy by means that are socially benign and ecologically are at least sustainable, by feeding pigs and poultry on leftovers and surpluses and cattle and sheep on pasture or land that is too hot, cold, wet, dry, high, or steep for horticulture or arable—as was and is traditional. Emphatically, less meat need not mean austerity. We simply need to-learn how to cook.

Again, the real driver is commerce. With modern high-tech we can produce huge surpluses—in the short term!—and the problem then is how to dispose of the excess profitably. The easy answer is to feed it to livestock—and then charge a lot for the meat (which, after all, *ought* to be expensive). Another wheeze now becoming popular in high circles is to burn the surplus cereal and call it 'biofuel.' It has been suggested that 40% of US maize—one of the world's most important food crops—could and should be turned into ethanol for fuel.

3: *We need ever more productive crops and livestock.*

We are told that the extra food that in fact we don't need can be provided only by raising, yet further, the already prodigious output of cereals and livestock: wheat that yields at least 10 tonnes per hectare on average, about three times the yield of 100 years ago (the British average is already eight tonnes per hectare); cattle that give at least 10,000 litres (2000 gallons) per lactation—about six times as much as a wild cow—which many do already; broiler chickens that reach supermarket weight even more quickly than the present ones that are slaughtered at six weeks.

But all this is of course unnecessary, and cruel, and obviously unsustainable. According to the UN's *Global Land Output* of September 2017 about a third of all the world's agricultural soils are now seriously degraded, largely or entirely because of intensive, industrial farming.

4: *Only high-tech can save us now.*

We are also given to understand that to go on feeding ourselves we need the highest of high tech—and above all, GMOs: 'genetically modified organisms,' tailor-made by genetic engineering; and, now, 'gene-editing'—re-structuring the crop's or animal's own genes. Yet it is very hard to find any clear examples of GM crops that have been of unequivocal benefit to humankind (more in chapter 13). They solve no problems that really need solving, and (despite vehement and sometimes litigious denials) are causing enormous collateral damage. Contrariwise, more traditional techniques that are now being swept aside could easily provide all the food the world will ever need, sustainably and at far less cost.

5: *Fewer workers means greater efficiency—and efficiency is all.*

It depends how you measure 'efficiency.' Measured in money then as long as oil is affordable NI oil-based agriculture is very efficient.

It's efficient too in terms of money generated per worker—since, after all, the main point of high tech in agriculture is to reduce labour. But measured in energy terms—total energy in *versus* total energy out—it is grossly inefficient compared with artisanal agriculture. It is grossly inefficient even in financial terms, too, if we add in the cost of the collateral damage—social and ecological—which in practice tend to be dismissed as 'externalities.' We should recall, too, that nature manages to be as resilient and sustainable as it is because there is so much built-in redundancy—the very opposite of what industrialists mean by 'efficiency.' ***The more 'efficient' farming becomes by the measures of industrialists and accountants the more precarious it becomes—and the more precarious our own existence.***

6: *Organic farming is a middle-class indulgence—strictly niche. It cannot possibly feed the world.*

Traditional artisanal farming is 'organic' by default—it developed before artificial fertilizers or pesticides were invented. Yet artisanal farms with little or no industrial input still supply half the world's food; and Professor Bob Orskov, who was himself born into a traditional farming family in Denmark and then spent much of his traditional life amongst Third World farmers, asserts that many or most artisanal farms could double or triple their output if given a little support simply of a political and economic kind, and some good basic science (as opposed to industrial high tech). Modern organic farming with guidance from science—ecology, physiology, microbiology—is a key component of agroecology and agroecology offers the *only* plausible, sustainable, long-term solution to the world's food problems. In addition, if agroecological farming (with modern organic know-how and plenty of skilled farmers and growers) was the global norm then much or most of the world's ecological ('environmental') and social problems would disappear too, or at least be seriously ameliorated.

Yet again it seems that in this as in most things the wisdom that is poured down to us from above is the precise opposite of what is really required.

What's to be done?

Although, on the face of things, agriculture and the entire food chain seem to be sewn up—a few handfuls of corporates seem to have taken over the whole show, backed by the world's most powerful governments with access to public (our) money—food and farming still offer the greatest opportunities for grass-roots movements and people's takeover. In *Six Steps Back to the Land* I suggest a six-step route whereby individuals who may never have thought seriously about farming may progress from patio-scale gardeners to bona-fide mixed farmers. The key to large-scale success, though, as always, is through cooperation—communities joining together to buy land or otherwise acquire the rights to use; and then combining either to employ full-time professional farmers or to farm themselves. For my part, I am collaborating with like-minded friends to build the College for Real Farming and Food Culture to provide the necessary intellectual and spiritual background to underpin the whole endeavour. Worldwide, many millions of individuals and many thousands of organizations are on the case. The whole together is the first stirrings of an ***Agrarian Renaissance***—key component of the cross-the-board Renaissance that is now so urgently needed. In short, desperate as the world now seems, and undoubtedly is, the game is far from over (unless we choose to cave in).

A NEW FOOD CULTURE: 'PLENTY OF PLANTS, NOT MUCH MEAT, AND MAXIMUM VARIETY'

Or

THE FUTURE BELONGS TO THE GOURMET

No system of agriculture can operate for very long—or not at least in a free, convivial society—unless people are prepared to eat, and preferably positively desire, what the farmers produce. In other words, all systems of farming need a corresponding, complementary **food culture**. So: what kind of food culture is needed to complement Enlightened Agriculture?

According to the jeremiahs, the to-the-death defenders of the status quo, if enlightened farmers are given their head, enabled and encouraged to farm according to the dictats of agroecology, then we, people-at-large, will have to tighten our belts, turn vegan (or very nearly so) and generally learn to embrace austerity. Only high-tech, we are told, can save us from this dour scenario—including artificial, aka *ersatz* meat spun from the protein of beans and fungi or even—some suggest—from bacteria, all laced with additives or suitably engineered, genetically, so as to mimic, up to a point, the flavours of the original.

As usual, the truth is more or less the diametric opposite of what we are being told. In reality, ***the future belongs to the gourme***t. The produce of enlightened agriculture is exactly of the kind and in the proportions recommended by the world's best-informed nutritionists, and perfectly matches the requirements of the world's finest cuisines. In short, ***all we really need is to farm properly (in the manner called enlightened) and re-learn how to cook.***

One—large—problem is that the science of nutrition—the science that should tell us what we *need* to eat—is still full of uncertainties. I have been taking a serious interest in nutrition for about 60 years and in that time a host of theories have come and gone and now we are left with a whole variety of opinions pulling in different directions. More than that: nutrition over the past few decades—like all science—has undergone what the American philosopher of science Thomas Kuhn in the 1960s called a ***paradigm shift***, or rather a series of paradigm shifts—away from the idea that nutritional science, or indeed any science, can ever tell us all there is to know, or provide us with absolute certainty. All our explanations of everything are almost certainly incomplete and could well be wrong. Furthermore, the more we move away from the abstractions and mathematical rigour of physics and start to study nature as it really is, the more the uncertainties grow. Thus:

SIXTY YEARS OF NUTRITIONAL THEORY: A LIGHTNING HISTORY

As was seen to be right and proper, traditional nutritional science of the kind that I was first taught in the 1950s and '60s was rooted in chemistry—essentially benchtop chemistry—and in thermodynamics.

Very reasonably, food in general was and is divided into 'macronutrients' which provide the stuff of flesh and fuel for energy, and 'micronutrients' which fill in the cracks and generally enable the metabolism to do its thing. It was generally understood that the macronutrients—carbohydrates, fats, and proteins—were broken down completely in the gut into their component parts—sugars, lipids, and amino acids—so the detailed nature of the original didn't matter very much. The micronutrients included a shortlist of vitamins—complex, essential molecules that the body could not make for itself, or not at least in sufficient amounts, and had to be supplied ready-made from a somewhat unlikely inventory of foodstuffs that included things like blackcurrants and spinach and liver, plus sunshine for vitamin D. The micronutrients also included a fair slice of the periodic table—metals and non-metals, collectively known as 'minerals.' Finally, we were told, food contains what in those days was known as 'roughage,' consisting almost entirely of plant cell walls. But roughage, more or less by definition, was seen to be 'inert,' indigestible, serving primarily to scour the bowel, an alimentary chimney-sweep. Roughage was the stock in trade of school matrons but avant-garde doctors generally had very little time for it.

The bowel was also home to various bacteria which mostly did nothing very interesting—they were merely 'commensals,' essentially lodgers and hangers-on. Some of them, however, including *Escherichia coli,* could turn rogue and cause disease that was sometimes fatal.

Body weight was a matter of simple physics—thermodynamics. Energy can neither be created nor destroyed so if you ate more than you burned off the surplus had to be stored as fat; and if you ate less than you burned off you would grow slimmer. Obvious.

That was more or less it. That, roughly, is what generations of medical students have been taught. The overall conception—the paradigm—did we but know it, derived from René Descartes (1596-1650) in the 17th century. For he declared in Enlightenment fashion that although human beings have ethereal souls that are conduits to God, our *bodies* can be conceived as machines; and, like machines, can be exhaustively studied by the methods of physics and chemistry, and thoroughly understood.

Things changed dramatically since the mid-20th century, though not of course in a straight line. Theories came and theories went. Opinions swung to and fro, with wave on wave of dietary advice, some based on respectable science and some essentially fanciful but none of it cast-iron. No corner of traditional nutrition science and the advice it gave rise to have gone untouched. The swings continue as vigorously as ever. Thus:

Protein

In the 1950s and 1960s when I was at school and university we were told to eat loads of protein—up to 15% of the diet, measured in calories. This advice apparently derived from observations before World War II on kwashiorkor in Africa: the nutritional disease of children that leaves them swollen-bellied (with oedema), and light-skinned, with reddish, frizzy hair. It seemed that lack of protein was the cause—and this was assumed to be a prime cause of malnutrition worldwide. The war interrupted research and this initial hypothesis became the accepted theory by default. Human beings, it seemed, need lots of protein and it had to be 'first class'—with a near-perfect balance of amino acids. So it had to be animal protein. Plant proteins were said to be 'second class.' We were told, not least on children's television, to eat as much cheese and eggs as possible. Even bread was written off as 'empty calories.' Fat *per se* was hardly mentioned.

The pre-war observations that led to the emphasis on protein were made very conscientiously by excellent physicians working in difficult conditions and with the best of intentions. Yet it seems they were wrong. Kwashiorkor, it now seems, like marasmus—wasting—is caused primarily by lack of calories: a body starved of calories 'burns' the protein in the muscles and so appears to be protein-deficient. But as is the way of the modern world, science and good intentions were overtaken by commerce. Agrochemistry (making use not least of the factories that had recently been producing explosives and agents of biological warfare) provided huge arable surpluses on which to raise poultry, pigs, and cattle on the grandest scale. Yet this, it seemed, wasn't just commerce in pursuit of money. It was seen to be *necessary*. A service to humankind. Truly good and solid medical research had apparently shown that animal protein was vital, in large amounts, and only industrial farming, rooted in agrochemistry, could supply what was needed. Commerce and piety together swept all before them (and still do).

In the 1970s, though, it began to seem that the zeal for protein was misguided. Indian physicians in particular pointed out that many millions of Asians functioned very well indeed and could raise large families although most of them had very little meat or fish and many had none at all. Various albeit limited trials suggested that healthy non-pregnant adults could make do on remarkably little protein—nearer seven per cent than 15. Clearly, too, some of the world's cleverest people were vegetarian or vegan, including a great many Asians and a minority of westerners who included Leonardo and Tolstoy. The proteins from cereals or pulses were perfectly adequate for most purposes, especially when the two were eaten in combination. Notably, the surplus of the essential amino acid lysine in beans and other pulses makes up for the relative lack of it in cereals. The cereal-plus-pulse combination occurs in all the world's traditional cuisines: dhal and rice; *tortilla con frijoles*; beans on toast. Professor N.W. ('Bill') Pirie from Rothamsted pointed out too that all the great cuisines use meat only as garnish or occasional feasts—and they also use meat and bones to make stock. Stock is the key to risotto and to noodle soup, and who should ask for more?

If diet followed scientific theory in any simple way then we might have expected that the vogue for meat would have faded with the vogue for protein. But there is much more to meat eating than that. Meat is a sign of wealth and hence of status. It is also the original fast food, epitomised by the burger. 'Slam in the lamb' said a recent TV ad—and that indeed is all you have to do. Besides, meat tastes nice and it's filling. In the 1970s and 1980s steak and salad was the standard executive lunch, the up-market way to lose weight. Yum yum.

Sugar and starch

In the 1960s the first serious doubts were raised around sugar and carbohydrates in general, primarily by the London-based nutritionist John Yudkin in his book *Pure, White and Deadly*. The doubts continue, not least around fructose, which combined with glucose makes sucrose, which is what most people call 'sugar.' Among other things, fructose is said to upset the production of insulin whose job it is to regulate blood sugar levels, and this in turn may predispose to diabetes. In general it seems that the simple and related sugars glucose and fructose have very different effects on the body—which illustrates a more general principle that has often been overlooked: that the body is very discerning. It is alert to fine chemical distinctions and we cannot assume that it will treat two molecules in the same way just because we with our present knowledge perceive that they are similar.

Good or bad, fructose derived from corn syrup is widely used as a sweetener (it is very sweet). Few, though, have many good words to say for sugar in general—although sweet foods are high in energy and surely should be good in the short term for anyone who is truly short of calories, which a great many people are, worldwide.

Others extended Professor Yudkin's antipathy to sugar to embrace carbohydrates in general—including starch, the principal energy store of plants: macromolecules compounded from many molecules of glucose. People on low starch diets can still eat plenty of plants in the form of leaves and fruits but they miss out on what for most of humanity are the staples—cereals (the seeds of grasses, (Poaceae)) and pulses (the seeds of legumes (Fabaceae)); and tubers such as potatoes and cassava. So a low starch diet by the standards of most of humanity is on the one hand very luxurious—generally high in meat, fish, and fruit—but is also austere: no bread, no rice, no tortillas, no potatoes—foods that for most people through most of history have formed most of the diet. Some nutritionists and anthropologists have gone on to argue that the birth of arable farming not long after the last Ice Age was a huge nutritional mistake, even though it is widely seen to have given rise to modern civilization. Human beings simply are not equipped, say the doubters, to cope with all that cereal. The 'paleo diet' (where paleo is short for 'Palaeolithic') has enjoyed some vogue in recent years, based on the idea that our pre-agricultural, hunter-gathering ancestors must have got their calories from nuts, fruits, tubers, and the lean meat of wild animals. This idea appeals too to those, including many farmers, who are now reacting against the low-fat diets that were recommended in the 1970s and beyond and are now telling us that we should eat more meat and eggs and dairy (provided the relevant livestock have not been fed on cereal). More on this later.

Whatever the benefits if any of the paleo diet, the theory on which it is based seems highly speculative, not to say flimsy. I have written a lot about human evolution in my time and the widely accepted theory, backed by a great deal of fossil and geological evidence, is that our australopithecine ancestors broke away from the ancient apish line as the world grew cooler and drier in the late Miocene and early Pliocene, and they left the dwindling forests of southern and eastern Africa to make their living on the savannah. There presumably they ate whatever plants were growing and whatever animals they could catch—but animals are elusive, and fight back. Savannah basically is grassland and grasses were abundant, not to say dominant, and our savannah-dwelling ancestors must surely have eaten their seeds. Cereals too are the seeds of grasses so why are we supposed to be so ill-adapted to them? Particular indispositions such as gluten intolerance are surely caused by modern high-gluten cereals and modern processing rather than by cereals per se. Besides, in his excellent book *The Diet Myth* (Orion Publishing 2015) Tim Spector points out that even if we were ill-adapted to eating cereals 10,000 years ago (a very big 'if'), we have had plenty of time to adapt. Favourable mutations are not common but they do happen and westerners on the whole have for example adapted to lactose, the sugar in milk, even though our ancestors did not retain the enzymes to cope with it after they had passed infancy.

In short, common sense and evolutionary biology suggest that a high cereal diet should be perfectly good (although the special case of gluten intolerance seems to need far more research than it is getting). The idea that bread is the staff of life (and rice and oats) seems to have served most of the human species pretty well over the past 10,000 years. There is a lot wrong with modern diets but surplus of cereals per se (at least in their more pristine forms) does not seem high on the list.

Overall, though, the position on carbohydrates remains unresolved, not to say confused. Some advisers in evangelical vein condemn sugars and starches out of hand—yet for health food shops, variations on a theme of cereals (muesli, wholemeal bread, and mixed loaves of wheat, barley, and rye) are the stock-in-trade. There's something wrong somewhere. (Quinoa and buckwheat are non-cereal grains. Quinoa is a relative of Good King Henry and Fat Hen, and buckwheat is related to Dock.)

Fibre

'Roughage' too underwent a serious overhaul from the 1970s onwards, and re-emerged as 'dietary fibre.' There were significant advances on three fronts. First, physicians such as Denis Burkitt and Hugh Trowell perceived that the people of Africa in particular on a traditional, plant-oriented, high-fibre diet suffered none of the 'diseases of affluence' that were besetting the affluent world—obesity, heart disease, various cancers, diabetes, and indeed gallstones; and they proposed that fibre could be protective. Secondly, botanists and nutritionists alike pointed out that plant cell walls do not consist solely of cellulose, which does tend to be 'inert,' but also include a host of 'hemicelluloses' which incorporate some recondite sugars, and pectin (described as a 'heteropolysaccharide': its molecules are compounded of various sugars and other things as well). All of these could be broken down in the colon and then become active players. Clearly, too, not all plant fibres are chemically or physically the same. Thirdly, by then it had long been obvious that the colon is not merely a conduit, designed to return the remains of previous meals to the wider world, but is a vital player in the whole digestive and absorptive process. Among other things, bile salts, squirted into the gut from the liver to assist the digestion of fat, are resorbed by the colon, and re-used. But they are also altered chemically in the colon—and the way they are altered depends in part on the amount and on the particular nature of any fibre that's present. Bile salts are stored in the gall bladder and some kinds of bile salt are more likely to cause stones than others, so here was a possible physiological link between dietary fibre and gallstones. So long as fibre was seen as 'roughage,' a kind of Brillo pad, it was hard to see how it could influence the various diseases with which it was being associated. But once it was called 'fibre' and recognized as an active player in the metabolism of the gut, the whole fibre story became, not proven, but eminently plausible; and plausibility is the start of serious interest.

Fats

Arch rival to John Yudkin, intellectually and, I understand, personally, was the Minnesota epidemiologist Ancel Keys. Keys, from the 1950s onwards, argued that the main cause of the world's dietary ills was not carbohydrates, but fats.

The simple message from Ancel Keys was that too much fat is bad for people—and this is still widely accepted. In the meat-rich diets of the western (northern) world, fat provides around 40% of total calories whereas in the low-meat diets of what Gandhi called the 'Third World' it's nearer 20%. In the traditional diets of Japan fat may account for only a tenth of total calories. In the mid-20th century it was Westerners who suffered the 'diseases of affluence.' The focus in those days was on coronary heart disease, sometimes shortened to CHD: blockage of the coronary arteries which feed the heart muscle itself.

But fat is not simple stuff. It takes many forms and does many different things. The 'essential' fats are key components of body structure, not least cell membranes. Others serve primarily as long-term stores of energy and as insulators, not least in seals and penguins.

Fats of the kind that concern us here are of two main kinds. The ones we normally think of as 'fat' are triglycerides: they consist of three long chains of fatty acids yoked together. Cholesterol is also a form of fat: one fatty acid chain attached to a sterol molecule. Thus, cholesterol is both a fat and a steroid.

Cholesterol often features in popular medical literature as the arch-villain—but again the picture is not simple. It is, after all, an essential component of cell membranes and a precursor in the synthesis of steroid hormones. But if there is too much cholesterol circulating in the blood then it tends to get deposited on the walls of arteries to form 'plaques'; and plaques blocking the coronary arteries lead to CHD and so perhaps to heart attack. In the light of this doctors have often advised their patients to steer clear of high-cholesterol foods such as eggs, including those of hens and the roes of fishes, although in truth, we normally consume very little cholesterol. But, it seems, diets high in fat of the triglyceride kind, as in lamb chops and burgers, also raise blood cholesterol. So it is that from about the 1960s onwards, many doctors and scientists have advised us to eat less carbohydrate (and particularly less sugar) while others have told us to eat less fat. Since fat and carbohydrate between them provide us with at least 80% of our calories, and sometimes well over 90%, it's clear that if we followed both streams of advice slavishly we would starve to death.

There are further complications. To begin with, cholesterol molecules are carried in the blood attached to protein molecules; and the two together form 'lipoproteins' (where 'lipo' means fat which in this instance is in the form of cholesterol). In some lipoprotein molecules the protein content is high, and since proteins weigh more than fats these are called high-density lipoproteins or HDLs; and in some lipoprotein molecules the protein content is low and these accordingly are of low density, and are called LDLs. It's the LDLs that can build plaques. They are the bad guys. Cholesterol in the form of HDLs are en route to the liver—which means they are being removed from the blood. So both LDLs and HDLs contribute to 'high cholesterol.' But while high LDLs can mean trouble, high HDLs are a sign that all is well. The cholesterol is being safely chaperoned out of harm's way.

Triglycerides, too, are immensely various—they range from oils like those of fish, sunflower seeds, and olives to beef dripping and lard. The fats that are liquid at normal temperatures are generally of the kind known as 'unsaturated.' Their long carbon chains contain far less hydrogen than they theoretically could. The hard fats tend to be highly saturated (with hydrogen). The two kinds in general seem to have different effects. In the last decades of the 20th century it became clear that while saturated fats tend to raise blood cholesterol and in particular to raise LDLs, unsaturated fats tend to lower LDLs, reducing the total level of blood cholesterol and increasing the ratio of HDLs to LDLs.

Then again, the polyunsaturates in food belong to two main 'series': the omega-3s (which include alpha-linolenic acid), and the omega-6s (which include linoleic acid). Omega-3s and omega-6s should ideally be consumed in equal amounts. Both are found in plant oils and omega-3 is largely associated with fish oil.

Then there are trans-fats. They are uncommon in nature but have been produced on the grand scale in industry by adding hydrogen to unsaturated fats to 'harden' them; that is, turn them from an oily to a solid form so they can be used in margarine and for baking. Adding hydrogen means that the formerly polyunsaturated fat becomes more saturated—and it now seems that such artificially hardened fats are more likely than most to lead to CHD. The hardening of plant oils to make a substitute for butter could be seen as yet another example of scientific hubris.

There are suggestions too that the ill effects of eating meat may not be due primarily to the fats. The culprit may be the protein carnitine, which is associated with fat metabolism and, it seems, with the onset of atherosclerosis (fatty plaques on the artery walls of the kind that lead to CHD). There isn't enough evidence to allow serious comment. Suffice to say only that the carnitine story is coming up on the rails—and who can tell what else might turn up in the years and decades to come?

Complicateder and complicateder, as Alice might have said. But then, why should life be simple? If it was, it wouldn't work. To borrow a thought from Immanuel Kant and to misquote Samuel Johnson, the wonder is not that life is hard to understand but that we should understand it at all.

As things turned out, thanks not least to aggressive PR, Ancel Keys's fat story won out over John Yudkin's sugar story. Thus in 1976 Britain's Royal Society of Physicians (RCP) advised westerners to reduce their total fat intake from around 40% of total calories to nearer 30%, although they said that 20% was probably better still. They also advised us all to switch from saturated fats to unsaturated fats. Saturated—hard—fats are mainly produced by animals, so we were advised in general to eat less meat, and especially red meat, with special reference to beef. Instead we should eat more unsaturated fats—the polyunsaturated kind which come mainly from fish and from seeds such as sunflower; and the monounsaturated fats which mainly mean olive oil.

I read the RCP report in great detail when it first came out and can attest that it is excellent. Its advice is clear but also cautious. The evidence is less than perfect, said the physicians (more on this later!) but on what they called the 'balance of probabilities' it seemed that if we ate less fat in general, and switched as far as possible from saturated to unsaturated, this could and should significantly reduce the risk of CHD—which, in the post-war decades, from the 1950s to well into the 1980s, was of epidemic proportions.

Although the evidence for all this was clearly less than perfect, what there was seemed very convincing. For example—just to take one anecdote—the people of Naples in those days apparently suffered far less heart attack than the people of Bologna. But then, the Neapolitans are southerners, who traditionally ate a 'Mediterranean diet': low in fat (but not ultra-low) but with a high proportion of fish and olive oil. Bolognans were rich northerners with a far higher intake of meat. We should all, it seemed, eat more like Neapolitans.

That is how the fat story stood for about half a century and a great many people including me feel there is still a great deal in it. Tim Spector in *The Diet Myth* says he favours the Mediterranean diet (and for what it's worth, so do I). The logic behind it and the many threads of data add up to a powerful story. But the game is not over (and never can be). There are several further twists.

One of these further twists seems to be letting beef off the hook big time—providing the beef is pasture-fed. Thus it seems that the fat of cattle fed on grass contains far more unsaturated fat than that of cattle fed on concentrates. Ancel Keys based his recommendations largely on epidemiological studies of seven nations, some of whom (like the Americans) ate large amounts of red meat and some of whom, like the Italians, ate far less. But now it seems that some people who eat a lot of red meat, like some Cretans, do not have particularly high LDL levels and very little CHD, and evidence from elsewhere suggests that it may be the diet of the cattle that makes the difference. In his latest book *Grass Fed Nation* (2016) Graham Harvey argues that some of the British in times past ate a lot of beef and revelled in butter, yet did not suffer heart attacks. Again the evidence is less than perfect but there surely is enough for governments who are concerned about more than economic growth at least to take a serious interest—to encourage pasture-feeding and assess the consequences as far as this is possible.

All of the above, or nearly all, was and is rooted in the traditional idea that the methods of science as outlined in chapter 13—observation, quantification, testable hypothesis, experiment, mathematical analysis—could and eventually would enable us to explain all aspects of the natural world exhaustively and with certainty; and what we could understand, we could surely control. The one real deviation from this was, I suggest, provided by the Royal College of Physicians in their 1976 report on CHD. Physicians know and have always known that life is not so easily pinned down. It is always one step ahead of us—or several steps. It is infinitely complex and full of unknowns and indeed of unknowables—things we simply cannot find out and things we didn't even realize we needed to know. Thus in practice it is almost impossible to conceive of a trial that would pin down the relationship between fat intake and heart disease in human beings who were leading their normal lives; and even if such a trial could be conceived it would be impossible to carry it out. We can do mass trials on microbes in petri dishes over a few days or weeks but not on real people living real lives over decades. What we don't fully understand we cannot predict or fully control. Indeed, doctors in general are always careful to point out to those who consult them that results cannot be guaranteed—not just for fear of being sued but because it is literally the case. Nature in the end is beyond our ken and in detail is beyond our control.

What physicians have known for millennia is now becoming obvious in all science. Real life cannot be pinned down completely and with certainty—and a series of insights over the past few decades has shown this to be abundantly true in the field of nutrition. This realization amounts not simply to a change of mind but to a ***paradigm shift***.

From changes of mind to paradigm shift

Four insights in particular have contributed to the paradigm shift in nutritional science:

First, there is growing interest in which I have been calling ***cryptonutrients***. 'Cryptonutrient' may be a neologism, so I will lay claim to it.

Secondly, it has become obvious that the zillions of microbes that live in the gut—there are more individual micro-organisms in the human gut than there are cells in the entire body—are not mere spivs and hangers-on. They are key players in digestion and absorption and hence in the whole physiology. Indeed, nutritional science to a significant extent has become an exercise in ***microbial ecology***.

Thirdly, there is growing interest in ***epigenetics***: based on the realization that the genes are not aloof dispensers of instructions but are very responsive to what is going on around them.

Finally, and most importantly, there is the general realization that ***nutritional science cannot sensibly be seen simply as an exercise in the 'hard' sciences of chemistry and thermodynamics***. Our diet influences and is influenced by *all* the mechanisms of the body and indeed by all aspects of human existence: genetics, immunology, endocrinology, psychology, sociology, personal history; and it affects and is affected by our general outlook on life. No wonder there is so much conflicting dietary advice out there.

In slightly more detail:

Cryptonutrients

Food isn't just nutrients—materials that build flesh and bones and brains, and/or provide fuel for energy. It also includes agents that behave more like pharmaceuticals or tonics, helping the works to run more smoothly. These include the vitamins, which are known to be essential: deficiency leads to disease and death. But in the 1990s it began to seem that there could be and probably is a whole host of subsidiary agents that if not necessarily vital are at least beneficial; agents that are somewhere between a nutrient and a tonic. The pharmaceutical industry seized on this idea and called these agents 'nutraceuticals.' The food industry called them 'functional foods.' Plant sterols are an example. They are chemically similar to cholesterol but, evidently, they help to lower cholesterol levels in the blood.

My own contribution to this discussion, written up here and there, has been to class all these subsidiary agents as ***cryptonutrients*** and to suggest an evolutionary reason why there should be such things. To begin at the beginning: human evolution did not begin when our apish ancestors took to the plains. It began long before our ancestors were human at all—with the origin of life on Earth, 3.8 billion or so years ago. After all, we still share some biochemical pathways and the corresponding genes with our fellow mammals and indeed with vertebrates in general. Evolutionary biologists commonly point out that we have inherited many of the features that enabled our australopithecine and early hominin ancestors to survive the Pliocene and Pleistocene but we have also inherited at least some of the adaptations that enabled our fishy ancestors to survive in Palaeozoic times. Indeed, we still retain a fair slice of the genes and metabolic pathways that are common to all animals and even to microbes.

Through all those millions and billions of years our ancestors must have been assailed with many thousands of different chemical entities, some of them produced by plants and other organisms for the express purpose of keeping predators at bay—in other words, toxins. Other such agents arose simply as by-products. Notably, oxygen gas appeared in the atmosphere as a by-product of photosynthesis. Our ancestors had to adapt to this relentless chemical assault. Sometimes, presumably, they just avoided trouble: didn't eat things that they 'knew' to be harmful. Often they evolved mechanisms of detoxification. Often, too, they went one step further and evolved the means to make positive use of the extraneous chemical agents that hitherto had harmed them. Oxygen is a case in point. For organisms that cannot cope with it, it is the mother of all toxins precisely because it is so chemically active. For creatures like us, which can cope with it, it has become vital—its chemical potency turned to advantage as the supplier of instant energy. Even so, our bodies are packed with 'anti-oxidants,' including some of the vitamins, to deal with rogue oxygen that escapes the normal coping mechanisms.

The cryptonutrients, I suggest, arose as agents in the environment, generally produced by other species, that our ancestors were obliged to deal with and which, as their evolution progressed, they turned to advantage. The vitamins can then be seen as cryptonutrients on which we have come to rely more or less absolutely, so they are indeed vital. The rest, possibly many thousands of them, may well be good for us, but the effects are generally too small to notice or to quantify. A regular dose of cryptonutrients—a plant sterol, for example—may well add two years to a life that is already long. But it would be very difficult in practice to demonstrate such an effect. Such an effect would not show up for example in a six-week trial on laboratory rats.

Overall however, we can be sure that cryptonutrients of many kinds are very important. But there are probably a great many of them, and the effects of any one may be very difficult to pin down and surely must vary from person to person. It seems very reasonable to suggest in a general way that a very varied diet based on natural ingredients is more likely to contain the required range of cryptonutrients than an artificial diet which on the whole will be simplified. Those who advocate natural diets are likely to be accused of 'muck-n-mystery' —but to a significant extent that may be the best we can do. In reality, nutrition cannot be an 'exact science.' 'Physics envy' is inappropriate.

Cryptonutrients also lead us very nicely into one of the greatest of all insights in the history of nutritional science: the absolute importance of microbes.

Microbes

I was brought up as was usual in my childhood days to be afraid of 'germs.' Polio, a virus, was the great fear. Measles, another virus, was seen largely as a routine childhood ailment although it was a prime cause of infant mortality in parts of the tropics and was the main cause of non-congenital blindness and deafness in the west. There were plenty of nasty bacteria too, including TB which mainly affected the poor and malnourished, although mothers still lived in fear of whooping cough and diphtheria. Hygiene was stressed. Food poisoning could kill too and the most minor cuts could lead to blood poisoning. Penicillin was produced on the mass scale only in World War II and in the years immediately afterwards it was still not universally available. All bacteria and indeed all microbes tended to be classed as germs and were commonly seen to be seriously bad news. We had to put up with the ones that were known to thrive in the gut but mainly, it seemed, because there wasn't much we could do about them.

This kind of mentality lives on. Young mums on daytime television are still being urged to spray their kitchens and their children's high-chairs with disinfectant. The message still goes out that our and our children's surroundings should be as sterile as possible; one big intensive care unit. There was even a vogue in the 1960s for germ-free piggeries.

Even in my schooldays, though, the story wasn't entirely negative. Industrial microbiology has flourished since the 19th century (Louis Pasteur was a seminal figure) and its triumphs include the control of fermentations of all kinds from bread to cheese to wine and beer, and large-scale production of antibiotics. Before World War II Albert Howard introduced the world to the modern age of composting which of course is primarily an exercise in fungal and microbial decay. The essential role of mycorrhizas in extending the range of roots was known since the 19th century, and so too the role of *Rhizobium* bacteria in legumes in fixing nitrogen. Microbiologist Bernard Dixon, a former editor of *New Scientist*, wrote an excellent summary of all these positives in *Invisible Allies* in 1976 and John Postgate excellently summarized nitrogen fixation in 1976 (both books later up-dated). All who wrote in such veins stressed that most microbes including most bacteria are our friends and indeed, as Bernard Dixon stressed, that the world would rapidly grind to a halt without them.

All such observations helped to lay the ground for what is perhaps the most significant nutritional insight of the past few decades: that the microbes in our guts are not spivs, out for a free lunch and ever ready to put the boot in. They are our partners—mediators between us and the world at large—and at least in net are our benefactors. To a mostly unknown but certainly to a very large extent the gut microbes determine how we respond to any particular kind of food; whether it makes us fat or doesn't; whether it makes us ill or does us good. The differences in individuals in their responses to particular foods or indeed to entire diets can at least in part (probably in large part) be ascribed to differences in their gut microbiota; and those differences in turn probably reflect differences in previous diet—or indeed may reflect differences in childhood experiences, not least around the time of birth; and even reflect the microbial status of our mothers. Antibiotics and food additives or novel foods of the kind cooked up in the laboratory can alter the gut flora dramatically. Again, the general idea from health food buffs that natural food is generally good and artificial food is likely to be bad begins to seem highly plausible, although it is still mocked in some circles of commercial science.

Two anecdotes from *The Diet Myth* illustrate the extraordinary influence of microbes. The first involves identical twin sisters, one prone to put on weight and forever dieting, while the other was forever slim. They were genetically identical, so why the difference? The answer, apparently, was that their gut flora was very different—and the reason, it seems, is that they were born by Caesarean section and thus had no opportunity to pick up bacteria from the birth canal and general nether regions of their mother; and were handled by different nurses from the word go. Each nurse passed on her own microbiota to the particular baby in her charge. The microbiota of the two sisters remained very different into adulthood.

Spector also tells of an American doctor who, to get around this problem, wiped a swab around the relevant areas of his wife when she gave birth by Caesarean section, and then applied the swab to the face and mouth of the newly emerged baby. So far all is well and some Scandinavian hospitals have unofficially adopted the swab technique as standard practice in Caesarean birth. It's becoming fairly common practice too to enrich impoverished gut microbiota with faecal implants from other people. We have come a long way since my schooldays, when bacteria were just 'germs.'

The parallels with organic husbandry are obvious. Both now recognise the supreme importance of microbes. Above all, it seems, it is essential to maintain their diversity. At least as a rough rule of thumb it seems that in the gut, as in a tropical forest or on a farm run on agroecological lines, the greater the diversity the better. Diversity can be encouraged with 'prebiotics,' which typically means mixtures (as mixed as possible) of biochemically various plants—herbs, nuts, recondite roots. Impoverished gut floras are enriched by adding 'probiotics': suites of new microbial species as contained for example in active yoghurt or real cheese, or fermented plants including miso and sauerkraut (and of course with faecal implants). The whole procedure is hit and miss but it surely must be taken seriously. In fact, says Professor Spector, 'You won't go wrong if you just treat your own microbes like you would treat your own garden. Give them plenty of fertilizer—prebiotics, fibre, and nutrients. Plant new seeds regularly in the shape of probiotics—foods that already contain useful bacteria. Give the soil an occasional rest by fasting. Experiment, but avoid poisoning your microbiotic garden with preservatives, antiseptic mouthwashes, antibiotics, junk food and sugar.'

Finally, the growing appreciation of gut microbes and microbes in general adds weight to the cryptonutrient idea. It's a fair bet that most of the peculiar chemical agents to which our human and pre-human ancestors were obliged to adapt were and are microbial in origin. Oxygen certainly was. Cyanobacteria (known in earlier times as 'blue-green algae') invented photosynthesis. Plants acquired the skill by turning cyanobacteria into chloroplasts (or so all the evidence suggests).

Clearly, there has been much confusion in nutritional science this past half century, and there still is. As Spector says, while some nutritionists advise us to nibble more or less continuously ('grazing'), others recommend a few big meals. Over the past 30 years, too, 'almost every component of our diet has been picked on as the villain by some expert or other' and yet 'our diets continue to deteriorate.' The focus is largely on losing weight, yet the average western waistline continues to expand by about an inch per decade and there's evidence that repeated dieting may make people fatter. Two generalizations that seem to make sense are, first, that most diets are monotonous, and a surfeit of grapefruit or cabbage soup (one of Spector's examples) suppresses the appetite wonderfully. Secondly, the many and various dietary adventures affect the microbiota in ways that are not understood, with consequences that are equally mysterious—but in the light of what is known, seem eminently plausible.

In short, in nutrition as in farming (did the powers-that-be but realize it), the greatest of all the paradigm shifts of recent decades is the rise and rise of microbiology. It's clear now in all contexts that microbes are not just spivs and rivals. They, more than any living creatures, make the world the way it is—the soil, the air, the state of the sea, our own nutritional status. They are the great intermediaries, between us and the universe at large. Instead of zapping them willy-nilly, spraying kitchens with disinfectant and trying in general to live in an intensive care unit, we need to open an intelligent dialogue with them. Eve Balfour said when she founded the Soil Association in 1946,

Look after the soil and the plants will look after themselves

and it is clear now that care for the soil in very large part means care for its microbiota. Now we can see very clearly that the same principle applies to the gut. If we want to be as healthy as we can be, we must nurture and cultivate or at least not unduly molest our on-board microbes.

One last, very big caveat. We learnt at school in the 1950s that microbes can turn nasty and cannot be taken lightly—and Covid-19 has rubbed that lesson home all too emphatically. So on the one hand we need to acknowledge that microbes are principal players in the world's and our own ecology and strive as far as possible to forge a symbiotic relationship with them; not assume *a priori* that they are the enemy and contrive to live in a sterile bubble. But neither can we afford to be cavalier. At the time of writing (July 2020) with the pandemic in full spate, ultra and even obsessive hygiene seems *de rigueur*. But in normal times, surely not. It's a narrow path we need to tread.

Epigenetics

In the mid-20th century it was generally assumed that our genes are virtual despots, loftily issuing orders from the security of the cell nucleus. Now it is clear that the genes of all organisms are very responsive to the circumstances: to the cell around them, which in turn is tuned in to the whole organism, which in turn must respond to the world at large. The past decade or so in particular has seen the rise of **epigenetics**—ad hoc mechanisms that turn particular genes on and off and thus change the behaviour of the genome, sometimes in the short term, sometimes through a whole lifetime, and sometimes over several generations. So it is clear now that the way we respond to food, and whether or not for example we became fat or stay slim, depends in part on our own diet in infancy, in part on our mother's diet when we were *in utero*; and the way our mother doles out nutrients to her foetus depends in part on her own experiences in infancy, and *in utero*; and all these influences are mediated via the genes.

As Nessa Carey describes in *The Epigenetics Revolution* (Icon Books, 2011), all this is illustrated wonderfully by the Dutch Hunger Winter from November 1944 to late spring 1945 when the war prevented food imports into Holland. Many starved and many of the survivors were permanently affected—like Audrey Hepburn, sixteen at the time, who remained thin (or enviably slim) though rarely in good health through all of her somewhat foreshortened life. Others were *in utero* at the time, and for some weeks or months were deprived of nutrient as their mothers went hungry. If women were already pregnant by the time the hunger began, so that their foetuses were well fed in the first months and then deprived, their babies were likely to be born small—and they tended to stay small throughout their lives, and were not so likely as the rest of the population to grow fat. The foetuses of women who conceived towards the end of the famine were deprived in the first months of their gestation but then were well fed—and then, generally, they caught up, and at birth were of normal weight. They, though, were more likely than usual to be obese in later life and also suffered other problems of health. Truly intriguing, however, is that some of these effects lasted into the following generation. That is, the *grandchildren* of the women who were starved in pregnancy also tended to be small, or else to be more than usually prone to obesity and ill-health. The inference (for which there is much independent evidence) is that epigenetics was and is the cause. Malnourishment in the womb did not cause the genes of the foetus to mutate, but it did impose epigenetic controllers onto some of the genes which altered their behaviour—and the effects continued after birth and into the next generation.

That is just one example of the power of epigenetics. Nessa Carey is right to speak of the 'epigenetic revolution.' Presumably, the gut microbiota is involved too. The gut flora of women starved in late pregnancy must surely have been affected. Perhaps the microbes themselves cause at least some of the epigenetic effects. We might assume, too, that the interaction between the genes and the microbes is two-way. Microbes and their hosts are in constant dialogue, each responsive to the other. All in all, the narrative of nutrition grows richer and richer.

Put all this together and the Cartesian model of the body-as-machine seems most inappropriate. Wind up the clock, stoke up the boilers, press the right levers, and a machine will behave exactly as it is designed to behave. But the bodies of living creatures are not machines. They are intelligent beings. Even those that don't have brains behave as if they were intelligent. Even trees have their own agenda, and how they respond to any one stimulus is conditional. It depends on what else is going on—whether it's spring or autumn, for example: time to grow or time to shut up shop. For animals, each individual molecule imbibed is a potential stimulus and each, at least in principle, is treated on its merits depending on the circumstances and on the individual's own history. Of course there are general patterns and there is some consistency, for if there were not then the science of biology as a whole would be impossible. But we can never hope to predict precisely the effects of any one dietary component on any one individual or on the population as a whole. Most of all, we can never hope to *control* the bodies of human beings or other animals to the nth degree as sometimes seems to be the ambition and the promise. Of course, physicians and farmers who deal with real creatures have always known this. Science can take us so far but for the rest we need experience and intuition.

Indeed, when all is said and done, it is hard when issuing nutritional advice to improve on traditional knowledge; and cooking, like enlightened farming, in the end must be rooted in craft.

BACK TO THE FUTURE: THE ABSOLUTE IMPORTANCE OF TRADITIONAL COOKING AND FOLK KNOWLEDGE

Truly modern nutritional advice, as opposed to the magic-bullet, snake-oil kind that has become the norm, veers closer and closer to folk wisdom. Thus we were told in the old days—

Eat what grows naturally

—which accords perfectly with the modern insights into gut microbes and cryptonutrients: the evolutionary idea that our gut flora and our general physiology have largely become adapted to the myriad products of nature over the millions and billions of years through which our human and pre-human ancestors have been exposed to them, and are not adapted to laboratory novelties. The fact that it has sometimes been shown that those novelties do not cause cancer or general collywobbles in laboratory rats tells us little about their total effects on human beings throughout their lives.

In wondrous contrast to the general germ warning, our grannies were also wont to tell us to—

Eat a peck of dirt before you die.

I confess I have met only one other person—an octogenarian—who remembers this adage, but it was certainly current in my day. It can of course be taken too far. Hygiene still matters of course. *E coli* and *Listeria* are always ready to pounce and the horrors of Covid-19 remind us yet again that rogue microbes can turn up at any time, created either through genetic mutation or—as seems to be the case with Covid-19—acquired from some wild creature. Then they may cause havoc; bring the whole world to its knees indeed. Yet the old motto makes sense nonetheless. We need to nourish and cultivate the gut flora just as farmers need to nourish the microbes that turn dirt into soil. Extreme hygiene may be necessary in extreme circumstances but in normal times it can very definitely be counter-productive.

Our forebears were also wont to assure us that—

A little of what you fancy does you good.

Again this seems perfectly in line with most modern theory, including the advice to eat a diet that's as varied as possible. These days too zoologists and vets are very impressed by the ways in which animals may go to great lengths to seek out particular herbs and minerals that they know, by whatever means, will make them feel better. Thus enlightened zoo-keepers and farmers provide their charges with patches of herbs which, demonstrably, the animals seek out when they are feeling poorly (as revealed, for example, by loose stools and general mopiness). Land animals of all kinds know when they are short of salt and may walk many miles to the nearest lick, as elephants and Arabian oryx do; and macaws stoke up on kaolin to sequester the toxins that perfuse their natural diets; and so on.

The stress, though, seems to be on 'a little' because as Waldo Emerson advised, and I remember being advised, we should adopt—

Moderation in all things

—which seems pretty sound in most contexts.

Overall, too, the modern nutritional advice as outlined above—a moderate intake of protein, high fibre, plenty of micro- and cryptonutrients and the rest—can be boiled down to nine words:

Plenty of plants, not much meat, and maximum variety

This irreducibly simple motto tells us more or less everything we need to know. Just cook and eat with these nine words in mind and you should not go far wrong.

This little adage too leads us into a series of huge serendipities—suggesting that God really is on our side.

First, agroecological farming focuses primarily on arable and horticulture, both as various as possible, with livestock fitted in as and when. So indeed it provides plenty of plants, not much meat, and maximum variety. Secondly, as N.W. Pirie pointed out, all the great cuisines use meat sparingly but to maximum effect, and we may also observe that all the great cuisines make maximum use of all the herbs, nuts, wild fruits, and spices that grow locally (and they sometimes import spices from far and wide, which it is perfectly reasonable to do). In other words, plenty of plants, not much meat, and maximum variety also describes the basic structure of all the world's greatest cuisines on an axis from Italy to China.

In other words:

There is perfect correspondence between agroecology, sound nutrition, and the world's greatest cuisines.

In other words, if we want to be healthy, and really want to keep the world as a whole in good heart, we just have to take food seriously; value whatever grows, and has been grown with tender loving care. In other words—

The future belongs to the gourmet.

This again is in the sharpest contrast to what we have been told from on high, which is that if we want to survive in large numbers then we have to tighten our belts and/or live on the various kinds of ersatz, like the various kinds of 'textured vegetable protein'—textured, that is, to resemble the fibres of meat. Such life-savers can, of course, be produced only by courtesy of high-tech food companies; and so we are invited once more to give thanks to the corporates for our salvation.

In fact, all we really have to do, if we don't ourselves want to become farmers, is—

Re-learn the arts and crafts of cooking.

It would of course be good to emulate the world's great cooks but that doesn't necessarily mean the most famous. In the history of the world many millions of people were and still are great cooks, albeit working in tiny kitchens (or indeed with a pile of brass pots over a single tiny fire, as I have seen on the streets of Mumbai, though that is clearly far from ideal). Raymond Blanc is among the world-renowned chefs who emphasize the absolute importance of traditional cooking, which largely means peasant cooking. He learnt to cook at home, he says. So, surely, did many or most of the world's greatest.

Coda

More and more, in all aspects of food and farming (and other areas too, but they can be discussed elsewhere) it's clear that the people who have most influence in the world, the oligarchy of governments, big business, and their chosen expert and intellectual advisers—including selected scientists—have sold us horribly short and are leading us more and more deeply into the mire. Truly we need enlightened agriculture rooted in agroecology, which means skills-intensive, primarily organic agriculture in small units—and governments like Britain's and big-time commerce promote the precise opposite: high-input, zero-labour monocultures, while land, the *sine qua non*, is on sale to the highest bidder to be used, in effect, for whatever purpose. We need to promote home cooking and to place cooking at the heart of all school curricula, together with gardening, especially of fruit and vegetables. Again, though, this isn't what's been happening. In British schools, 'domestic science' became 'home economics' and both were and are commonly reduced to the arts of defrosting and the splitting of polythene.

Even more broadly, science needs to come off its high horse. Scientists need to acknowledge the paradigm shift within their own *métier*, which clearly for the most part they have not. For example, the Royal Society no less has now taken it upon itself to promote GM. Intellectuals in all fields need to ask themselves whether they seriously improve on folk wisdom—and to ask why they apparently assume they should be able to do so. After all, folk wisdom at its best encapsulates the experience and insights of all humankind over thousands of years. Why should anyone suppose that their own particular wheeze should improve on that? How can western agriculturalists presume to sweep aside the world's traditional farming, developed by men, women, and sometimes children over centuries, in favour of some untried algorithm (untried in all but the shortest term), and assume that this is *ipso facto* progress? Mercifully, some people including some intellectuals in high places *are* asking these questions, and are seeking to develop whatever knowledge and skills they have to offer in true collaboration with people at large. The role of science is not—surely?—simply to sweep aside all that has gone before. Even less should it seek to transfer wealth and the power to act from people at large to a ruling minority, which is what it is tending to do at the moment as it helps to replace traditional farming, and cooking, with industrialized systems controlled by corporates. What the world really needs—another slogan—is:

Science-assisted craft.

That, I suggest, really would be progress.

Part IV

INFRASTRUCTURE

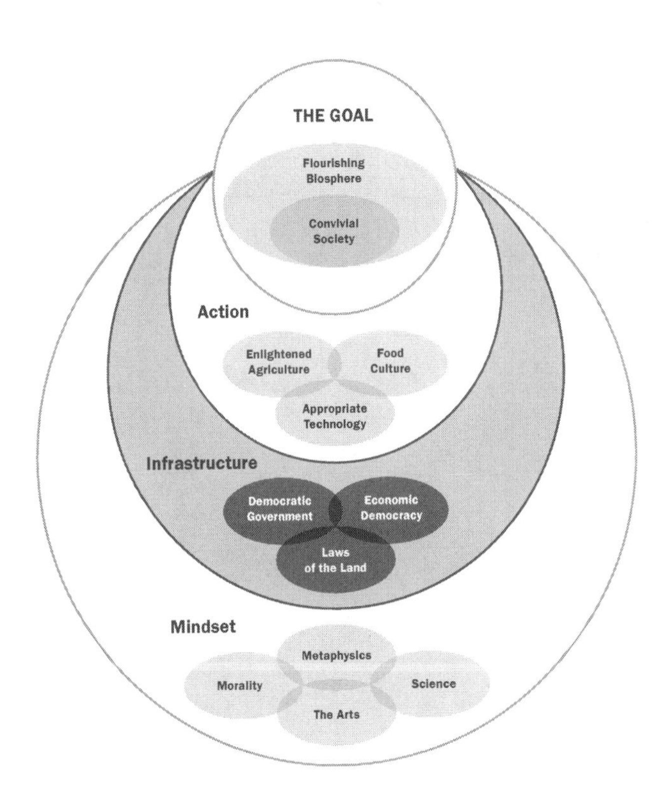

8

WHAT'S GONE WRONG WITH THE WAY WE RUN THINGS?

INFRASTRUCTURE IS CRUCIAL: HOW WE ORGANIZE OUR SOCIETIES; how we run our affairs; the framework and the mechanics of day-to-day living. Get it right and we could—surely?—deliver what I am suggesting would be most obviously desirable and achievable: *conviviality and personal fulfilment within a flourishing biosphere*. Get it wrong, and we have no chance. Clearly, right now, we are getting it horribly wrong. Clearly, the present infrastructure is far from what is required. This, in large part, is why the world is in such a mess.

Why should this be so? Why is the world so mismanaged? There surely are no definitive answers but here are a few suggestions:

1: Not everybody agrees with the goal. To me it is self-evident that we should be trying to achieve 'convivial societies in a flourishing biosphere,' for what could be more important? But some people, apparently, don't want that, while others don't think it is possible, so they feel it is not worth trying. Some, it seems, of metadarwinian mien, seek above all to be at the top of the social and material heap while others (very reasonably) just want a quiet life and so go along with whoever seems to be in charge, however nasty they may be, at least until they can stand no more. As for the biosphere: many seem indifferent to the natural world except perhaps as scenery and real estate; or a place to walk the dog; or—for the rich—to shoot grouse; or—for the super-rich—to shoot bears.

2: Politics decides who is in charge and what, in practice, is actually done, and politics is innately messy: endlessly complex and ultimately non-linear. There is no simple relationship between cause and effect; we never know how things will turn out—

The best-laid schemes o' mice an' men
Gang aft agley,

—as Robert Burns put the matter in 1785, and no-one has ever said it better. Aristotle said that human beings are political animals and indeed that is so—but politics is not confined to our own species. *All* intelligent social animals are political up to a point, jostling for kudos and social position (on which, in the end, the quality of their lives depend—and whether they are ever to find a mate, and reproduce). In short: the arts and wiles of politicking lie deep in our biology—which means, among other things, that much of what we do in the name of politics is unfathomable, for as Freud and Jung emphasized, we can never get truly to grips with the deep stirrings of our own psyche (which didn't stop them trying).

3: It is also all too horribly true that once political schemes are set in motion it can be impossible to stop them, even when it becomes obvious that they are disastrous. World War I is the prime example. Once the troops were mobilised they could not be called back. Nobody knew how Brexit would turn out, and we still don't. In short, the forces that in the end determine how we live and the fate of the world are, to a large extent, beyond our control. In practice, people in positions of influence—politicians, economists, scientists, technologists, priests—are wont simply to light the blue touch paper and then see what happens. They press the panic button and hope for the best.

The folly is glossed over with rhetoric. Recklessness is passed off as 'boldness.'

4: Then again: the theories dreamed up by intellectuals which largely determine the way the world is run are, to a much greater extent than they are wont to admit, guesswork; and the expertise of experts is far less expert than they are wont to claim. No human pursuit is more painstaking or mathematically impeccable than engineering, of all kinds—yet computers crash, and planes fall out of the sky, and bridges fall down.

Reality is always one step ahead; and what is true of engineering is a hundred times more true of the vital but far less tractable pursuits of economics and sociology. All theories in all contexts are abstractions; sometimes accurate, no doubt, or near enough, and often useful, but abstractions nonetheless. Nice clean theories are nice and clean because they miss out the details—but the details remain and sometimes bite us. Physicians since the times of Hippocrates and Galen have always known and stressed that life is innately unpredictable and that their knowledge is imperfect, and that they can but promise to do their best. Economists and politicians whose knowledge is far less certain are all too apt to promise that things will turn out just as required, if only we follow the rules and do as we are told. In medicine, only quacks have such confidence.

To make things worse, as government ministers in all departments constantly demonstrate—not least, these past few decades, in agriculture, the thing we absolutely have to get right—those with most power may hardly begin to understand their subject. Often they don't care (agriculture in Britain is a political also-ran) and even if they do, they very rarely have time to get properly stuck in. A few lunches with captains of industry must serve as an education. In short, we may reasonably doubt whether our governments are in any worthwhile sense *competent*. In 2002 the English politician Estelle Morris resigned from her post as Secretary of State for Education because, she said, she could not handle it. Would that others in high places were as honest!

Even when the intent and the theory are good they may be impossible to put into practice. Some laws that are very good in principle may be unenforceable. No one seems to have the power to tell modern corporates what to do. In any case, once the corporate machinery is in place—the technologies, the finance, the modus operandi—even the chief executives cannot truly control the thing that they have helped to create. The system itself takes over.

5: By the same token, there has been these past few hundred years a tendency to suppose that politics and economics can and should be treated as sciences; that the ideas of economics in particular can be reduced to formulae, as certain as $E=mc^2$, and then applied as algorithms—recipes for solving problems that are sure to provide the right answers, like the rules we used to learn at school for doing long division. Marx apparently felt that both politics and economics could be treated as bona fide sciences. For a time at least he was a disciple of Wilhelm Hegel (1770-

1831), who in effect treated all history as a science. Neoliberalism too, albeit with a quite different philosophy, is in effect a giant algorithm: just leave our affairs to the market and all will be well.

This is a huge mistake. Economics may borrow the trappings and some of the methods of science—but no more than that. Science depends above all on testable hypotheses which economics does not always supply, and on controlled experiments which economists cannot usually organize on a worthwhile scale even if it occurred to them to do so. Besides, as outlined in chapter 13, even bona fide science does not deal in certainties, as is commonly supposed, but only in probabilities.

Nonetheless, politicians and economists continue to apply their particular 'isms' in the hope and apparent belief that they will deliver what's intended. Usually, it just isn't so. ***What really matters, always, are the bedrock principles: morality and ecology***. The principles don't translate easily into isms and still less into algorithms.

6: Indeed, it is the core premise of this book, as outlined in Part I, that if we are truly to put the world to rights then we need to found all our policies on the bedrock principles of morality and ecology. Both are underpinned in the end by metaphysics, and taken all together are the stuff of 'the perennial wisdom.' Indeed we might say, grandiosely, that the task of the infrastructure is to translate the perennial wisdom into everyday life (roughly in the manner that St Benedict described when he founded the Benedictine order in the early 6th century).

But how many politicians, economists, or lawyers, or those who teach these subjects, think in such terms? Well—some do. In all branches of politics in most countries we find politicians who truly are dedicated to the wellbeing of humanity, and all the best economists have been serious moralists with a clear vision of what is *right*, and some lawyers are certainly a force for good, often heroically so. Many lawyers too and some politicians have a deep concern for the natural world. So the position is not all bad, by any means. There are a great many good people in positions of influence who are seeking to make the world more convivial and to keep our fellow species in good heart. Commonly, though, at least by their mainstream peers, they are seen as mavericks. It is a huge pity that those who seek to do good must so often swim against the tide—and often, like Mahatma Gandhi and Nelson Mandela in modern times, they finish up in prison, or worse. It is a crime, apparently, to seek justice, or at least to do the things that are necessary to secure it. No wonder the world is in a mess.

For the most part, what politicians call 'principles' are really just ideologies, typically made manifest as 'isms': communism, capitalism, Toryism, and all the rest. Ideologies claim to be rooted in deeper principles, moral and metaphysical, but in reality they are merely sets of rules by which some authority has decided we should live. As the writer and former Czechoslovakian President Vaclav Havel (1936-2011) put the matter in 1978 in an essay entitled *The Power of the Powerless*

> *Ideology is a specious way of relating to the world .... [Its] primary excusatory function is to provide people with the illusion that the system is in harmony with the human order and the order of the universe.*

From: *Living in Truth*, edited by Jan Vladislav,
Faber and Faber, London, 1987. p. 43.

Worse: in practice ideologies tend to be equated with party manifestos, and politicians, anxious as most of us are to preserve their status and their way of life, commonly fight not for bedrock principles, or even for ideologies, but to ensure that their party stays in power and they themselves have a job. Much of what they do and vote for is guided by expediency. Who does not know this? Often indeed politicians vote against their conscience—but they excuse this, at least to themselves, by making a virtue of *loyalty*. Loyalty is a virtue, no doubt—at least as the antithesis of treachery. But it really does matter who or what a person is loyal to. 'I was only obeying orders' was the standard defence at Nuremberg.

Then again, all politics in practice—which means the fate of entire societies and of the world as a whole, human and non-human—is swayed this way and that by charismatic individuals. 'Charisma' is a dubious quality, at least as dependent on illusion as on reality. Right now the world is in thrall to Donald Trump and Vladimir Putin (though both live in the shadow of Xi Jinping). The whims of such individuals are a million miles from anything that can properly be called principle.

In the end, in the words of Germany's most celebrated statesman, Otto Bismarck (1815-1898):

> *Politics is the art of the possible*

—no more, no less; and what is possible depends, in the end, on chance and circumstance, and the whims of those who for whatever reason have most power. Yet politics shapes our lives.

7: Corruption at all levels plays a huge part in the world's affairs. Corruption is so deeply embedded that it is commonly taken to be the norm, and may indeed be perfectly legal. Off-shore tax-free banking is a prime example. All in all there is a very broad grey area between the legal and illegal. Indeed we may reasonably ask whether the legitimate economy could in practice function at all without the black economy to fill in the cracks.

Some enterprises that are very definitely illegal are nonetheless huge. According to *National Geographic* (November 12, 2018) the trade in exotic animals is worth between $5.5-$18 billion per year. According to the Wildlife Justice Commission an elephant is killed every 30 minutes for its ivory and one rhino is sacrificed every eight hours for its horn and every five minutes a pangolin is poached. Heroic people risk their lives to stop this horror but the powers behind the trade are ruthless, rich, and clever and the people who may risk their lives to steal the animals are for the most part desperate, with no other adequate means of making a living. Some trades the world over have a conveniently ambiguous legal status. In Britain some aspects of prostitution are legal and some are not but even those that are *verboten* are supposed to be taxed.

More broadly, as Lord Acton put the matter in the late 19th century:

Power tends to corrupt, and absolute power corrupts absolutely.

He added:

Great men are nearly always bad men.

Lord Acton was not some bearded firebrand shouting from the sidelines. He was a historian and a statesman—a pillar of the Establishment. He was speaking of his peers. Indeed it truly is remarkable how many heads of state finish up in jail—albeit only a small proportion of those who *ought* to be in jail. Many are surely corrupt to begin with (see below) but many seem to slide into unspeakableness as their power increases, just as Lord Acton described. Robert Mugabe of Zimbabwe (1924-2019) comes very obviously to mind. Indeed the world is largely run by idiots, gangsters, and vainglorious psychopaths—for the somewhat obvious reason that those who are most obsessed by the psychopathic traits of money and power are the most likely to become rich and powerful. ***So although most people surely are nice, they finish up being ruled by the minority who are nasty***. But surely this could be avoided.

But then again; a politically active friend has pointed out to me that powerlessness is corrupting too. It leads to the feeling that nothing we do really matters—a form of what Marx called alienation; the feeling that we do not really belong to society—that we have indeed been rejected by it and therefore owe it no allegiance. How much does the rise in street crime that is now so obvious in Britain's cities spring from such a feeling?

The urgent question, though, is not 'What's gone wrong?' but 'How can we do better?' Are there any precedents out there—any models—that we can follow, or at least adapt to present needs?

Again, no one can provide definitive answers, although many have affected to do so. But here are a few pointers, as I see things, arranged under three chapter headings: Governance, the Economy, and the Law.

GOVERNANCE

Power tends to corrupt, and absolute power corrupts absolutely. Great men are almost always bad men.

Lord Acton (1834-1902), historian and statesman

IF WE SERIOUSLY WANT TO CREATE CONVIVIAL SOCIETIES then, I suggest, the prime task of governments must be to help good things happen and to create conditions in which what Abraham Lincoln called the better angels of our nature can safely poke their heads above the parapet.

In practice, though, governments of every kind in the history of the world have commonly done the precise opposite, and still do. Many or most use taxpayers' money to support enterprises that at least in net do far more harm than good. Most have presided over and sometimes actively promoted gross injustice. Some have been downright vicious. To be sure, some have done some good things for the biosphere—created national parks, for instance, like Kruger in South Africa and Yosemite in California—but most at best have treated the natural world perfunctorily and no government with anything resembling global influence has fully embraced the idea that human beings are not the only creatures that matter. So incompetent and cruel was the governance of 19th century Russia that many intellectuals embraced anarchism which literally means 'no ruler.' Prominent among them was the scientist-activist Peter Kropotkin (1842-1921). So too was Leo Tolstoy no less (1828-1910) who in his *Essay on Anarchy* in 1900 declared:

> *The Anarchists are right in everything; in the negation of the existing order; and in the assertion that, without Authority, there could not be worse violence than that of Authority under existing conditions. They are mistaken only in thinking that Anarchy can be instituted by a revolution. But it will be instituted only by there being more and more people who do not require the protection of governmental power ... There can be only one permanent revolution—a moral one: the regeneration of the inner man.*

Alas, though, large and inevitably complex societies probably do need *some* form of government, at least to provide some coordination and to take big decisions. Most of all, perhaps, some special group is needed to dispense justice. Any of us, however well-intentioned, might at some point find ourselves in conflict with our neighbours. Then, as Steven Pinker points out in *The Better Angels of Our Nature* (2011), we need some kind of ruling power to sort things out—or else are forced to take matters into our own hands. This would take us back to the Wild West, or land us in feuds and vendettas that may rumble on for decades or in effect forever, like the fictional Montagues and Capulets in **Romeo and Juliet,** or the all-too-real Campbells and Macdonalds in the Scottish Highlands, or the rival families of the Mafia. It matters, though, what *kind* of justice is meted out: whether the intent is to punish the wrongdoer, which is 'retributive'; or to recompense the victim and, with luck, effect some *rapprochement* between the wrongdoer and the wronged. The restorative, conciliatory route seems to work better but justice in most countries most of the time, if it is applied at all, tends mainly to be punitive.

But who should govern? How much authority should a government be granted? How do we ensure that we get the government we want and need? And as the Roman poet and satirist Juvenal put the matter in the 2nd century:

> *Quis custodiet ipsos custodes?*
> Who shall guard us from the guardians?

Many and probably most people in the history of the world have not had the opportunity even to ask such questions. Most people through all of history have simply had to let those who are most obsessed with power slug it out—although they were usually dragged into the fray—and then have had to live as best they could with the outcome. Wars are always between power groups, not between people at large, even though people at large get to fight them. Democracy is supposed to enable us to elect the kind of government we need—but democracy is immensely difficult to get right and societies that are supposedly democratic including Britain and the US are still dominated by power groups that still perpetuate injustice and still wage unnecessary wars and of course, for the most part, take no proper care of the biosphere. Oddly—it really is odd! —we vote such people into power when, in theory, we should be able to vote them out.

So how can we do better? The following is a preliminary checklist of principles and problems. To begin with—the *sine qua non*:

Government must be on our side

Jesus summarized the matter unimproveably, as recorded by St Mark (10:42-44):

> ... *whoever would be great among you must be your servant, and whoever would be first among you must be slave of all.*

Incoming Presidents and Prime Ministers typically vow as they take office to serve their people tirelessly and selflessly—but somehow it doesn't always feel like that. Some surely do mean what they say in the beginning, but lapse. Robert Mugabe of Zimbabwe (1924-2019) was a spectacular example. Some apparently see high office simply as a step up to even higher things—even greater wealth and/or a charmed, post-political life as a superstar, not least on the extremely lucrative lecture circuit. In some countries it seems to be taken for granted that high office is just a way of filling the boots and those of one's family.

All governments in practice are supported by elites. Monarchs have their courtiers. Communist dictatorships are dominated by the party faithful. Ultra-civilized Britain, refined by a thousand years of tradition, has 'the Establishment'—powerful individuals not least from the land-owning classes who in the main were educated in what the English for historical reasons call 'public' schools, although in truth they are very expensive and hence exclusive. Those who are thus privileged dominate, so they tend to feel, by *right*. At the heart of the Establishment sits the Church of England, the 'established' church, propping up the *status quo* although, as many priests agree, it surely should be striving to bring the very different morality of Christ into the general domain. All governments, inevitably it seems, identify more with some subsections of society than with others: if not with some elite then, contrariwise, with what is unsatisfactorily called 'the working class.' Some governments, including David Cameron's Tory government of 2010-2016, have sought to create 'One Nation.' As the British economy struggled to recover from the banking crisis of 2008, Cameron's Chancellor George Osborne assured us that 'We are all in this together.' But again, that is not how it seemed. Everyone suffered, it seems, and many or most are still suffering, and some always will, except for the bankers and other financiers who had caused the trouble. They have grown richer (chapter 10).

To be sure, some politicians including some leaders or potential leaders are truly well-intentioned—but they tend to fall short nonetheless. Some lack political skill, like the erstwhile leader of Britain's Labour party, Jeremy Corbyn. Many are brought down by their enemies, either from within their own country, like Russia's Mikhail Gorbachev, or by some outside force, like Chile's elected President Salvador Allende (1908-1973). Some are murdered, like Bobby Kennedy (1925-1968), Martin Luther King (1929-1968), and the Labour Party's Jo Cox (1974-2016). Others just die before their time, like the Labour party's John Smith (1938-1994) and Robin Cook (1946-2005). For some reason or another, the people who really want to do good in this world seem particularly unlucky, if unlucky is the word.

Whatever the cause, governments rarely if ever quite live up to the standards that society ought to demand of them. In almost all societies there is a sense of 'us and them.' Often, governments and their allies act not as servants but as predators, or indeed as parasites, draining the wealth and sucking the energies of people at large as a leech sucks blood. The debt economy, which has become the global norm, puts this process on a formal footing. Prime Minister Margaret Thatcher promised that the wealth of the rich would 'trickle down' to the poor but the reality is the precise opposite: wealth is systematically siphoned from the bottom to the top (chapter 10).

In practice, of course, both the governors and the governed are always required to strike a balance between conflicting interests and points of view. Not everyone by any means agrees on the principles of morality. Some, to misquote Gordon Gekko in *Wall Street*, evidently feel that compassion is for wimps. Some have tried virtually to stamp out free enterprise and free trade while others have contrived virtually to abolish public ownership. In particular, there is tension between

Societies and Individuals (Left vs Right)

Top-down and Bottom-up

Anthropocentric and Gaiacentric

Briefly:

Societies vs Individuals: Left and Right

There are tremendous advantages in living in societies, or as part of a colonial creature like a polyp in a coral reef, or as a cell as part of an organism. Eusocial creatures like us *need* each other. No man is an island. No person is *complete* if cut off from all others—because individuals of social species like ours *evolved* as components of larger societies. People who are completely isolated always languish and usually die in short order. The hermits we know about in truth were the sociable ones, like St Cuthbert (634-687) who was recalled from his eyrie on the Farne Islands to take charge of Lindisfarne Abbey, or Julian of Norwich (b. 1342, d. after 1416) who lived as an anchorite—literally walled up within her cell—but nonetheless ministered to passers-by. Goodness knows what happened to the hermits who were really cut off.

If individuals *need* society, and society is composed of individuals, then it seems to follow (does it not?) that whatever is good for individuals ought to be good for society, and *vice versa*. Yet, in reality, there is always tension between the needs and aspirations of individuals (or of particular groups) and the needs and aspirations of the society as a whole. Social life requires individuals to exercise restraint and sustained restraint is difficult.

We can see this tension at work even among honeybees. The workers—the females—spend their lives raising the offspring of the queen, who alone is allowed to breed; and, when called upon, they are prepared to die in defence of the colony. Thomas Henry Huxley (1825-1895), the arch-defender of Darwin ('Darwin's Bulldog'), saw honeybees as models of altruism, a lesson to us all. But although worker bees are generally celibate they are still fully functional and may, occasionally, kick over the traces and lay eggs of their own—unfertilized but able nonetheless to develop into drones (males). The other workers, their sisters and half-sisters, usually make short work of those upstart would-be offspring—but the lesson is there. Even in honeybees, models of eusociality, there is always the possibility of breaking loose and, apparently, the latent urge to do so. The tension between individuals and their societies has very deep biological roots.

Worker bees occasionally rebel even though, like other social insects, they are genetically programmed to behave socially and to fill their own prescribed niches. Human beings are probably more programmed than we like to think but we also have an intelligence that allows us to see alternative courses of behaviour and to make choices. Hence we can in theory *choose* at any one time to behave sociably or just to do our own thing for what we perceive to be our own benefit.

Because sociality requires restraint and unselfishness and some degree of altruism it is easy to conclude as Huxley did that this must be the morally superior course—but again, life is not quite so simple for (surely?) self-fulfilment matters too. Bees, it seems, are not deeply reflective creatures. They are programmed by their genes to behave as they do. We, by contrast, are intelligent, feeling creatures with freedom of choice—and what is the point of being an intelligent, feeling creature if we don't give ourselves a chance to think, feel, and act in our own way? A religious person might reasonably argue that to sacrifice our God-given freedom to think our own thoughts is to thwart God's purpose, and so is a kind of blasphemy. There is the matter of rights, too. The concept of rights does indeed come with caveats (see below) but it seems indispensable nonetheless and we feel, do we not, that although we may have a *duty* to behave sociably we also have a *right* to exert our own individuality, at least up to a point. At least in the western world individual freedom is seen as one of the great desiderata. The US Declaration of Independence and the slogan of the French Revolution both stress *liberty.*

This is what distinguishes the political ***Right***—otherwise known as *individualists*—from the political ***Left***—properly known as *socialists*. The Right in general emphasizes the rights of individuals while the Left stresses our responsibility to the society as a whole. In truth, while Left and Right are matters of degree the division between the two is in practice as profound and far-reaching as the perceived and sometimes actual divide between the sexes or between religions or ethnic groups.

Neither Right nor Left can claim to be wholly good and both taken to extremes become seriously unpleasant. The extreme Right is Fascist and the extreme Left all too often is Stalinist/Maoist, and seriously oppressive. Yet both claim the moral high ground. The philosophies and doctrines of the two groups are often called political *principles* but in truth they are merely ideologies, which is not the same thing at all. As argued at the start of this book, the only principles that can properly be called 'bedrock' are those of morality and ecology, and the fundamental ingredient of morality is compassion. Political ideologies commonly lack compassion and at least in their conventional, historical forms both Left and Right have generally taken the biosphere as a given; a resource; a cornucopia for us to exploit at will and in effect *ad infinitum*.

Both Left and Right are highly heterogeneous. Each is represented by several different political parties that often are bitter rivals (at least in countries that allow more than one political party to exist). Labour is the main party of the Left in the UK but there are about twenty smaller left-leaning parties, as listed in Wikipedia. Extreme right-wing parties in Britain include the National Front and Nigel Farage's short-lived Brexit party but the mainstream party of the Right is or are the Conservative Party, otherwise known as the Tories.

The parties of the Right: Britain's Tories and the US Republicans

The Tories of Britain include at least four quite different groups. First there are the remains of the aristocracy, whose distant ancestors found favour with some Mediaeval monarch and so were granted large tracts of land which their descendants have guarded jealously ever since. Their right to do so has often been questioned but never decisively, since whoever is in power at any one time makes the rules. Money goes to money and power goes to power (see below). This on the face of things may seem dreadful but again, all is not so simple for although some aristocrats have often behaved high-handedly and cruelly, some at least have lived and still live by the ancient chivalric principle of *noblesse oblige*—that with power comes responsibility, practical and moral. So some aristocrats look after their lands extremely well and care deeply about the welfare of the villagers and farmers who occupy the land they are deemed to own (although we should always ask whether anyone can truly 'own' land at all. See chapter 11). Thus we may feel that it is at least absurd to allow ourselves to be dominated by people who, for the most part, have done nothing tangible to justify their status, yet we should always pause to ask whether *in practice,* at least in the short term, we could do better (and the long term, as has often been pointed out, is a series of short terms joined end to end).

Also in the Tory party, and now the dominant force, are the business people and financiers—who in turn include two distinct groups. First there are the 'traditional' businesspeople who often have a strong moral sense and feel that business is the natural underpinning of a free and democratic society: 'business with a conscience,' as Britain's Tory elder statesman Ken Clarke has put the matter. Harold Macmillan (1894-1986), Britain's Prime Minister from 1957 to 1963, was of this kind. As housing minister from 1951-54, in Churchill's government, he built 300,000 houses a year. But then the Tory manifesto that brought Churchill's government to power in 1951 declared that:

> *Housing is the first of the social services. It is also one of the keys to increased productivity. Work, family life, health and education are all undermined by crowded houses. Therefore, a Conservative and Unionist Government will give housing a priority second only to national defence.*

Thus Toryism in the style of Clarke and Macmillan combines benign intent with economic pragmatism—and we can see the same combination in traditional businesses of all kinds, from corner shops and smallholdings to (some) large and powerful companies. Some of the extreme Left would do away with private enterprise altogether but in practice, when contained within a moral framework, it can be the best option. Many a good left-winger has thought so.

Since about 1980, however, the world has seen the rise and rise of a quite different approach to business—that of neoliberalism. The neoliberals take it as their mantra that the economy in effect *means* the 'free' market—meaning that the market should not be constrained by anything except market forces, meaning money. Indeed, the market itself decides what morality *is*. What is considered good is what people are prepared to pay for. What people will not pay for falls by the wayside and is *ipso facto* bad. This may sound vile—and, as discussed later, vile it certainly is. Among other things, it means that morality is defined by those with the most buying power who are, of course, the rich. When combined as it often is with uncritical technophilia, neoliberalism and the crude moral philosophy it gives rise to, is the greatest threat by far to the wellbeing of the world. Yet, paradoxically, the idea of neoliberalism was first introduced or at least clearly spelled out in the mid-20th century for moral reasons. Its perpetrators argued that people at large would *benefit* from a totally free market and that this was moral justification enough. Again we see that abstract theory does not necessarily or usually square well with reality—or as George Orwell said (although I paraphrase) there's nowt so daft as intellectuals, when they are carried away by their own flights of fancy. We really cannot hope to create convivial societies rooted in morality with an economic system that aspires to reject morality as a matter of principle, and a political system that is geared to it. Still less can we hope to take proper care of the biosphere. More in chapter 10.

There has, traditionally, been huge tension between the aristocrats and the business people—but also, these past few centuries, there has been *rapprochement*, because the aristocrats need the money that business can supply and businesspeople have often longed for the one thing that money itself cannot buy, which is commonly called 'class.' The tension between the two factions is ever-present in the novels of Jane Austen at the turn of the 18th and 19th centuries and is a favourite theme of Henry James at the turn of the19th and 20th.

Fourthly, Britain's Tories also include a wide swathe of what might be called hangers-on, including Hooray-Henries who perceive that the Tories give the best parties.

Finally—again, it seems, paradoxically—the Tories rely heavily and absolutely on the votes of the working class. The motives of the latter are mixed. Some aspire to be rich and hence to join the ranks of the dominant classes. Others simply want a quiet life and feel that this above all requires the law and order which is what, above all, the Tories invariably promise. Some are just out-and-out jingoists.

In the US the Republican Party, traditionally seen as the main party of the Right, is similarly mixed, albeit without the feudal aristocracy. The actor James Stewart (1908-1997), himself a Republican, conveyed the essence of traditional Republicanism in *It's a Wonderful Life* (Frank Capra 1946). Small businessman George Bailey (Stewart) stands for what most Americans would agree are the core principles of the USA: he is hard-working, creative, and uses his talents and energy not simply to keep his family in good fettle but also to serve his community. He defends his town—Bedford Falls—against the ravages of Henry F. Potter (Lionel Barrymore) who seeks to take overall control. Potter is the archetypal, ruthless fat cat (though Barrymore in reality was rather lean). Nowadays, Potter would be called a neoliberal. In short, both Bailey (Stewart) and Potter (Barrymore) were Republicans but Bailey was very obviously the good guy and Potter very obviously was bad.

But the world that Stewart and Barrymore portrayed has largely disappeared. By the 1980s, as the British historian Adam Tooze commented in *The London Review of Books* (April 4, 2019, p. 3):

> *... the Republican Party was an uneasy coalition between a free-market, pro-business elite and a xenophobic working and lower-middle-class base. This was always a fragile arrangement, held together by rampant nationalism and a suspicion of big government.*

In short: the Right, at its worst, is indeed morally despicable: the bloated, entirely self-centred aristocrat as depicted by the English cartoonist Thomas Rowlandson (1756-1827) *circa* 1800; and/or the bloated, entirely self-centred, champagne-swilling capitalist as depicted in our own times not least by the English cartoonist Martin Rowson. At its best, though, the Right includes what the English call good blokes and Americans call regular guys—and also includes some real philanthropists: literally, 'lovers of humanity,' who are keen to use their money and influence for the general good. But again, inevitably it seems, we find that philanthropy has its dark side. Ostensible philanthropists often distribute largesse as an exercise in personal vanity, or (in the US) to avoid taxes. Even if they do strive truly to do good, we may ask whether the wellbeing of the world should depend on the whims of individuals over whom the recipients have no control, and have often grown rich by dubious means. This trap is avoided to some extent if the philanthropist puts his or her money into a trust to be administered by trustees who really do give a damn about its use—but then we must rely on the acumen and good will of the trustees. In reality, though, we are always dependent on *somebody,* and properly appointed trustees who don't stay in office too long are as good as anybody.

For my part, I claim to be a socialist, definitely of the Left. But not the extreme left. Not everything that's done under the broad umbrella of 'the Right' is bad and we should not, I feel, throw babies out with the bathwater. Small businesses run by people like George Bailey, and especially small family farms, are a very large part of what the world really needs, and have often found shelter under the Tory or the Republican umbrellas, at least as those parties have often been construed. We really do need to be radical if we are to rescue humanity and the world but it's a mistake to be more radical than we really need to be. As they say in the backwoods, 'If it ain't bust, don't fix it.' And as the Nobel Prize-winning economist Paul Krugman pointed out in the *New York Times* on January 10, 2011:

> *... welfare-state capitalism—a market economy with its rough edges smoothed by a strong safety net—has produced the most decent societies ever known.*

It's a mistake, too, as Tolstoy intimated, to try to effect change too quickly—to rush at our perceived problems like a bull at a gate. For starters, we would do well to re-visit and in many cases restore the kinds of systems and technologies that have existed in some countries, including Britain, in the recent past. That could at least help to prepare the ground for more radical change in the future. *Reculer pour mieux sauter* (retreat the better to jump) as the French have it. Go back a bit and start again.

The two rival species of Socialist

The Left emphasises the need and the obligation to ensure the wellbeing of society as a whole for reasons both moral (it's the right thing to do) and practical (when the society is functioning well *everybody* benefits). Particular concern for society is properly called ***socialist*** therefore. But the Left too is split into many different parties—and most obviously, and damagingly, into two very distinct camps, which on the whole do not live well together.

The first kind of socialist is loosely called 'communist' or 'Marxist'—although the kind of communism that Marx envisaged was very different from most of what, in practice, has been on offer. The best-known and most influential Communist states were those of the USSR, centred on Russia but embracing most of Eastern Europe, and Mao Zedong's China. The two differed markedly in detail but they had much in common. Both, very clearly, were dictatorships. Mao emphasized the importance of the peasants which implies some concern for local control while the USSR was orientated towards the cities and the factories but both imposed top-down governance, typically with serious penalties for those who deviated. In Mao's China recalcitrant intellectuals and artists were sent to spread sewage on the fields while in Stalin's Russia the salt-mines awaited. In both societies what George Orwell was happy to call 'ordinary people' were required in effect to dedicate *all* their endeavours to society as a whole—or rather to the particular social structures that the government permitted. In both regimes, crucially, the economy was ***centralized***. The state, represented by the government, was deemed to own everything of any substance and made all substantive economic decisions. Religion—an alternative voice—at best was sidelined and sometimes actively obliterated, or at best was state-controlled. So everyone worked for the state and took their lead from the state. Emphatically, individuality was not encouraged.

Despite all this, at their best—so many visitors attested—the results could sometimes be truly convivial: village and small-town people working hard, but together, cooperatively, all worked ostensibly for the common good. But other observers, both inside and outside the regimes, reported and report that more or less total rule by government was generally oppressive and often cruel and that life was hard and generally ant-like. The loss of private initiative and hence of creativity and the need to refer all decisions upwards to some government-approved committee led to some huge inefficiencies—one result of which, in both regimes, was unnecessary famine. So both regimes were largely dysfunctional as well as harsh.

This, the top-down imposition of ideology and dogma and the resulting inhumanity, were not what Marx meant by communism. Although he took a hard line on religion, the form of communism he seemed to have envisaged seems far closer in spirit to the communality, equality, and sharing that we see in many religious communities, not least as introduced by St Benedict (*c* 480–*c* 547). Indeed we might say (although I am not sure that Marx would) that the task facing would-be communists is to translate the spirit of the Benedictine community into the everyday living of the entire society. However: the men and women who give up their everyday freedoms to join Benedictine monasteries and convents do so of their own volition (or that at least was and is the idea). Would-be monks and nuns vow to give up their personal freedoms and indeed their egos but they are not forced to do so as, in effect, was and is the case in the nation states that have called themselves communist. Marx himself acknowledged that his own idealized vision of communism would not be achieved in his lifetime, or any time soon. In truth, both the USSR and Mao's China were rushed jobs, not up to the task. Both resulted, after all, from revolution. They did not arise in situ in the spirit of Renaissance. In particular, I suggest, primarily because they both abandoned or oppressed organized religion, they lacked the necessary underpinning of metaphysics (chapter 14). The whole operation in both cases was too cavalier by half. Radical does not mean cavalier.

However—and again it's a very big 'however': many Russians felt that life under Lenin and then Stalin was better and offered more hope than the centuries they had endured under the Tsars—vindicating Tolstoy's point that it could not be worse. I visited Latvia, on the edge of the USSR empire, soon after the Berlin Wall came down and the USSR was broken up, and many people there said that although they were glad to say goodbye to Russian rule they much preferred the security offered by the top-down, regimented economy to the uncertainty of its capitalist, neoliberal replacement. Women in their 60s sold amber beads on the streets of Riga because they had lost their pensions. China before Mao was a disaster, horribly and cynically exploited by all-comers, including the British, Americans, and Japanese. Again, for many at least, what Mao offered was preferable. Many worshipped, more or less literally, the names of Stalin and Mao and some still do—and it would be arrogant in the extreme to suggest that this was, and is, all down to brainwashing. Neither is such leader-worship unique to dictatorships. Modern-day Americans are required to swear allegiance to their country and at least by implication to their president. ('My president right or wrong,' as the somewhat chilling expression has it.) Human beings, it seems, like strong leaders, whatever form they take. So too do baboons and gorillas and we are good primates too.

But it is a huge mistake—or a deliberate deception—to conflate USSR-style or Mao-style communism with socialism: to suppose or pretend that state-run communism and the centralized economy are what socialism *is*. This is the message dinned down to us by the western, right-inclined media. We are given to understand that if we go down the socialist route, then we are bound to finish up with some dysfunctional, inhumane dictatorship. Jeremy Corbyn's Labour opposition (2015-2020) apparently lacked the wit or the will to point out the error of this. Contrariwise, the Right in Britain and the US presents free enterprise and the unfettered, de-regulated global market as symbols and as essential components of freedom itself. This is simply not true, and in practice may be the opposite of the truth but the power game doesn't require truth.

For there is another, quite different version of socialism—which, I suggest, it would be to almost everyone's advantage to adopt.

Keir Hardie (1856-1915) summarized what I and a great many other people feel socialism should be, and which should be the core philosophy of the British Labour party which he helped to establish, and of which he was the first leader. As he wrote in *From Serfdom to Socialism* in 1907 (p. 53):

> *To the Socialist the community represents a huge family organization in which the strong should employ their gifts in promoting the weal of all, instead of using their strength for their own personal aggrandizement.*

Later he wrote:

> *I claim for socialism that it is the embodiment of Christianity in our industrial system.*

Much later (1961), in the spirit of Keir Hardie, Harold Wilson famously declared:

> *The Labour Party is a moral crusade or it is nothing.*

This way of thinking does not lead us towards despotism or to the centralized economy. ***It requires us instead to embrace democracy, wholeheartedly, and leads us too towards a mixed economy*** (of which more in chapter 10).

Keir Hardie-style government clearly can work. The achievements of Clement Attlee's Labour Government from 1945-51, when Britain was bankrupt after World War II, were little short of miraculous. Those years saw the introduction of the National Health Service and consolidated the idea of secondary education for all for which my generation and our children and grandchildren have cause to be eternally grateful. Attlee's government also sponsored publically-owned housing on a large scale—although this, as outlined above, reached its peak under Harold Macmillan.

Wilson's Labour governments, from 1964-1970 and from 1974-76, in effect continued from where Attlee left off. His governments were not an unalloyed success, not by any means, though they did chalk up some significant achievements—not the least of which was to continue borrowing money from the US to keep Britain afloat without getting us dragged into the Vietnam War. Driven in particular by Jennie Lee, too, (1904-1988) the Wilson government founded Britain's Open University, which was operational by 1971.

But under James Callaghan, Prime Minister from 1976-79, Labour seemed to lose its moral compass, degenerating it seemed into the crudest kind of class war, a kind of short-termist parody of Marx. I was a minor official in a trade union in the early 1970s and the union behaved in effect as a protection racket, although it wasn't the worst by any means. Thus the Callaghan government and all that went with it opened the door for Mrs Thatcher and neoliberalism, the global market that makes its own moral rules. Oddly—as if to demonstrate that politics is non-linear, or indeed that 'there's nowt so queer as folk'—the so-called 'New Labour' government of Tony Blair and Gordon Brown positively embraced neoliberalism and more or less banished the term 'socialism,' placing it in effect on their *Index Expurgatorius*. Labour's recently deposed leader, Jeremy Corbyn, seems simply to be confused. He certainly confuses everybody else. For some decades now the great vision of Keir Hardie has been lost. With luck Hardie's partial namesake, Keir Starmer, elected Labour leader in 2020, will restore the original spirit of the whole enterprise.

The world *needs* to return to Keir Hardie style socialism, or something very like it; to re-align the organization of the country and the economy with deep-rooted moral principles of which the chief is compassion. One major politician to espouse this notion in recent years was and is Bernie Sanders, who stood in opposition to Hillary Clinton as potential presidential candidate for the US presidency. He was and is extremely popular and might, had he been selected, have defeated Donald Trump. The world would look very different if he had won—which, if the Democratic

Party had had the courage to nominate him, he might well have done. At the time of writing (Spring 2020) he has just lost the Democrats' nomination for the second time.

Top-down vs Bottom-up: the absolute importance of Democracy

The Greeks invented the word 'democracy,' which literally means rule by the people. Democracy *feels* right, morally. Ideally, one feels, everyone in a society *ought* to have some say in how the society is run. As Kazuo Ishiguro remarks in *The Remains of the Day* (1989), if we are going to make mistakes then we should at least make our own mistakes. World War I was a huge and horrible mistake but the mistake was not made by the millions who died in it and in the aftermath but through the false pride and anachronistic conceits of governments. The same can surely be said in our own time of the invasion of Iraq. What George Orwell was happy to call 'ordinary people' would not have been so hubristic.

Democracy has many connotations, nearly all of which are beneficial. It encourages and results from a sense of social equality. It leads us, or should lead us, to ***bottom-up*** as opposed to ***top-down*** governance. Whatever kind of government we install it should be, as Abraham Lincoln put the matter in his famous Gettysburg Address in 1863 at the height of the American Civil War

Of the people, by the people, and for the people.

Indeed we might reasonably ask:

How did the world slump
From Lincoln to Trump?

There are practical as well as moral advantages in bottom-up governance too. Notably, as more and more intellectuals are stressing, the know-how and general wisdom of people at large, inherited and refined over many thousands of years, and largely seen simply as 'common sense,' may be far more in tune with the realities of the world than the imposed abstractions of academics. In particular, as noted in chapter 6, leading agriculturalists now emphasize the importance and significance of traditional practice. Michel Pimbert, now a professor at Coventry University, has long insisted that programmes of agricultural *science*—let alone of farming practice—should always be carried out in close collaboration with the people they are intended to influence. By contrast, most of the time, in most contexts, science is considered to be too esoteric, too specialised, to bother 'ordinary' people with. Yet local farmers understand their own problems far better than any outsider could do, and often already have the solutions, of at least the germs of the solutions, if only they were given a chance.

What's usually needed is what might be called '***science-assisted craft***' as outlined in particular in chapters 5 and 6. Certainly, to sweep aside traditional practice to make way for neoliberal-industrial high-tech farming of the kind that is now considered 'modern' is hubris writ large, the height of folly, yet this has become the norm. These days, governments and commercial companies in all contexts—mining, farming, civil engineering—are supposed to consult the people in whose midst they elect to operate but the 'consultation' is typically *post hoc*: the people in effect are invited to rubber stamp a *fait accompli*. It's a sham, in other words. They also claim that their policies are 'evidence based'—but usually at best, only in parts. The phrase keeps recurring: 'No wonder the world is in a mess.'

Finally—although this remains speculative—if it is true, as it surely is, that most people are *nice,* or would prefer to be if given half a chance, then a society that truly reflected the wishes of the people ought to be nice too; certainly a lot nicer than most societies tend to be.

But—and it's a huge 'but'—democracy is difficult. It is impossible to consult everyone on every detail—and most of the time, most people don't want to be bothered. Brexit—Britain's departure from the European Union—will affect the people of Britain and the whole world profoundly in the decades to come but a distressingly high proportion of people interviewed on television during the build-up said they were simply fed up with the whole discussion, and just wanted the government to get on with it, whichever way the dice may fall. Boris Johnson won the 2019 general election by promising to 'Get Brexit done!' as if all we needed was a *fait accompli*, whatever it was that was accomplished. Many issues too—which certainly includes Brexit—require specialist knowledge which only the specialists have time for. Democracy in practice requires us to sit through hours and hours of tedium in draughty village halls ('On a point of order, Madame Chair')—or as Oscar Wilde (allegedly) put the matter:

Democracy takes up too many evenings.

In practice, then, what might be called *true* democracy—everyone consulted on everything—is replaced by ***representative democracy***: people at large are invited to vote for dedicated souls to represent their views. This solves the too-many-evenings problem but raises a whole lot more. Sometimes the people who put themselves forward for election really do see it as their duty to serve their community. But others are vain mountebanks. All too often the mountebanks, fired by their own egoism, prevail. Britain at the time of writing is dominated by Boris Johnson, surely the doyen of mountebanks. Often we find that none of the candidates who put themselves forward for government really reflects our views, so we are obliged to vote for the least bad. Hillary Clinton or Donald Trump really wasn't much of a choice. In most countries, as has been the case everywhere through most of history, only some of the people are allowed to vote. Even in Britain—not the most democratic but by no means the least—men who were not property owners could not vote in national elections until 1918. Women were granted the vote in 1918 too—but only about 40% of them: only those who were over 30 and married to respectable men. Universal suffrage for both men and women over 21 had to wait until 1928. In 1979 the minimum age for both men and women was reduced to 18.

However, the right to vote is only half the story. In practice few people stand for election unless they belong to some political party—and even when the votes are in it still is not clear which of the contending parties should form the government. Should it be the one that wins the most votes overall or the one that wins the most seats? Some countries do one thing and some do another and none is entirely satisfactory. All too often, too, the voting system is seriously corrupt. Whole tranches of ballot papers mysteriously go missing, or are peremptorily declared to be spoiled. Black people in the southern United States sometimes find they must jump through extraordinary, gratuitous hoops before they are allowed to vote even though it is their constitutional right to do so. When the reigning world chess champion Gary Kasparov dared to challenge Vladimir Putin for the presidency of Russia in 2007 he found that civic halls and other likely meeting places were closed to him. Sometimes armed militia stand guard over the polling stations. In some despotic states the despots may apparently win more votes than there are voters. In countries like Britain where voting is voluntary and more than two parties stand for election we typically find that the winner may form a government with only about 25%—or less—of the available votes, and yet may finish up with a commanding majority in the House of Commons with literal powers of life and death over the rest of us (since governments have the power to make war).

In *Against Elections: The Case for Democracy* (2013) the Belgian writer David Van Reybrouck seeks to cut through the Gordian knots by invoking the old idea of ***sortition***, as practiced in ancient Athens and in the Renaissance states of Venice and Florence. In this system, particular matters of policy are decided by what in effect are juries: assemblies of citizens chosen at random to consider the matters in hand. As with conventional juries, citizens are required by law to take part in these assemblies if called upon to do so. The decisions they reach would not be worse than those arrived at by governments. There is less opportunity for corruption or grandstanding and the participants are truly 'of the people' and so, presumably, would be inclined to act 'for the people.' There are obvious snags but the idea is being taken seriously in some influential circles and may yet play a part in the world's affairs.

It is clear though, all in all, that the complexities of democracy are endless. There are no sure-fire ways to ensure that decisions are taken democratically and certainly no guarantee that the decisions that are made democratically are necessarily the best. After all, the Brexit referendum of 2016 was supposed to be democratic but most people who take a serious interest agree that the process was deeply flawed and that the outcome has been disastrous. Small wonder that Winston Churchill commented (although he wasn't apparently the first to say it) that

> *Democracy is the worst form of government. Except for all the others.*

In the present world, however (yet another 'however') democracy is hugely threatened by neoliberalism, which has long since ceased merely to be an economic device and has become a political movement, and indeed a religion, and one that flouts, or does not even recognize, the bedrock principles of morality and ecology. Truly it is the enemy of humankind and of the biosphere. More in chapter 10.

Finally, socialism and democracy together lead us to prefer societies that are ***egalitarian***. Thus:

The ideal of Equality

It seems morally right—*just*—that everyone should have a fair share of what's going. No one should be filthy rich, with the personal power that goes with extreme wealth. Still less should they make a virtue of their wealth, as if wealth necessarily implies merit. Indeed as Pope Gregory (St Gregory the Great) put the matter about 1400 years ago:

> *Those who make private property of the gift of God pretend in vain to be innocent, for in thus retaining the subsistence of the poor they are the murderers of those who die every day for the want of it.*
>
> (Quoted by A.S. Attack in *John Clare: Voice of Freedom*, Shepheard-Walwyn 2010. p. 84)

A more egalitarian society with more even distribution of wealth has practical advantages too. As Richard Wilkinson and Kate Pickett point out in *The Spirit Level* (2009), *everyone* benefits in egalitarian societies. The better off as well as the less well-off are measurably healthier and less stressed than in unequal societies. That is, it is better for your general wellbeing to be averagely rich in an egalitarian society than to be seriously rich in an unequal one. Ask yourself: would you rather have a modest but agreeable job in, say, Copenhagen, or live in some hacienda in Patagonia, protected from the discontented peasantry by big dogs and *pistoleros*?

Many a government or would-be government has recognized the virtue and advantages of equality and so it is that The American Declaration of Independence of 1776 tells us in the second and most famous paragraph that

> *We hold these truths to be self-evident, that all men are created equal, that they are endowed by their Creator with certain unalienable Rights, that among these are Life, Liberty and the pursuit of Happiness.*

The Declaration is beyond doubt a brilliant document, penned by some of the outstanding thinkers and doers of modern times including Thomas Jefferson and Benjamin Franklin. Yet many people (including me) feel that it is deeply flawed, and got the US off to a very dubious start, to the detriment of us all. Thus, although the second paragraph may be taken to read that all men (which we may infer albeit anachronistically was meant to include all women) are created equal, the wealth of the US at the time was largely dependent on slavery, and the people now known as native Americans were systematically done down. Evidently, as Napoleon the Pig declared in George Orwell's *Animal Farm* (1945), 'some are more equal than others.'

Then again, although the Declaration tells us that all men are *created* equal, it does not suggest that we should stay that way. In practice American society is maximally competitive, with some racing far ahead of others; and although there is a strong humanitarian tradition, with the strong and the rich taking care of the less fortunate, there is nothing in the Declaration to suggest they *should* do so. 'Rights,' too, many would say, is a necessary but dubious concept, not to be taken for granted. 'Life, Liberty, and the pursuit of happiness' seem reasonable enough. But Al Capone and all those merciless corporate bosses could legitimately claim that they too are merely pursuing happiness and exercising their freedom—which, according to the Declaration, is their more or less incontrovertible right. In short: the Declaration talks of ***rights*** which, as the first modern Americans strove to shrug off the yoke of British rule, was high in the minds of radical thinkers. But it does not speak commensurately of social ***obligations***; or as lawyers put the matter—an excellent expression—*duty of care*. The Declaration is not, innately, a compassionate document although compassion, if we truly desire to create a convivial world and to take due care of our fellow creatures, is the *sine qua non*.

The slogan that emerged from the French Revolution a few years later

Liberty, Equality, Fraternity

is far more to the point. Here, equality is seen not simply as the initial condition but as a *goal*; and compassion is implicit in the idea of 'fraternity' (though this of course should be expressed in non-sexist terms). It is one of history's great tragedies that the French Revolution turned so sour. But that, it seems to me, is the nature of revolutions. This is why we should prefer Renaissance. Build the alternative *before* the status quo is brought down. Allow the status quo to wither on the vine.

All in all, then, absolute equality is probably not a sensible ambition. It can, however, in the manner of utopian visions, be seen as a virtual, moral goal; at least to provide an antidote to the extreme inequality that now prevails worldwide which surely is morally vile and in practice is a prime, direct cause of all the world's ills. But if we combine the slogan of the French Revolution with a famous adage of Karl Marx—

From each according to their abilities; to each according to their needs

—then I reckon we more or less say all that really needs saying.

Anthropocentric vs Gaiacentric

Quite a few governments in the history of the world have embraced the socialist ideals spelled out by Keir Hardie and have tried in various ways to be truly democratic—but none to my knowledge has ever been sufficiently ***gaiacentric***—which is what 'green' ought to mean. David Cameron's Tory government of 2010-16 promised to be 'the greenest government ever' but then reduced support for conservation projects, along with the public services. All governments that I know of refer to the biosphere as 'the environment' and then treat 'the environment' as an add-on, to be attended to, perhaps, as and when they are rich enough, though it is never made clear when that golden day has arrived or how we will know it if it does. All governments that I know of take an anthropocentric view of the natural world if they consider it at all. Our fellow creatures and the places they live in are valued only insofar as they provide 'natural capital' and/or 'ecosystem services.' Otherwise they are neglected or actively done in. The Australians in recent decades used heavy tractors to 'clear' the bush—which now in large part is desert. Governments worldwide seem to have had a particular down on wetland: the upland peat bogs of Britain; the marshes of Iraq; the bayou country of the southern United States. Influential lobbies, including that of the traditional landowners, are allowed or encouraged to render vast areas of wild landscape hostile to all but the few creatures—grouse, pheasants, or deer—that they raise expressly to be shot. Various forms of ecological destruction have often been declared illegal but are rarely punished with the severity that such crime deserves. No government at least in the western world has ever actively embraced the idea that nature is sacred and that to despoil and destroy wild creatures and landscapes is beyond mere secular crime and indeed should be classed as a sin. None has fully embraced and promulgated the idea that humanity is part of the biosphere and the biosphere is part of us, and truly incorporated the needs of the natural world into the economy. The growth of the world's Green parties is encouraging but none is quite Green enough.

In short, the world, and our approach to governance, has yet to engage with the need to strike a balance between the anthropocentric and the gaiacentric. That essential step has yet to be taken.

Perm any three from eight

Political groups are conventionally divided along one main axis: Left vs Right. But, I am suggesting, they should in reality be divided along three axes:

Left (socialist) vs Right

Bottom-up (democratic) vs top-down (hierarchical)

Gaiacentric (green) vs exclusively anthropocentric

In reality, either alternative from each of the three essential dimensions can be combined with any of the others—giving eight possible permutations in all. That is, it is possible to devise governments that are:

Left wing, democratic, and green

Left wing, democratic, but entirely anthropocentric

Left wing, top-down, and green

Left wing, top down, and entirely anthropocentric

Right wing, democratic, and green

Right wing, democratic, but entirely anthropocentric

Right wing, top-down, and green

Right wing, top down, and entirely anthropocentric

So we find that some governments that claimed or claim to be socialist have in practice been autocratic—the epitome of top-down-ness; and some individuals if not entire governments have been extremely top-down and autocratic and yet have been, or claimed to be, thoroughly gaiacentric—happy indeed to banish human beings altogether to make way for wilderness.

I suggest that if we really want to create convivial societies (with personal fulfilment) within a flourishing biosphere then what we need is governments that are

Socialist—in the style of Keir Hardie

Democratic *and*

Gaiacentric (Green)

No government and no political party that I know of has ever grasped all three nettles as tightly as they need to be grasped; or if there is such a party, anywhere, it has never to my knowledge ever come to power, and certainly has never become a world power. The world in general is and always has been dominated by governments that may claim to be democratic but in truth are always highly hierarchical, and at best make only grudging concessions to the natural world. Such governments commonly lead the world in precisely the opposite direction from where we need to go. Above all, as discussed in chapter 6, the world needs Enlightened Agriculture, and Enlightened Agriculture leads us to favour mixed, low-input, skills-intensive farms geared primarily to local distribution which perforce means that ideally they should be small to medium-sized. But in all kinds of ways, all over the world, bureaucracy and the details of the economy make life even more difficult for small farmers than farming unavoidably is. These days for reasons of short-term economy and their desire to control, governments like Britain's favour high-input monoculture with minimal to zero labour on the largest possible scale, geared to the commodity export market, and ultimately run by a handful of corporates; and this is what they put their weight and our money behind.

The idea that we need benign forms of socialism and democracy has been around in one form or another for centuries, and the idea that nature is sacred and should be treated with extreme respect is surely as old as humanity. So why—given that these ideas are so obviously desirable and necessary—has almost all the world, almost all the time, opted for something so completely different? In particular, why do so many societies who have the vote so often elect governments who so obviously are not on the side of the people and still less of the biosphere and in truth seem to be leading humanity and the rest of the biosphere to the buffers with all possible speed?

The reality: Metadarwinism and rule by Oligarchy

Actually, I don't reckon that people as a whole ever did *opt* to appoint the kind of government we have now, and have usually endured. Rather, humankind and therefore the world as a whole (given that whatever affects us affects everything else as well) are victims of game theory. More particularly, we are victims of what in chapter 3 I called ***metadarwinism***: ostensibly Darwinian theory that in practice goes well beyond Darwin's teaching and his intention.

For although life and the universe are, I suggest, prevailingly cooperative (and if they were not, neither would be possible) competition is a fact of life too. Cooperative systems must work much better in the long term but in the short term competition brings advantages, at least for the winners; and day-to-day life operates in the short term. The long term—jam tomorrow—requires constraint today. If you want jam today, then put the boot in and take what you can while the going's good.

Many people, perceiving that this is so, make a virtue of being competitive. In the neoliberal economy competitiveness is the *sine qua non*. Budding businesspeople straight out of university are *trained* to be aggressive. They stand in front of mirrors baring their teeth. Their model is the Rottweiler. They are taught in effect that the purpose of life is to come out on top; to become rich, and to achieve power and to dominate.

I have taken part in a course for young businesspeople where this way of thinking was justified on Darwinian grounds. The students were told that to compete unwinkingly is natural, the way of the world, and is therefore right; which is bad biology and even worse moral philosophy, but what the hell. I am pleased to report that as a course teacher I was off message, and my services were no longer required. Friedrich Nietzsche (1844-1900) is sometimes dragged out of the philosophical woodwork to add weight to the metadarwinian message. He after all taught that human beings should strive above all to achieve personal excellence, in all that they did, and indeed to achieve the status of *Ubermensch*, which translates roughly as 'supermen.' This he saw as our duty. Ultimately, the drive for personal excellence would raise humankind as a whole to a new level. Those who were not up to the mark should be left by the wayside—with the accent on the 'should.' It was, and is, positively reprehensible to waste time and effort on the less than able. Compassion, to misquote Gordon Gekko again, is for wimps.

Those who seek power and wealth obsessively are more likely to achieve it than the rest of us, who for the most part prefer to get on with our own lives. So the world is inevitably dominated by people who are obsessed with power and wealth. More: those who are so driven form ***a self-reinforcing positive feedback loop***. The corporates generate wealth, because that is their *raison d'etre*. Governments like those of Britain and the US happily work in partnership with the corporates because they are concerned above all with 'economic growth'—ever increasing 'Gross Domestic Product' or GDP—and this is what the corporates, above all, seek to provide. Often indeed, modern governments in practice are extensions of the corporate boardroom.

Both government and the corporates finance intellectuals and experts—with governments like Britain's happy to leave university funding more and more to the corporates ('the private sector') so as to reduce public spending, and make their own lives easier. Corporates are not charities and cannot be and so therefore, perforce, support only those lines of research and thinking that reinforce their own position. Inevitably, high-tech methods, which can be hugely profitable and allow control to be centralized, are favoured above low-tech, artisanal approaches, even though the latter are often socially and ecologically superior.

In short: corporates make the wealth which governments rely upon and governments in turn smooth the path for the corporates and both support the kind of practical and intellectual endeavour that supplies the ideas that keep that cosy combination ahead of the global competition. The three groups between them—corporates, government, and their selected intellectuals and experts—form the oligarchy—an oligarchy of enormous power, since it has all bases covered: wealth, statutory power, and expertise. There is no need to invoke conspiracy theory to explain how such oligarchies come about. Darwinian (truly Darwinian) natural selection is explanation enough. Those who support the oligarchy become part of it, and flourish, with money and the might of government on their side. Those who question the actions and motives of the oligarchs and their right to dominate, are left out in the cold.

I suggest that the prime political task for humankind, if we truly want to look forward to a long and agreeable future, for us and all creatures, is to break the feedback loop that keeps the oligarchy in power and to expose the crude thinking that lies behind it. As always, Renaissance must be the way: build the alternatives, despite the status quo, and show that they work.

Coda: the absolute importance of the grass roots

It occurs to me, albeit without any formal study to back it up, that all the truly worthwhile reforms throughout history have been or at least began as grassroots movements—democracy in action. In absolute contrast, not least in my own dealings with British agriculture, it has often seemed to me that the oligarchy in general and governments in particular emerge not as the initiators and leaders of much-needed radical change but as obstacles to be overcome. That, surely, is not how things ought to be.

10

AN ECONOMY FIT FOR PURPOSE

The point is, ladies and gentlemen, that greed, for lack of a better word, is good. ... Greed, in all of its forms; greed for life, for money, for love, knowledge has marked the upward surge of mankind.

Michael Douglas as Gordon Gekko in
Wall Street (Oliver Stone, 1987)

If economists could manage to get themselves thought of as humble, competent people on a level with dentists, that would be splendid.

John Maynard Keynes. Allegedly a throwaway
remark though widely quoted e.g. by Tim Harford
in the *Financial Times*, January 18, 2017.

TO PUT THE MATTER HIGH-FALLUTINLY, the economy is, or should be, the medium through which we translate our aspirations into reality: our needs and reasonable desires into action and material goods. Indeed it is the matrix of our lives. What human beings do, too, affects all other creatures—so the fate of all life on Earth, and the fabric of the Earth itself, depends in the end on economics.

In practice, though, to put the matter crudely, the economy is played out as a game of money. So the task before us is, or should be, to create a game of money that can deliver 'convivial societies with personal fulfilment within a flourishing biosphere.' This at least, I am suggesting, is what the world really needs and what most people would surely prefer, if the option was there.

But no economist that I know of—or none that has so far had any great influence on the world stage—has devised a game of money that really would help us to create convivial societies within a flourishing biosphere. None that I know of has expressly set out to do so. To be sure, most of the best known economists have been moralists at least of a conventional kind, who did set out expressly to improve human wellbeing. Two of the most influential, Adam Smith and J.S. Mill, were moral philosophers before they were economists. A few have at least acknowledged the existence of the natural world. But none of the front-line economists who feature in standard courses of economics in the world's leading universities and business schools have been ecologists, truly with a *feel* for the biosphere. None have felt as I suggest in chapters 4 and 14 it essential, that human beings are *part* of the natural world, and beholden to it, and must have a sense of the sacred, and have sought to shape the economy accordingly. None have felt that the natural world is more than a 'natural resource'—or if they have, this did not play a significant part in their thinking.

Even worse—the death-blow indeed—is that not all economists or the governments and industrialists who call upon their services agree that we should be seeking to create convivial societies within a flourishing biosphere. Most of the world's most powerful leaders—Donald Trump, Vladimir Putin, Xi Jinping—are strictly materialist Machiavellian metadarwinians or at least they behave as if they are which is what matters to the rest of the world. They see life as one long ultra-competitive punch-up and regard the natural world simply as natural resource. There is a ray of hope, however. There usually is, somewhere. As Kate Raworth demonstrates in *Doughnut Economics* (Random House, Business Books, 2017) a new generation of economists is gaining ground that is on the case; she herself describes what an economy might look like that was geared to the real needs both of humanity and of the natural world. She also draws attention to the growing, radical initiatives including the student movement, Kick It Over. So far, however, the radicals are far from the frontline of power. The money games that are now played out on the world stage and are taught in the world's most prestigious centres of learning do not and cannot help us to create a world that is convivial and just and is in good heart ecologically. The standard money games are not designed for this. In the main they are dedicated simplistically to the multiplication of wealth and to a great extent they are leading us *away* from where we need to go—*creating* injustice and wreaking ecological havoc.

As always, we need to start again from first principles. Since the economy is, in the end, a game of money, we might reasonably start by asking what money is and how it works. I am not an economist but Raworth is and as she says

> *Every now and again, being untutored can be an intellectual asset—and this is one of those moments.*

The following, then, is the fruit of my own very considerable intellectual asset.

Money

Money, beyond doubt, is extremely useful stuff—and, more importantly, an extremely useful idea. Above all, it facilitates trade; and trade is one of humanity's defining qualities. Trade is an exercise in cooperation and sharing, and only by sharing and cooperating can we truly release our own talents—build cathedrals and frame philosophies and scientific theories and be truly fulfilled. Speech and our infinitely versatile syntactical language enable us to pool our thoughts, which is what *really* makes us special; and trade enables us to pool material goods, and to exchange goods for services, so that all of us, in theory, can partake of all that the natural world and our fellow human beings have to offer. Other animals pool their thoughts to a greater extent than is generally appreciated. Some, like lions and wolves and vultures, do share material spoils from time to time and some courting males, especially birds, bring gifts for their would-be mates. A freshly-concussed lizard can make all the difference. But no other animal that I know of actually *trades*. This again makes us special and gives us the ecological edge. Among humans, trade is clearly ancient. Neanderthals have been found with tools made from stone that came from other people's territories in far distant places.

Trade can simply mean barter—but barter has obvious limitations. It is hard to barter cattle, if that is what you have to sell, for clothes pegs, if that is what you need. Currency is needed: some universal token of exchange. Currency in principle can take any form—sometimes intrinsically valuable and useful, like gold or arrow heads, and sometimes not, like cowry shells. Anything may serve as a token, so long as both parties acknowledge its validity. But of all the currencies so far conceived money is the most useful. Its value is easily quantified. The amount that a coin or a note is worth is written on it.

But although money is useful stuff—almost vital in fact, in a complex society that depends on trade—we put far too much store by it. Indeed in the modern world we feel obliged to build our entire lives around it. It is assumed, first of all, that wealth—the things that money can buy, and indeed the mere possession of money itself—makes us happy. It is taken to be self-evident that happiness is good and it is further assumed that to seek happiness is self-evidently rational; and the philosophers of the Enlightenment, which reached its apex in the 18th century, emphasized the need to be rational above all. Thus the Enlightenment gave birth to the system of ethics known as 'utilitarian' which the English philosopher Jeremy Bentham defined as 'the greatest happiness of the greatest number.' Utilitarian ethics still prevails even though it has serious shortcomings as discussed in chapter 12. Ethics these days is often treated as an exercise in cost-effectiveness. All in all, it has commonly been assumed these past few centuries that it must be both rational and good to generate wealth since wealth, it is assumed, leads to happiness.

The above may sound very simplistic, and is. Yet, I suggest, this line of thought is the rationale behind and the moral justification for the economic system that has prevailed for the past 300 years; that of ***capitalism*** and its variants. The whole idea was beautifully summarized by Anthony Trollope in his novel of 1875, *The Way We Live Now*. The banker, Augustus Melmotte, tells his would-be clients:

> *What is the engine of this world? Profit. Gentlemen it is your duty to make yourself rich!*

Melmotte was of course fictional and Trollope intended him to be a villain—almost a pantomime villain. But modern economists and politicians, some with enormous influence, have embraced his philosophy wholeheartedly. Some indeed have gone one step further. Thus in January 1980 Margaret Thatcher, Britain's newly elected Prime Minister told Brian Walden in an interview on London Weekend Television's *Weekend World* that

> *No one would remember the good Samaritan if he'd only had good intentions; he had money as well.*

The good Samaritan, as related in Luke 10:25-37, helped a poor wounded Jew by the side of road while many other people, most of whom were Jews, 'passed by on the other side.' The Samaritans and Jews were not good friends at the time and most Christians have taken the parable to mean that goodness—compassion—knows no boundaries, whether racial, political, or religious. Mrs Thatcher seemed to be suggesting, however, that we have to be rich in order to do good at all. Obviously money can be used to do good and common sense suggests that the more money we have the more good we could do—but what really counts is the intention: the moral impulsion. Absolutely not is money an essential prerequisite, and of course it is absolutely not the case that *in practice*, more wealth leads to more good. Often the precise opposite.

In truth, in a society that depends on money as complex societies do everyone needs *some* money if they are to survive at all, and they need somewhat more than is needed for mere subsistence if they are to live with dignity and achieve personal fulfilment. But once we are comfortably above the breadline it very obviously is not true that more and more wealth makes us happier and happier. Gold taps and designer undies are no cure for depression. Only psychopaths really get a kick out of wealth per se, and measure their own worth by it. The folly of such thinking is a powerful theme of literature from the story of King Midas in the 2nd millennium BCE who turned his own daughter into gold and then realized that gold is nothing compared with a flesh and blood person and the love of a child, to Scott Fitzgerald's story of 1925 about *The Great Gatsby* who had boundless wealth but no real friends and burned with unrequited love for the capricious and somewhat vacuous Daisy. A great many studies show us that above a certain, fairly low threshold there is no simple relationship between wealth and fulfilment, though that was already obvious.

Yet all of us in the modern economy are encouraged above all to earn lots of money, or otherwise to acquire money, and this is seen to be both rational and virtuous. Indeed, in the modern world, entire nations are dedicated above all to 'economic growth,' measured as 'Gross Domestic Product,' or GDP. GDP is a measure of all the measurable wealth produced in a country by every means—although, in reality, it measures economic activity rather than positive gain. Thus demolition and war contribute to GDP because the demolition and the arms industries are lucrative—yet the purpose of both is to destroy. The concept of GDP was introduced in the 1930s for technical reasons, and is useful for some purposes, but it was never meant to be a measure of human wellbeing and clearly it is not—although that is how it is commonly construed. I well remember an African leader at an international conference praying out loud that no one would discover oil on his land. Sure, it would increase GDP no end. But, so a great many precedents tell us, the oil would in practice be extracted by foreign corporations and the wealth that did stay in the country would almost certainly create a super-elite while the poor stayed poor—or indeed became poorer for they would lose their traditional ways of life and be reduced to lackeys, or banished to the slums. The precedents are all too obvious the world over. Mrs Thatcher sought to assure us that the wealth of the rich 'trickles down' to the poor but as President Barack Obama observed some decades later:

Guess what. Trickle-down doesn't work.

Even if it did work, in an economy that relies on trickle down in effect is accepting that the rich—in practice a tiny minority—should act as gatekeepers of the world's wealth. What gives them the *right* to adopt such a role? What gives them the right to lay claim to the bulk of the world's wealth and then to dispense whatever is expedient to the rest? John F. Kennedy no less spoke of economic growth as

the rising tide that lifts all boats

—but the tide of money does not lift all boats equally, and some are caught in the eddies, and sink.

What really matters of course is not how much money we have but ***how the money is produced; who gets their hands on it; and what it is used for.*** The way things are at the moment, in the ultra-competitive, metadarwinian, self-centred, entirely anthropocentric zeitgeist of the present world, money is often produced in ways that are extremely destructive. Indeed

the most destructive enterprises can be the m
mining of precious metals and hyper-intensiv
practice, too, as outlined below, most of the w
hands of a few and serves primarily to make ric
new or at least proposed generation of high-spe
case in point. Local buses and light railways tha
people at large are neglected while the government
from whoever is richest around the world to build sup ... the
alleged benefit of businesspeople. We should rather b ... g, as people
were urged to ask in World War II, 'Is your journey really necessary?'

Nevertheless, we can accept that *some* money is necessary—and the money we do produce should not be wasted. The general method by which money is generated and manipulated, developed, refined, and elaborated since its first *bona fide* stirrings in the 18th century, is called ***capitalism.***

Capitalism and its variants

Capitalism employs a number of mechanisms designed to deploy money in ways that generate more money. These mechanisms include: ***lending (or borrowing) money with interest; free enterprise; investment***—which commonly means buying a share of a business and then sharing the profits (or losses); and ***trade***—buying goods and then 'adding value' (if only by taking them within range of the customer) and selling them for more than was paid. The general aim is to return a ***profit***: meaning that more money is received in the end than is expended; and the profit is then re-invested, as opposed to being put in a box, as a miser would do. Or that at least is the idea. Typically the mechanisms of capitalism are deployed by private individuals and companies but entire states and communities can and do operate as capitalists too.

All the various mechanisms come with caveats. Since ancient times, long before the birth of formal capitalism, traditional Jews and Muslims objected and some still object to lending or borrowing with interest. They call this ***usury***. After all, they take it as read that money should reflect work and a person who gains just by lending grows richer without any obvious endeavour—which is a kind of cheating. Others though point out that lending always involves an element of risk, which should be compensated. It is the case, too, that new enterprises could not get off ss their initiators were very rich to start with, or else e money to get started. So judicious borrowing and lending, ould argue, is *necessary*, or very few people would ever be able to nch out or try anything new and the whole economy would grind to a halt. Lending these days is generally called usury only when the lenders charge extortionate rates of interest.

Personally, good socialist though I claim to be, I see no serious moral objection to most of the main *mechanisms* that are commonly associated with capitalism. If capitalism operates within the bedrock principles of morality and ecology, as all human activity must if we are seriously to contemplate a long-term future, then those mechanisms can deliver what is needed. Britain's senior Tory MP of recent years, Kenneth Clarke, talks of 'business with a conscience.' The mixed, low-input, small-to-medium sized farms of the kind that Enlightened Agriculture is most likely to give rise to, are good examples of this and could certainly be created within the context of an essentially capitalist economy, and sometimes are.

All too obviously, though, capitalism and the capitalists who practice it do not always respect the bedrock principles of morality and ecology. Indeed they can be vile. Capitalism in a recognizable form grew alongside the industrial revolution which in Britain got properly underway with the factories of the 18th century and came fully to fruition in the 19th century and as everyone knows, those factories and mines were often immensely cruel. The workers, including small children who came cheap, worked 14-hour shifts with an inadequate diet and a hovel to live in while armies of slaves or virtual slaves in far-flung countries provided the raw materials. All this is outlined in all school history books and is described in all its horrendous detail by the Irish historian-journalist Brian Inglis in his excellent book of 1971, *Poverty and the Industrial Revolution*. The relationship between workers and factory-owners was competitive—each competing to get the best deal. But the balance lay very much with the employers—not least because the employers were heavily represented in parliament and could adjust the law in their own favour. The result was and is extreme wealth on the one hand and extreme poverty on the other. The obvious injustice was excused on the grounds that the poor were poor because they were lazy, and would be even lazier if they weren't desperate. All this got capitalism a very bad name, and quite rightly. It was the injustice and cruelty they saw in England's industrial north that prompted Karl Marx and his friend and benefactor Friedrich Engels to write *The Communist Manifesto* in 1848, and Marx to formulate his alternative to capitalism in *Das Kapital* in 1867. But the injustice and the cruelty are with us still. The modern off-the-peg clothing industry depends on the sweatshop, and despite the fancy technology there would be no cheap food without sweated labour, cruelty and ecological destruction.

Yet—surely? —capitalism does not have to be vile. It should be possible to set up factories that do genuinely useful things in ways that do not result in social injustice—as demonstrated at least in part by the great Quaker enterprises of the mid-19th century such as Cadbury's, Rowntree's and Fry's (the Quakers apparently had an inordinate fondness for chocolate); and by the Lever brothers who made soap and established Port Sunlight on Merseyside for the benefit of their workers. To be sure, these factories were run on patriarchal lines which is not ideal but they were a huge improvement on what had gone before and a sincere attempt to create a (capitalist) economy that was good for society as a whole. Societies run on capitalist lines can indeed be foul but, I suggest, the blame rests primarily not with the basic mechanisms of capitalism but with the mindset: the absence of morality, and especially the virtue of compassion, and of any worthwhile sense that the natural world is anything other than a resource to be ripped off. The same point recurs again and again; if we are not guided by the bedrock principles of morality and ecology then all hell is liable to break loose, whatever the technicalities of the system. If we are guided by the bedrock principles then various systems of governance and economics can be made to work for the general good—although some, of course, work much better than others.

Here we encounter a great irony. For one of the principal founders of recognizably modern capitalism was Adam Smith (1723-1790), a pillar of the Scottish Enlightenment and best chum of his fellow pillar, David Hume (1711-1776). He gave public lectures in philosophy in the 1740s and in 1752 he became the head of Moral Philosophy at Glasgow University. His first book, published in 1759, was *The Theory of Moral Sentiments*. It began:

> *How selfish soever man may be supposed, there are evidently some principles in his nature, which interest him in the fortune of others, and render their happiness necessary to him, though he derives nothing from it except the pleasure of seeing it.... As we have no immediate experience of what other men feel, we can form no idea of the manner in which they are affected, but by conceiving what we ourselves should feel in the like situation.*

In particular, throughout this book and throughout his life, Smith spoke of ***human sympathy,*** clearly akin to the ancient concept of compassion and the modern concept of empathy. Clearly he believed in the essential goodness of human beings—it's in there somewhere—and in its central importance.

But Smith is better known as an economist and indeed is sometimes called 'the Father of Economics' or 'the Father of Capitalism.' In volume IV of his most famous book *The Wealth of Nations,* published in 1776, he discusses the importance of the market, conceived as the general meeting ground, the interface, between traders and customers. In one of the most quoted paragraphs he wrote:

> *... by directing that industry in such a manner as its produce may be of the greatest value, [the trader] intends only his own gain, and he is in this, as in many other cases, led by* **an invisible hand** *to promote an end which was no part of his intention. Nor is it always the worse for the society that it was no part of it. By pursuing his own interest he frequently promotes that of the society more effectually than when he really intends to promote it. I have never known much good done by those who affected to trade for the public good.*

So (and this is the irony, at least as I see things): here is Smith the moralist describing and indeed advocating a system that apparently produces a good, just outcome without anyone needing to think in moral terms at all. Provided the market is 'free' (which he discusses elsewhere) then its own internal mechanism—'the invisible hand'—will produce a morally acceptable outcome even if everyone simply pursues his or her self-interest—which is not what morality is generally taken to mean. Indeed he seems to be saying—or indeed is saying—that in practice we get a *better* moral outcome if we deliberately avoid thinking in moral terms. Just think of number one, seems to be the message, and all will be well. Those who try to impose moral rules are just interfering busybodies, who screw up the works. Smith's argument over the following centuries has been simplified and coarsened and re-emerged in the late 20th century in Gordon Gekko's infamous comment as quoted above:

> *Greed is good.*

Smith himself, however, supported his idea with logical argument. In a healthy, fully functional market, there will be plenty of traders offering a wide variety of options. The customers then will have plenty of choice—which is what modern, freemarket enthusiasts such as Britain's Tories and the former 'New Labour' Prime Minister Tony Blair see as *the* great desideratum. The traders must therefore compete for custom and must raise their act in order to do so. If any sell inferior goods, or are overpriced, then they will lose custom and go out of business. Hence the general standard is raised over time. Smith was writing 100 years before Darwin, but this is all very Darwinian (except of course that Darwin did not suppose that natural selection produced general improvement—merely that it enhanced adaptation). Many have taken it to be the case that if the system is Darwinian then it is *ipso facto* scientific and if it is scientific it can't be wrong. Can it? In short, Smith's idea of the invisible hand chimes very well with the general desire to turn economics in general into a science, of which more later; and it is very much in line with the 18th century emphasis on rationality.

Presumably the invisible hand could work in the way that Smith envisaged if there was an infinite number of traders offering infinite choice and if the potential customers had perfect knowledge and had infinite time in which to shop; and if they were bold enough to haggle and if their decisions were always 'rational.' In reality none of the above can ever apply. In the modern world indeed the corporate-owned supermarket may be the only place to shop and modern customers learn most of what they know about the goods on offer through the ads put out by the traders themselves. And in the modern world that puts such store by convenience and leisure many or most people are far too busy to spend time shopping—or at least on shopping for food. They grab what they need on their way home from work at the station Tesco.

Smith must have known that the perfect market conditions in which the invisible hand could work its magic did not and could not exist. I can't help thinking, however, that Smith was forever the moralist. He believed in human sympathy, and surely believed that real people in the real world would not in general be out-and-out crooks. They would not set out deliberately to cheat; and even in an imperfect market, with less than an infinite number of traders and with customers who are not particularly well informed, the invisible hand would be helped out by what people commonly call 'decency.' Alas, apparently, that is not the case. In reality, as demonstrated by the vile factories of the industrial revolution and the modern sweatshop, in a 'free,' deregulated market, ruthlessness prevails. The point is not that most people are ruthless. The point rather is that the ruthless minority tend to dominate through the mechanism of the positive feedback loop, as outlined in chapter 9. It is also true, of course, unfortunately, that not enough people care enough to take enough interest in what is going on.

Neoliberalism may be seen as the market principle of Smith taken to extremes. The whole neoliberal economy is built around the market, which is supposed to be as free as possible. Free in this context means that anyone can join in (which in practice they cannot) and that the traders are as free as possible of regulation. If the free market ever seems to fail then the neoliberals can always claim, and do, that it was not allowed to be free enough. In the same way when Marxist economies fail, Marxists claim that they were prevented from operating in a truly Marxist style. Similarly, too, dyed-in-the-wool Freudians argue that all who object to their theories are suffering from mental blocks which in turn can be explained away by the theories of Freud.

In the neoliberal market, the value of everything is measured purely in money. At least, everything that the economist chooses to attach any value to, is given a price. Producers are obliged to make what people are prepared to pay for. Otherwise they go bust. This, the neoliberals argue, is democratic—for what is democracy for if not to give people what they want? In practice, though, this means that the market—not moral philosophers or prophets or priests or indeed humanity at large with our built-in human sympathy—becomes the arbiter of good and bad. What people are prepared to pay for is deemed, *ipso facto*, to be good. What they will pay most for is best. What people will not pay for must be undesirable or unnecessary and either is left to gather dust or is never produced at all.

In line with Smith's idea of the invisible hand, the theory has it that if everyone just sets out to get rich, in the manner of Trollope's Melmotte, and if the market is given a free rein, then the mechanism of the market itself will produce a good and fair result. Thus the result is morally acceptable even though no one needs consciously to be a moralist. Since human beings are notoriously fickle, and not everyone is morally good, it seems far safer to install an economic mechanism—an algorithm—that can deliver an agreeable outcome without relying on human honesty and goodwill. Just leave the market itself to sort things out.

Of course there are snags. I once took part in a debate on the rights and wrongs of human cloning at the World Economic Forum no less in which one bright spark solemnly declared that cloning ought to be allowed because there was a 'demand' for it—and he was warmly applauded. I dared to suggest that all moral edicts must above all be rooted in compassion and that cloning when you think it through seems far from compassionate. Not relevant said the chairman. Clearly Tudge has failed to grasp the problem. The same market logic would tell us that since some people will pay big money for child pornography then that too should be allowed. In truth, in all societies that I know about child pornography remains taboo, despite the market—yet according to neoliberal logic, there should be no taboos at all. In the US, what is called 'the gun culture' is booming. Thanks largely to an unfortunate clause in their constitution Americans are brought up to believe that they have a *right* to carry guns and as mentioned in chapter 9, the second paragraph of the American Declaration of Independence of 1776 stresses *rights* above all, with no mention of social obligation. The coronavirus lockdown is still in full flood as I am writing this and all but essential shops are closed—but America's gun stores are allowed to stay open. Indeed they are doing a roaring trade for as the virus bites more deeply, Americans may feel obliged to shoot each other. Deregulation does not necessarily bring out the better angels of our nature.

Neither does the free market dispense its favours equally and in this important sense it is far from democratic. All traders must compete for investment and so must seek to maximize their profits to reward their investors and so inevitably must cater primarily to those with the greatest ability to pay. Unless the market is very firmly regulated by governments or the community, then the poor may not be catered for at all and public service goes by the board. Modern, right-wing, neoliberal governments are wont to argue that markets should be as free as possible, sometimes appealing to Smith's invisible hand. But, I suggest, it is the prime task of governments, or at least of democratic governments, to ensure that the economy works in everyone's interests, which the deregulated market clearly does not.

Proof of the pudding

The neoliberal economy was and is designed to maximize wealth in general, and as J.F. Kennedy implied, we were all supposed to benefit thereby. But neoliberalism has prevailed these past 40 years and that is not how things have turned out.

In an essay entitled 'Neoliberalism and the End of Democracy,' (in Simon Springer; Kean Birch and Julie MacLeavy, eds. *The Handbook of Neoliberalism*. Oxon: Routledge, 2016) Jason Hickel of Goldsmith's College, London tells us that whereas in the years up to 1980 per capita incomes in the US and Britain increased by around 3.2 per cent per year, the rate of increase fell to 2.1 per cent after 1980—which is when neoliberalism first began to become the norm. In the US too before the 1980s the richest one per cent of the population collared eight per cent of national income—but under neoliberalism this has risen to 18 per cent. The discrepancy is now as bad as it was in the so-called 'Gilded Age,' from around 1870 to 1900, when a few families were conspicuously rich while most were deprived and often seriously so—hence 'gilded' meaning surface glitter, as opposed to golden. In Britain since 1980 the proportion of total wealth held by the richest one per cent has risen from 6.5 per cent to 13 per cent. In the 1990s, the salaries of CEOs in the USA increased by 400%, while average household incomes stagnated and in real terms, wages actually declined.

On the world stage, even more alarmingly, an Oxfam report prepared for the World Economic Forum in January 2016 told us that ***just one per cent of the world's people own as much as the rest of us combined.*** Just 62 *individuals* own as much as the poorest *half* of the world's population—which in 2016 meant 3.6 billion people. Simple arithmetic suggests that if the wealth of the top one per cent was shared among the rest of us we would all be twice as rich, or very nearly; and if the distribution was skewed towards the poorest people, we could end the problems of poverty at a stroke. Why do we, the 99%, put up with this? Why do we vote for governments that encourage this to happen? In practice, too, the wealth of the poorest 50% has fallen by a trillion dollars since 2010 (where a trillion means a million million) while the wealth of the 62 individuals has risen by half a trillion (and in 2016 totalled $1.76tr).

Since neoliberalism seems to have delivered such disastrous results we might conclude that the economists who thought it up were monstrous too. But again that is not the case. Perhaps the chief architect of neoliberalism was the Chicago economist Milton Friedman (1912-2006) who in turn was inspired by the Austrian-British economist and philosopher Friedrich von Hayek (1899-1992). Both had suffered or seen from close hand the rigours of the early 20th century—Fascism, war, economic depression. Hayek in particular emphasized the importance of freedom, which included economic freedom. Friedman concluded that free enterprise and a free market offered the best route out of poverty and the best guard against it and also felt that poverty perhaps above all makes human fulfilment impossible. In particular he criticized the economic strategy of President Franklin D. Roosevelt (1882-1945). Roosevelt pulled America out of its Great Depression with his economic New Deal. His government took the economy into its own hands and invested and changed tax laws in ways that rebalanced the economy and generally got it moving again. Most people felt this was brilliant—but, said Friedman, if Roosevelt had simply kept his nose out, the market would have sorted things out more quickly and put the economy back on to a surer footing, albeit with more pain at the very beginning.

For all that, in his obituary in *The New York Times* on November 23, 2006, the American economist Robert (Bob) Frank drew attention to 'The Other Milton Friedman'—who, he said, was 'A Conservative With a Social Welfare Program.' But, said Frank, Friedman recognized full well that

> *... market forces ... accomplish wonderful things* [but they] *cannot ensure a distribution of income that enables all citizens to meet basic economic needs.*

So Friedman proposed a programme of ***negative income tax*** whereby every citizen who earned below a certain amount would receive a top-up: an idea that at least is in line with the citizen's wage, outlined below. However, said Frank:

> *Mr. Friedman's proposal was undoubtedly motivated in part by his concern for the welfare of the least fortunate. But he was above all a pragmatist, and he emphasized the superiority of the negative income tax over conventional welfare programs on purely practical grounds. If the main problem of the poor is that they have too little money, he reasoned, the simplest and cheapest solution is to give them some*

more. He saw no advantage in hiring armies of bureaucrats to dispense food stamps, energy stamps, day care stamps and rent subsidies.

In short, the world's leading advocate of neoliberalism was not a bad man but even he acknowledged that the free market on its own cannot deliver what humanity really needs (and still less can it take proper care of the biosphere).

One more refinement of capitalist thinking needs a closer look:

Finance capitalism

Finance capitalism really is a game of money. The idea is to multiply money itself, without necessarily referring to the real, material world at all. Money is always, of its nature, an abstraction. It may in practice have an intrinsic value—as gold coins do—but it can be represented just as well by banknotes, which in themselves have no value at all except as wastepaper (unless they become collectors' items, but that is a different issue). Nowadays, money need not have to have any physical form at all. Even printed notes are far too cumbersome. Instead, the amount of money that any individual holds, or any company or any nation, is registered in the form of a few displaced electrons in a microchip. In fact the trillions of dollars spent on the Iraq war, say, never really existed at all in physical form. The vast wealth that was and is necessary is merely *deemed* to exist. It's all very weird. (No one quite understands it, any more than anyone really understands quantum physics. Much of what we make use of is in fact beyond our ken.)

The corollary of all this is the ***debt economy***. My mother's generation, and certainly my grandmother's generation, hated even the idea of debt. 'Never owed a penny in my life!' was a proud boast. At least, 'ordinary' people like most of our ancestors aspired to be debt-free, even if they could not always manage it.

Nowadays, however, *everyone* is in debt as a matter of course. People even measure their status by the size of their debt—since you can't borrow, at least from respectable lenders, unless you are seen to be credit-worthy. By judicious borrowing we can do things that we otherwise could not do while we are still young enough to benefit. People at large can borrow money to buy houses that they could not otherwise get a sniff of—and then live in them, which should be more to the point. Commercial companies can borrow money for start-up or to buy better machinery and take on more staff. Banks, financiers and ad hoc investors do the lending. In effect, though, the borrowers borrow against the future. Banks expect to be paid back with interest—with money that the borrowers are *expected* to earn in the future. Lending, for professional investors, *is* investment.

This is all very well as far as it goes but there are serious and obvious downsides. For instance:

The lenders are not always scrupulous. Loan sharks are a menace of course but, as always, it's the big, mainstream, respectable institutions—or some of them at least—that are the main cause of trouble. In recent decades various speculative yet eminently respectable bankers have lent large sums of money to people who have little or no hope of paying it back—using various arcane financial mechanisms to compensate for non-payment of bad debts. This has caused enormous misery. Such practice—essentially malpractice—was a prime cause of the great banking crash of 2008.

Reality into fantasy into reality. The British economist Ann Pettifor has spelled out very clearly what seems like a central absurdity of finance capitalism. Thus, a bank that agrees to lend someone £100,000 or so to buy a house (a modest amount in present-day Britain) need not actually *have* £100,000. Banks are required by law to own *some* money but nothing like the amounts that they are free to lend. The bank does not, as might be imagined, simply hand over a big bag of cash, as depicted in *Beano*. It is merely deemed to have lent the money and the borrower is then deemed to be able to afford a down-payment on a house. The borrower then does real work, making furniture or raising crops or helping people with their tax returns or whatever, and over time pays back the bank in the real money that he or she has thereby earned. Because the debt is repaid over a long period—commonly over decades—and because unpaid debt increases by compound interest, the amount paid back in earned money may be several times greater than the amount that the bank was initially deemed to have lent.

The system does work up to a point at least for some people but it feels precarious nonetheless, and of course it is. It means in effect that most of us live much or most of the time on money that doesn't really exist. Also, on a considerable point of detail, because Margaret Thatcher severely curtailed the building of public housing Britain now has too few houses so people must compete to buy; and because people at large are able to borrow enormous sums to buy houses and the price of houses has increased many times over in the past few decades, with many people spending a third or even half their entire income just on a place to live. Sixty years ago people expected to spend only 10 or 12 per cent of their income on a mortgage or a rent. My father had a modest income yet bought a house in South London, which I and my brother and sister grew up in, that now is being sold on for well over £1,000,000—several times more than I could afford. Largely because people in Britain are obliged to spend so much on somewhere to live, many cannot afford good food, even though the British economy is said to be the fifth largest in the world. The position is absurd and grotesque.

As always, the Third World suffers most. Third World countries in recent decades have been encouraged to borrow vast sums for 'development'—so that they can become more like the affluent west. (Some feel the expression 'Third World' is politically incorrect but it was the term preferred by Gandhi. 'Developing world' is a highly tendentious euphemism which implies that non-western countries should aspire to be like us—a highly questionable assumption). Anyway, although borrowing isn't necessarily bad and may indeed bring tangible benefits, it can also be a deep trap. As Jason Hickel points out, the loans from rich countries come with strings, to the lasting disadvantage of the borrower. Some strings are reasonable, as in 'Don't use the money to wage war on your neighbours' but often money is lent *only* if the borrowing country agrees to buy most of or all the goods it needs from the lender. Thus the borrower is drawn into the lender's commercial and political empire—for the imperialist mindset lives on, even though most of the great Empires of the past have been formally dismantled. Thus, says Hickel, in the past four decades or so incomes in Third World countries have grown by only 1.7% per year—about half what they were before neoliberalism became the norm. In the 1980s and '90s the total income of Sub-Saharan African countries fell by around 10 per cent. All told, developing countries lost roughly $480 billion per year in potential GDP. As he says, 'It would be difficult to overestimate the scale of human suffering that these numbers represent.' The references for all these statistics are in Hickel's paper. Because of compound interest the borrowing country generally finds that it has to pay back several or many times more than it borrowed and finds itself, if nothing is done, with a debt that continues to grow no matter how much it pays off.

Not trickle down but upward flow. The German architect-ecologist turned economist Margrit Kennedy (1939-2013) turned the trickle-down theory on its head. She pointed out that *most* people in the economic system that now prevails are in debt, for even those few who think they are not in debt must buy goods from people who are—and the debts of the producers must be passed on to the consumers or the producers go bust.

Now the final twist. In any one western-style society with a western-style economy, *most* people (probably around 80%) are net borrowers: paying other people's debts vicariously even if they apparently have none of their own. A few, however—about 10% including the bankers and other financiers—will be net lenders. The remaining 10% are neutral: receiving as much in interest from loans as they spend. The net borrowers are of course net spenders; and the net lenders are net receivers. Thus, said Margrit Kennedy, in absolute contrast to what Mrs Thatcher and other neoliberal zealots have been keen to tell us, ***there is a constant, net flow of money not from the rich to the poor but from the poor to the rich***—and it's not so much a trickle as an upward surge.

This mechanism alone seems enough to account for the enormous discrepancies in wealth both within nations and between nations. But of course there are other mechanisms too, pulling the same way—and above all the mindset which says that this is somehow OK.

Don't work. Just play the system. But what strikes me as the biggest flaw in finance capitalism is that people who are good at manipulating money can and do make vast sums *simply* by playing the game of money—and it is money that is merely deemed to exist. Street-wise graduates straight from business school can and do become immensely rich without ever leaving their swivel chairs or their computer screens, except to go skiing. But although the wealth that they are deemed to possess in truth is virtual—the fruits of abstract victory in an abstract game—it can then be translated into real goods that other people have laboured hard to create. Indeed—such are the present laws (chapter 12)—the victors in the money game are free to buy and hence to own whole slices of the natural world. So it is that people of no special talent yet versed in the tricks of the trade and with no concern for the state of the world may finish up owning vast estates on which to build pony paddocks and helicopter pads and imitation Palladian mansions or, more commonly, to buy all the most desirable properties in the most picturesque locations at prices vastly greater than any local who merely works for a living could ever hope to afford, just for weekends. In the Middle Ages the ancestors of today's aristocrats grew comparably rich by finding favour with the monarch. The rules of the game have become more complex but morally and socially we don't seem to have moved on at all. The dream of a convivial world in a flourishing biosphere seems to fade ever further into the distance.

Physics envy

Yet, despite the apparently obvious shortcomings of the present economy, the idea has grown up since the 18th century that economics should be seen as a *bona fide* science—and indeed that it's a science already. Proof of this is provided by the standard textbooks of the 19th century and beyond which informed the generation of economists who are now in positions of power, and are now being passed on to the next generation. As Kate Raworth relates, those textbooks have all the apparent gravitas of learned papers in journals of physics, festooned as they are with graphs and equations. But papers in physics relate to the tangible, material world. The equations of economics are based on assumptions—not least the Enlightenment assumption that it is 'rational' to want to be rich and that human beings ought to want to behave rationally; assumptions that are at least highly dubious. In truth the economist's claim to the status of physics is specious. As the Cambridge economist Joan Robinson (1903-1983) world-wearily observed:

> *All along [economics] has been striving to escape from sentiment and to win for itself the status of a science ... [but] ... lacking the experimental method, economists are not strictly enough compelled to reduce metaphysical concepts to falsifiable terms and cannot compel each other to agree as to what has been falsified. So economics limps along with one foot in untested hypotheses and the other in untestable slogans.*

She added:

> *I never learned mathematics, so I had to think.*

[Both the Robinson quotes are from Linda Yueh's *The Great Economists* (Penguin Books, 2019)]

The quest to create economic theories that are as solid as Einstein's relativity is known as 'physics envy.' Doubtless it is well-meaning but it is also misguided. Winston Churchill said that 'Scientists should be on tap but not on top.' Economists in practice *are* on top—politicians rely absolutely on their economic advisers—although they are nothing like as reliable as scientists. A double whammy.

Marx, incidentally, suffered from physics envy at least as much as the capitalists did and do. Indeed, as a one-time admirer of Wilhelm Hegel (1770-1831) Marx grew up with the idea that all of history unfolded in ways that are lawful and are therefore comprehensible and predictable, and hence that history itself can be treated as a science. Hence his idea that capitalism is *bound* to collapse under the weight of its own 'contradictions' and is bound then to be succeeded by worker-driven communism. Yet there is no 'bound to' about it. There may or may not be patterns in history but there are no intrinsic laws.

Clearly, an economy that really can help us to create convivial societies in a flourishing biosphere must be qualitatively different from anything the world has seen before—or different at least from anything that has ever been enacted on a large scale. What we need in fact may reasonably be called ***Green Economic Democracy***. A lot of people have already thought long and hard about this. The following is my own version of it.

Green Economic Democracy

Four basic premises

Since economics cannot truly be a science it must instead be rooted in premises of a moral and commonsensical kind, including:

No one should have less than is needed to live with dignity and to achieve fulfilment.

No one should have so much that their wealth interferes with others.

It is a prime tenet of all moral thinking that everyone should as far as possible avoid harming other people—or other creatures or damaging the fabric of the Earth. Rich people can compromise the lives of others in many different ways—not least by taking more than their fair share of what's available in a finite space, or indeed in a finite planet. Pope Gregory I, aka St Gregory the Great (560-604), made the point 1400 years ago:

> *Those who make private property of the gift of God pretend in vain to be innocent, for in thus retaining the subsistence of the poor they are the murderers of those who die every day for the want of it.*
>
> [Quoted by A.S. Attack in *John Clare: Voice of Freedom*, Shepheard-Walwyn, 2010. p. 84]

It isn't just absolute wealth that matters. Equality, or at least a sense of justice, matter at least as much.

As discussed in the last chapter *no one* is truly content in a markedly non-egalitarian society. The inequalities in modern societies would be seriously compromising even if everyone had enough (which of course is far from the case).

We must take care of the biosphere. More: we must feel that we are part of it.

As discussed in chapters 4 and 14 and indeed throughout this book. The sense of oneness is a *sine qua non* and the economy must reflect this.

The six key ingredients

Green Economic Democracy, GED is intended to translate these four grand premises into action; or, rather, to create a framework in which these desiderata become possible. At least as I see things GED has six essential ingredients:

Social enterprise

The tripartite mixed economy

Positive investment

Universal Basic Income

To achieve the vital but much neglected quality of greenness—with minimum damage to the biosphere, and enhancing biodiversity and resilience wherever possible—the economy must be:

Minimalist *and*

Circular

To take these key components one by one:

Social enterprise merely means that all businesses, of whatever kind, should strive to bring net benefit to society and more broadly to humanity in general, and/or to the biosphere. Such enterprises should make enough money to stay afloat—'wash their face' as the expression has it—but maximization of wealth is not their *raison d'être*. Thom Hartmann records in *Unequal Protection* (2nd edition 2004. BK, San Francisco) that in the early days of the United States, corporates were required to show that they brought social benefit, or else they were not allowed to operate at all. In *Prosperity* (Oxford University Press, 2018) Colin Mayer argues that corporates should always state their intended *purpose*, up front, in their statutes; and the purpose ought to be to bring net benefit to society as a whole.

Corporates right now have earned themselves a very bad name because they have in recent years used their enormous wealth and influence to override democratically elected governments, often to the very obvious detriment of societies and of the natural world. Yet corporates can, or could, bring enormous benefits. The problem, says Mayer, is not that they are big and powerful—for if they were bringing net benefit to humanity and to the biosphere, then we might argue that they should be as big and powerful as possible. It is that they have defined their purpose far too narrowly. It is assumed, and indeed has become the dogma, that the purpose of a corporate must be to maximize profit for the shareholders. Accordingly, the corporate managers see themselves as the shareholders' employees.

But the shareholders are only one of the groups affected by the corporate. The employees are important too—though that may simply be abandoned if the managers, dedicated to the shareholders, decide to merge, or sell up, just to make more money in the short term. The customers matter too; and it simply is not true, as Adam Smith supposed, that the invisible hand will smooth out all the glitches. In practice in many small towns the supermarket is the only practical option and the supermarket need not strive to do the best possible job if it has no competitors. Society as a whole obviously matters too—and people at large are hugely affected by the activities of corporates, often adversely. The natural world too should be uppermost in everyone's thoughts but in practice, as the profit-orientated juggernauts roll on, the biosphere is trashed. Enterprises that are designed truly with the society's and the world's best interests at heart are *de facto* social enterprises, even if they take the form of corporates.

The tripartite mixed economy. I first got this idea from Martin Large's book, *Common Wealth* (Hawthorn Press, Stroud, 2009). It is an extension of the well-established idea of the ***mixed economy*** which is the basic economic mechanism of social democracy—and was the norm in Britain and the west in general before Thatcher and Reagan swept all before them with neoliberalism and (almost) the whole world lurched to the Right. The traditional mixed economy combines private ownership and control, with public ownership and control—where 'public' in practice means control by governments, whether national or local or anything in between. Martin Large and others, however, have added a third component to the mixed economy—which could and perhaps should become the most important of all: ***community ownership***, where communities are defined either by geography (the village; the neighbourhood) or by common interest (the Honourable Company of Fishmongers; Britain's county Wildlife Trusts; Tranmere Rovers Supporters' Club; Friends of the Redsox; and so on).

Communities can be big enough to have real economic clout (some supporters' clubs have bought their own football club) but also small enough to be democratic, in the sense that everyone's voice can be heard; and members of communities, unlike members of nations that are run by faraway oligarchs, are likely to take a real interest. Particularly promising in the quest to make a better world is the widespread movement at least in the western world to take control of farms by Community Supported Agriculture, CSA, and community buy-outs of land, as by *Terre de Liens* in France, and the Ecological Land Cooperative in Britain. If all British farmland was community-owned and placed in trust we could ensure that it was farmed well by farmers who really care what they are doing, and this would go a long way to stabilize food prices. More of this in the next chapter. This 'people's takeover' should cost surprisingly little: around £8000 a head at present prices, although in practice this probably comes down to around £5000 per head since we don't really need to buy every last hectare, and some land is already in trust and some that is in private hands is already very well managed. £5000 isn't much if paid back over a lifetime. That's roughly half the price of a year's tuition fees at an English university, or a few weeks at Eton, or a five-year-old Skoda.

Community ownership is not a panacea of course—there are no panaceas. Community initiatives do not work well in practice unless there are charismatic, honest, dedicated individuals to keep them on track and to bring everyone on board—and such individuals are not always forthcoming. So community enterprises are all too liable to fade away and sometimes, like national governments, they may be taken over by self-seeking mountebanks. At least in theory, though, ***the community should emerge as the natural unit of democracy and community ownership should be at the heart of the economy.***

All 20th century UK governments of all parties, before Thatcher, favoured the mixed economy; and those who favour a mixed economy can properly be called ***social democrats***. The advantages of the mixed economy are obvious. Sometimes private enterprise really can deliver, and sometimes public institutions can be best—like the NHS; and community ownership can combine the qualities of both. Thus, one of the greatest spokesmen for the Labour Party in pre- and post-war Britain was the Welshman Aneurin ('Nye') Bevan (1897-1960). Like Keir Hardie he was raised in a mining community (Hardie in East Scotland, Bevan in South Wales) and had been a miner. He is commonly caricatured by Right-wing commentators as a loonie-leftie but in his personal manifesto of 1952, *In Place of Fear,* he wrote:

> *A mixed economy is what most people of the West prefer. The victory of Socialism need not be universal to be decisive ... It is neither*

prudent, nor does it accord with our conception of the future, that all forms of private property should live under perpetual threat. In almost all types of human society different forms of property have lived side by side...

As a good socialist he did of course add

But it is a requisite of social stability that one type of property ownership should dominate. In the society of the future it should be public property.

Still, though, as MP for Ebbw Vale, Bevan was a champion of small businesses and more importantly of small businesspeople, in practice defending private property. All the Tory Prime Ministers from the end of WWII until the neoliberal government of Margaret Thatcher took over in 1979 were social democrats too, albeit leaning towards private rather than public ownership. Indeed the conceptual gap between Labour stalwart Nye Bevan and the Tory Prime Ministers Harold Macmillan and Edward Heath was far smaller than the ideological gulf between Macmillan and Thatcher—or between the socialist Bevan and the socialist Mao Zedong.

Positive investment is a refinement of ethical investment. Ethical investment in practice tends to mean not investing in things that the investor feels are undesirable—like the arms trade, or CAFOs. Positive investment means investing only in things that the investor feels are good and worthwhile—like small mixed farms and local markets. Like all investors, ethical investors must follow the standard guidelines; that no one should invest more than they can afford to lose; that investors should *really* understand what they are investing in; and that any enterprise that offers more than the average return should be treated with extreme caution. In general, too, given that most truly good enterprises (like, say, microdairies) have a very difficult time in the present economic climate and can be slow to get going and often fail, returns on ethical investments are generally low, and in practice many ethical investors can expect merely to get their money back. But many people are content with this. They like to know that the money they or their parents spent their lives earning is doing good things, and not just stoking the fires of some offshore corporate.

Universal Basic Income or UBI, aka 'Citizen's Income,' means that every adult in a given society is given enough money at least to live modestly, but with dignity, whether they work or not, irrespective of age or gender or ability. All kinds of objections have been raised—that too many people would simply stop working all together; that they would spend the money frivolously; that UBI is not affordable; and so on. Yet as John Lanchester describes in *London Review of Books* (July 18, 2019 p. 5), wherever versions of UBI have been tried—in places as diverse as Manitoba, Iran, Finland, Kenya, Liberia, Honduras, Indonesia, and in Stockton in California and among the homeless in the City of London—these fears have proved unfounded. UBI seems to work at all levels: more just; more humane; and—counterintuitive though it may seem—UBI on the whole seems good for the economy. It is not more costly than the benefits that any humane society must pay to the disadvantaged. To be sure, if the citizen's income was indeed universal then rich people would receive it too—but they could pay it back in taxes.

An obvious yet unexpected bonus is that people in general perform better in all tasks—including IQ tests—when they are not stressed; and nothing is more stressful than the fear of destitution. Thus in North Carolina, researchers at Duke University found that Cherokee children did better at school when their parents were receiving income from the casino that the Cherokees had set up in the Snowy Mountains for the benefit of their community.

UBI is an old idea. A character in Thomas More's *Utopia* of 1526 argued that it was bad simply to hang thieves, as was the custom:

> *Instead of inflicting these horrible punishments, it would be far more to the point to provide everyone with some means of livelihood, so that nobody is under the frightful necessity of becoming a thief and then a corpse.*

UBI at least in some forms evidently appeals to the Right as well as to the Left. Thus the grandfather of neoliberalism, Friedrich Hayek, argued for:

> *a certain minimum wage income for everyone ... a floor below which nobody need fall even when he is unable to provide for himself*

—and Richard Nixon, Republican US President from 1969-74, proposed a 'Family Assistance Plan':

> *Let us place a floor under the income of every family with children in America ... and without those demeaning, soul-stifling affronts to human dignity that so blight the lives of welfare children today.*

As noted above, Milton Friedman said something very similar. Indeed we might compare Friedman to Dr Frankenstein. They were not monsters themselves but they finished up creating monsters; and neoliberalism is far more scary than the nightmare of Mary Shelley.

In short, after several centuries of shilly-shallying, it surely is clear that UBI's time has come. Governments hold back from it, it seems, primarily because, as is so often and so regrettably the case, those in power mistrust and in effect despise the people whose lives they largely control. Our rulers evidently believe that if we were 'given something for nothing' then we would all go to pot. But such evidence as there is shows that we are not like that. John Lanchester tells us that in its efforts to lift the UK out of its post-2008 recession successive governments have injected £425 billion into the economy, *all* of it going to rich institutions and people, yet to 'uncertain effect.' For the same money we could have paid everyone £50 a week for two years—which, one feels, would have boosted the economy far more.

Finally, many millions of people in countries like Britain already receive what in effect is UBI in the form of a pension. Some pensioners just wile away the time, some feeling that they have earned the rest and others unable to work, but many others say they are working harder than ever, albeit unpaid, often as carers or for charities—in other words as very valuable members of society. Many say they have never felt more contented. All public services—and enlightened agriculture!—could do with (many) more people on board. Why should people have to wait until they are old before they can start doing truly worthwhile things that they really want to do?

The minimalist economy requires us to reverse the prevailing economic and political mindset, focused on 'growth.' Instead of striving to maximize output, and to maximize consumption commensurately, and to maximize wealth so that we can all—or some of us at least—afford to buy more and more of the goods that modern technologies can produce we should ask, instead: ***what is the minimum that we need to produce, and consume, and earn, in order to create the kind of world that can remain in good heart for aeons to come?*** In similar vein, various economists have explored the possibilities of the 'no-growth economy'—but this to me sounds negative: the brakes applied to the runaway train. Minimalism is a positive desire to live well on as little material goods as possible. Luxuries are necessary but should be owned by everyone for the general good, like cathedrals and places of learning and dance halls and town squares (with cafes and shade trees as in Italy and France).

I don't live particularly luxuriously by some people's standards (although, like most westerners, well beyond the dreams of most people in the world) but I reckon that with an appropriate economy I could easily live comfortably on less than half of what my wife and I get through now. The idea that all of us—or any of us—should aspire to live like Californians with private swimming pools and spare SUVs for weekends, is ludicrous. Yet that does seem to be the shared dream of humanity right now—or at least of the people who have most influence over our lives. It would not be beyond the wit of humankind to devise an equitable and agreeable minimalist economy. I am told that the minimalist economy would be a hard sell but many, I am sure, would consider 'genteel poverty' to be most attractive—if it was a realistic option. In countries like Britain and the US right now it costs a lot of money to live a simple life of a half-way agreeable kind. Most of what most people earn, after all, is siphoned off by the very rich.

The circular economy requires us to devise methods of manufacture, and farming, and indeed all human activities, that do not simply turn raw materials into waste that has no further use, or indeed is toxic. Recycling is part of what's needed, but not the whole. The bigger point is to manufacture or to build whatever we need—houses, motorcars, washing machines, mobile phones—in ways that enable us to dismantle them when they are past their best and *re-use* the bits that have a long lifetime (as many bits do). Ideally, too, ad hoc rental of the things we need—cars for instance—would start to take over from ownership. The manufacturers would remain the owners—and, perhaps ideally, the factory, the 'means of production,' would be owned not specifically by the workers as Marx envisaged but by the community. The manufacturers and/or communities that own the cars or whatever it is would then have a vested interest in ensuring that they last as long as possible. As things are, it pays the manufacturer to build in obsolescence, so that their customers must buy again. The Monmouthshire (Wales) based company Riversimple, pioneers of hydrogen electric cars, has devised a new economic structure to ensure that it is in everyone's interests to create vehicles that last as long as possible. Ellen MacArthur tells us that while she was breaking the world record for single-handedly circumnavigating the world in a trimaran in 2005, it struck her very forcibly that she had to survive on whatever was on board—and that what was true for her and her precarious boat is true too for humanity and planet Earth. So on her return to England she established the Ellen MacArthur Foundation, based in the Isle of Wight, dedicated to the establishment, development, and promulgation of the circular economy.

How we get from where we are to where we need to be I will discuss in the concluding chapter. As always we need ***Renaissance***: building the kind of world we would like to see—beginning with small enterprises that provide life-rafts for people who would like to jump from the present, ill-fated economic ship and need somewhere to jump to. The task then will be to join the rafts in an ever-expanding network and so create a truly alternative world. Various economists are working on alternatives as outlined in the above and in the bibliography. We surely could do what needs to be done and some people around the world are already showing the way—not alas with the help of the powers-that-be but, as so often seems to be the case, despite the powers-that-be.

11

THE LAW OF THE LAND

Like Henry Longfellow's fictional little girl (the one with the curls), when the law is good it is very very good but when it is bad it is horrid.

The job of law and lawyers is to deliver justice—and justice, I suggest, is applied morality. The task of jurisprudence—the philosophy of law—is to translate moral principle into rules, i.e. laws, expressed in unambiguous prose—which, for the most part, it surely does very well. It's the task of lawyers to ensure that those rules are applied in everyday life—and I have sometimes seen good lawyers at work close-hand and been mightily impressed by their acumen and probity. Everyone who wants to create a better world sooner or later, and usually sooner, needs lawyers on their side.

Yet the law is not always just. Some laws, including a great deal of commercial and corporate law, clearly favour the 'rights' of corporates above those of small traders, or indeed of society at large, and enable corporates bent only on profit to override democratically elected governments—and that surely is not just or even half-way sensible. Some lawyers seem very content and indeed keen to work for whoever has the most money and power, and use their wits and their very expensive education to defend the indefensible—for example to sue small traders for no reason at all except to put them out of business, or to circumvent laws designed to protect the natural world. They defend such legalized nastiness with specious rhetoric as in 'Everyone is entitled to justice!'—including those, it seems, who are at pains to see justice overridden. Sometimes, too, of course, the law ruins people's lives even when the intent is good, just because it tends to be so slow: 'Justice delayed is justice denied.' Unscrupulous litigants add to the delays simply to wear down the opposition—helped by unscrupulous lawyers. Often, though, the wheels of law grind slowly simply because the details can be so intricate and the necessary expertise is in such short supply. Again, though, the necessary expertise is often so expensive that only the rich can afford it. But then—as with health care or education—to achieve perfection in matters of justice (if perfection were indeed possible) would cost the entire GDP, and then some. In the end, with the law as in all things, we just have to do the best we can. In the end, it's the intent that matters most: do we really care about justice, or do we just want to win the day?

For ***what really counts in law—as with government and the economy; as indeed with all aspects of life—is the underlying morality.*** As spelled out in the next chapter, morality is not just a relative thing, dependent on custom or the whims of whoever is in power. There is such a thing as universal morality—a key component of the Perennial Wisdom—and the universal morality is rooted in particular in the concepts of compassion, humility, and a reverence for the natural world. But the attitude that so often prevails in life, and particularly in modern life, is a maximally competitive, metadarwinian, pseudo-Nietzschean, supremely arrogant, ultra-materialist urge to possess and to dominate—which, although it is so obviously destructive, is said to be 'rational.' The technologies and economic mechanisms to which such an attitude gives rise prevail for the very obvious reason that they are expressly designed to prevail. Such a mindset, and the laws that protect and foster such a mindset, really is the root of all evil.

On the other hand, if people really do care about justice—rooted in compassion which in turn is rooted in a sense of transcendence (chapters 12 and 14)—then the law almost becomes superfluous. After all, the main reason most of us don't commit murder is not that there is a law against it, but because, for most of us, the very idea of murder is too horrible to contemplate. The point in the end is not to make bad things unlawful—murder, cruelty to animals, setting fire to rainforests—but to make them unthinkable. Truly to achieve the kind of world that can survive long term, which is what the better angels of our nature would surely prefer, we need to restore the sense of the sacred and the sense of taboo that goes with it. The law—or at least, good law—should merely be a pointer to bigger things; a reminder.

Clearly, jurisprudence and the workings of the law must be discussed at length and in detail if we seriously want to create convivial societies and to keep the natural world in good heart. But to keep this book to finite proportions, and because I don't know enough to do otherwise, I will confine the present discussion to just one topic—albeit the one that is supremely important: the laws of the land.

The land

Winston Churchill (1874-1965) summarized the matter in a campaign speech in 1906:

> *Land, which is a necessity of all human existence, which is the original source of all wealth, which is strictly limited in extent, which is fixed in geographical position—land, I say, differs from all other forms of property in those primary and fundamental conditions.*
>
> Quoted by Andro Linklater (1944-2013) in his last, excellent book, *Owning the Earth* (Bloomsbury, London, 2014. p.12).

To our ancestors, and indeed to a great many people today, land and wild nature were commonly seen as a gift—or a *loan*—from God or the gods, to be treated with extreme reverence. If and when it was deemed necessary to cultivate and so to disturb the land, or to kill an animal, this was done at least in some traditional societies only after asking the gods' permission. The Maoris are said to have held a thanksgiving ceremony whenever they cut down a tree—although, as a Maori high-court judge once commented world-wearily when I put that point to him, 'They must have held an awful lot of ceremonies!' Commonly, as with many other animals, people who occupied any one piece of land for any length of time and depend or depended on it, developed a sense of territory: that they had more right to it than anyone else. But, traditionally, nobody ever supposed that they actually *owned* the land they hunted on, or grew crops on, and certainly not in the sense that they owned their clothes or their cooking pots. Such an idea was—well: unthinkable.

In feudal systems, which prevailed in much or most of Europe until deep into the 19th century and still has a huge influence, all land was deemed to belong to the monarchy—but in societies that were truly feudal the monarch was seen to rule on behalf of God, and remained beholden to God. Only seriously twisted monarchs thought of themselves as the *supreme* rulers. Only madmen, in the spirit of the 1st century Roman emperor Caligula, supposed that they were gods themselves. Truly feudal monarchs also felt, in chivalric vein, the sense of *noblesse oblige*; that with power and privilege goes responsibility. It was the monarch's duty as God's viceroy to make sure that it was properly treated and disposed of. To be sure, feudal monarchs granted rights of use to favoured lords and those lords were and are the ancestors of today's 'old' families who are still among Britain's and Europe's biggest landowners. Yet the original feudal lords were not themselves seen as literal land*owners*. They held the land in trust, under the monarch, who held it in trust under God. They certainly did not have the right, as their modern descendants have now acquired, to treat the land as a *commodity,* to be bought and sold for their personal profit. There was no *market* for land. No speculators. The very idea would have seemed somewhat blasphemous (or indeed unthinkable).

Land that was not deemed to be in the domain of some lord was held in common—but this did not mean that it was unprotected or ungoverned. Far from it. A very great deal of English mediaeval law, including much of the Magna Carta of 1215, related to common land: what people of different rank were allowed to do on it, and what they were not. (Although I have yet to put it to the test I believe that I, as a very low-ranked commoner in my corner of Oxford, am entitled to keep geese on our local common. But not sheep.) Common land was not actually *owned* by anyone in a literal sense but absolutely not was it left to hazard. In 1968 the American ecologist Garrett Hardin argued in *Tragedy of the Commons* that in this crowded world land left ungoverned would very probably be trashed. This indeed can happen—but we don't need actually to *own* land in order to feel a duty to protect it. The same indeed applies to everything. I don't *own* other people's children, or even my own children in the sense that I own my woolly jumpers, but I feel a duty of care nonetheless. The idea that we need to own things in order to care about them or to act on their behalf is a deeply pernicious nonsense, but one that again sits comfortably with the prevailing, neoliberal idea that human beings are motivated only by self-interest.

But in England, says Linklater, the feudal mindset and the laws to which it gave rise began seriously to change in the 15th century with the rise of the merchant classes, precursors of modern capitalists. They did aspire literally to own land—and to treat is as a commodity. Henry VII no less, the first Tudor king, still feudal in mindset, tried to resist the trend, but even he, tough cookie though he was, could not prevail against the rising tide of commerce. In the late 16th century, Henry's granddaughter, Elizabeth I, seemed positively to embrace the idea of literal land ownership as she laid the foundations of England's (later Britain's) mighty Empire; and so it was that in 1578 she gave her support to a series of expeditions to be led by the soldier-adventurer Sir Humphrey Gilbert (1539-1583), half-brother of Sir Walter Raleigh, to explore the commercial possibilities of North America. She gave him permission to claim:

> *all the soyle of all such lands, countries, and territories to be discovered ... with full power to dispose thereof in fee simple or otherwise, according to the order of the laws of England*

—where 'fee simple' in effect means freehold with absolute rights of use.

So Gilbert, with a small fleet, set sail for Newfoundland—and there, in St John's harbour, he found some 40 fishing vessels already at work. We were all told at school that Christopher Columbus sailed the ocean blue and 'discovered' America in 1492—but, says Linklater, Basque fishermen were using the harbour long before that; and before them, it had 'belonged' to the Mi'kmaq people. Neither the Basque fishermen nor the native Americans thought they literally 'owned' the harbour. It was simply where they made their living. But Gilbert claimed it for his own, or at least on behalf of Queen Elizabeth, and began to charge the incumbents rent to do what they had long been doing for free. Linklater does not tell us why the residents did not throw him back in the sea. Gilbert was accompanied on at least one of his trips by the famous John Dee (1527-1608), the all-seeing Elizabethan magus—probably the role model for Shakespeare's Prospero in *The Tempest.* The stereotype has it that intellectual, spiritually-inclined dreamers like Dee should be other-worldly but that did not stop him asking his friend Gilbert for 5000 acres of North America, as 'twere for services rendered.

The idea that human beings could literally own land in the same sense that they owned their chattels and their movables lay behind the Enclosures. In feudal times England's countryside, as in most of mainland Europe, was 'open': not divided into discrete fields by fences and hedges. But increasingly after the 15th century more and more individuals—rich and influential individuals, that is—were given the right to enclose discrete areas, meaning to put fences around it, and to claim the land within *literally* as their own. The whole process was consolidated by a series of Acts of Parliament. Now it is taken for granted at least in Britain that land is, and should be, enclosed and owned. Common land in truth is most uncommon (and to judge from our own experience in North Oxfordshire, is constantly under siege from 'developers'). The myth has got around that unless somebody has paid money for land and has a direct financial stake in it, it will fall foul of 'the tragedy of the commons' and be neglected—and yet as our mediaeval ancestors demonstrated, the law can just as soon protect the public good, and indeed the biosphere, if called upon to do so. The law isn't *just* about private property.

Agriculturally, of course, it wasn't a bad idea to start enclosing land. Livestock in particular needs to be managed and although animals can be and are managed effectively even in open country, by shepherds and cowherds and swineherds and goose-girls, fences and hedges certainly help. The strife between Cain 'the tiller of the ground' and Abel the 'keeper of sheep' (Genesis 4:1-18) might surely have been soothed somewhat if Abel had kept his animals in fields (although that is difficult in semi-desert country where pasture is so diffuse). It is far easier, too, to improve the cultivation and the long-term improvement of crops in protected areas where the farmer has long-term tenure.

Yet even though it was often a good idea to enclose at least some of England's land, it isn't obvious that this should have required a change of ownership. After enclosure, land that was previously open and was often held in common was deemed to belong to whoever had been given it, or bought it, even though it was not and is not clear who had the right to give it away or to sell it in the first place. Fields that had been enclosed might still have been owned in common, or at least by the local community, just as it had been before there were fences, if the law had been framed that way. So whether or not enclosure was justified for agricultural reasons it was in practice a giant land-grab—theft indeed—by the rich, from people at large; ratified by a parliament that was mostly composed of people who benefited from it. Parliament had no real *authority* to enclose land and, in effect, to put it on the market. They just had the power to do so; and once it was done they declared the status quo to be the natural way of things. Thus the rich became richer at the expense of the poor—the same general effect that Margrit Kennedy described, as outlined in chapter 10. The root cause is always the same: that the rules are made by powerful people—the minority who benefit most from them.

Parliament continued to pass 'Inclosure' Acts until well into the 19th century—there was a flurry of enclosures between 1760 and 1820. The effects on the countryside and on ways of life were absolute. In particular, peasant farmers with a direct stake in the land became landless labourers, often seasonal labourers. 'Peasant' in England is commonly used as a term of abuse but in truth it describes a class of people who at best have a deep knowledge of nature and how to live with it, and are wonderfully versatile and self-reliant—models indeed of how agrarian humanity ought to be. The Midlands poet John Clare (1793-1864) was himself a peasant in the original sense and normally preferred to write about peasant life and the natural world but the enclosure of his native 'mores' (moors) stirred his political anger into verse—as in these lines from 1821:

Fence now meets fence in owners' little grounds
In little parcels little minds to please ...
Each little tyrant with his little sign
Shows where man claims earth no more divine
But paths to freedom and to childhood dear
A board sticks up to notice 'no road here.'

Clare himself was small in stature but great in spirit. He joined the army briefly to fight Napoleon and was seriously reprimanded at one point for duffing up a fellow soldier who had drawn attention to his littleness.

The injustice of the Enclosures was exacerbated through the 19th century as capitalism got into its stride and land increasingly became a commodity, like everything else. Often it could be bought for very little—especially in foreign lands from people who had no inkling that land could be owned at all—and sold a few years later for a great deal. Sometimes the land increased in value because the legalized owner improved it in the practical, commercial sense (by adding farm buildings, say) but often the price went up without the owner making any effort at all, for example if some third party ran a railway line or built a town nearby. Thus the titular owner grew rich entirely through luck and other people's efforts. How can that be sensible and just? Worse: if the cost of the land itself increases then so does the cost of everything subsequently built on it. Farmland in Britain now averages £10,000 an acre, or £25,000 per hectare. Britain needs a new generation of farmers (chapter 6). It is always hard to start a new business—and farms may be particularly difficult—and huge mortgages, meaning huge debts, make it even harder.

The cost of land for building is off the scale—and this hugely inflates the cost of housing. The house that one of my daughters and her husband now own in South London is now valued at around £700,000—which is *more than 100 times* more than I and my then wife paid for an almost identical house in the late 1960s. House prices were further inflated by Mrs Thatcher's decision around 1980 to sell off publically built and owned ('council') houses without replacing them like for like—so now there is a chronic shortage of housing. The chronic shortage, some commentators suggest, is a deliberate ploy to keep prices up in the same way and for the same reason that De Beers limits the supply of diamonds. Cost is related to scarcity. This strategy benefits house agents and bankers enormously, but socially it is immensely destructive. People in Britain right now are commonly obliged to spend 30-50% of their income on a place to live which is intrinsically ridiculous and in many cases leaves them too little to live on. Yet there is nothing inevitable about this. It is not so in all countries and it was not always so here. Sixty years ago when I was in my teens families commonly spent only about 11% of their income on housing and 30% on food. Now it is the other way round. Many people in Britain, though it's apparently the fifth largest economy in the world, cannot afford to buy enough food, certainly not fresh food. More than a million must now make use of food banks, or so it is estimated. The standard response from government is to urge farmers to produce food even more cheaply by whatever means, and as a result farmers are treated unjustly and thrown out of work, animals are treated harshly, the biosphere is trashed, and—an indirect effect but an important one—science is corrupted, pressed into the service of big business. What's really needed is a far more egalitarian economy so that no one is too poor to live with dignity and no one is damagingly rich, in the way that St Gregory warned us about as quoted earlier. That—and radical land reform.

Again we see—a key theme of this book—that everything is linked to everything else—and ***we cannot put right the wrongs of food and farming just by focusing on farming.*** A great many people even in rich Britain cannot afford enough food and certainly cannot afford fresh food not because food is too dear but because they are obliged to spend so much of their income just on a place to live. The policies that have brought this about are surely misguided to the point of wickedness.

To the rescue?

Yet the American journalist-turned-economist Henry George (1839-1897) presented at least the outline of a solution to all these problems in 1879 in his most famous book, *Poverty and Progress*. In effect he reverted to the ancient idea that land should not be literally *owned* by any individual but should belong to everybody—which in practice, he thought, should mean it should be owned by society as a whole. Land therefore should have no *intrinsic* monetary value. Individuals who wanted to use land for any particular purpose had to rent it from society at large. George was not a communist. Indeed he was a good capitalist and was happy to see land bought and sold. But what the seller sells and the buyer buys is not absolute ownership of the land itself but the right to use the land (for approved purposes), with security of tenure for as long as the contract lasts. Tenants who sell on their right to use the land are indeed entitled to make a profit—but they should be paid *only* for the improvements that they, personally, have made to the land they have occupied. They are *not* paid for any increase in the value of the land itself—because the land itself is not deemed to have any intrinsic monetary value. This policy at the very least would stop the rich becoming super-rich just by sitting on land, and would make the land far more accessible to people at large.

For a time it was widely agreed that George had indeed found the answer to a key problem and he was hugely popular with governments and intellectuals as well as with people at large. *Poverty and Progress* sold two million copies. In Britain, George Bernard Shaw, one of the architects of British socialism, was a huge fan. Two thousand people attended George's funeral in New York in 1897—the biggest turn-out for a funeral, so estimates had it, since Abraham Lincoln's. Despite all this, and even though his core idea seems so simple and just, and is surely workable, George seems largely to have been forgotten. There is a flourishing Henry George Foundation but people at large seem hardly to have heard of him. One problem—although surely not decisive—is that it has proved hard to decide to what extent any increase in the perceived value of any particular holding during any one tenant's lifetime did in fact result from the tenant's own efforts. It seems likely, too (though I have no chapter and verse on this) that the very rich who gained from land speculation would have opposed any attempt to rationalize land use and values—and, of course, the very rich, more than anyone, influence policy. Despite the difficulties, however, George's ideas are surely worth pursuing and developing. The policies of Britain's Land Justice Network seem very much in tune with his philosophy.

As things are, the distribution of land—who owns what—and the uses to which the land is put still cry out for wholesale reform. The first step in land reform (as is always the case in all contexts) is to establish the scope of the problem.

The status quo

At least in England, as Friends of the Earth campaigner Guy Shrubsole discovered as he researched his excellent book *Who Owns England?* (William Collins 2019), it is remarkably and shockingly difficult in an age that ostensibly places such store by freedom of information, to find out who owns what.

Shrubsole did discover though, albeit with considerable difficulty and some inspired guesstimating, that about 30% of England is still owned by the aristocracy (descendants of those who found favour with some ancient monarch) and the gentry (rich people who are accorded quasi-aristocratic status). Corporates—some of them based offshore—own a further 18%. Conservation charities, such as the National Trust and the Woodland Trust, collectively own two per cent of England, and the church another 0.5%. Home-owners in Britain own around five per cent. About 5000 individuals own half of Britain's farmland—and 5000 is less than one 10,000th of the total population. The public sector owns around eight per cent in total—although many councils have been selling off their (our) land of late to make ends meet, starved as they are of central funding. In particular, England's councils have been selling off county farms, set up by Joseph Chamberlain's government to alleviate the agricultural depression of the late 19th century and intended in part to provide a foothold for the new farmers that Britain so desperately needs. County farms dwindled from 426,695 acres in 1977 (about 170,000 hectares) to 215,155 acres in 2017 (around 87,000 hectares). ***This again is the complete opposite of what ought to be happening.***

The maldistribution of land in Britain, with its feudal past, its persistent class divisions, and its long and apparently ever-deepening commitment to an economy that values material wealth and personal possession above all else, is surely worse than in most other countries, but is probably not the worst of all. I don't have the stats for the world as a whole, if such stats indeed exist, and there is no room for them here in any case. But Guy Shrubsole's book on the state of England certainly gives a flavour of the prevailing, gross inequity. The dream of 'convivial society' seems to make little sense in the face of it. With greater equality—*not* simply with greater wealth, for the world is easily rich enough already—we could start to put things right. So long as the world is so unequal strife and degradation are inevitable.

The big question as always, is—

What's to be done?

Who owns the land, according to the law, is not the most important question. What really matters is what it is used for, and the underlying mindset: whether the *intention* is to serve humanity and the biosphere and in general to make the world a better place, or simply to enable the rich to indulge themselves and to grow richer. Even if the land is used well the problem remains—of how to ensure that the good things and the good intentions continue after the enlightened owner quits. History has shown all too often that those who come after the benign founders lose the moral thread and squander what has been achieved. The usual solution is to put the land in trust—though reliable, incorruptible trustees are then required to keep estates on track.

Often, though, alas, big estates owned by private landowners or commercial companies are horribly misused. Grouse moors on the whole are an abomination. The natural diversity of wildlife is sacrificed to clear the way exclusively for just one species of bird, to be shot by rich people and their hangers-on at grand slaughter-fests. Birds of prey (notably, in Britain, Hen Harriers) are laid waste to make way for them. Upland forest with all its diversity of creatures is replaced by moors of heather for the grouse to eat—which also hugely increases the chances of flooding in the surrounding valleys, as experienced of late not least at Hebden Bridge in Yorkshire. When land is not being used for the general good or indeed is used for general harm then public takeover of land is surely justified—and it indeed is necessary; a public duty. So how?

A truly powerful government could simply expropriate all land and put it into the public domain. But this surely would not be desirable, not least because governments that had such power would probably finish up doing far more harm than good, partly because governments are not omniscient and can make huge mistakes, and also because power really does corrupt and powerful governments tend to favour themselves and whoever is in favour or has to be bought off. In practice, too, wholesale land reform imposed from on high just is not going to happen. In short, we surely need to distribute land far more fairly and to use it far more sensibly than is now the norm but we need to find means of doing this which themselves are fair, and as far as possible are enacted democratically, and which do not, as radical programmes of land reform have so often done in the past, throw out valuable babies with the bathwater. Henry VIII's seizure of monastic land in the 1530s to raise money largely for war is a case in point. So too was Robert Mugabe's takeover of farmland in Zimbabwe, which surely was justified in theory but was far too draconian and sometimes corrupt in practice and sacrificed a great deal that was worth hanging on to, including much of the expertise and (often) the good will of some at least of the white farmers who were booted out. So what, in reality, can be done?

Although wholesale land seizure is surely not the best idea (unless push really does come to shove) we do need nonetheless to move towards a Henry George kind of solution: ***Land should be owned by everybody and rented to individuals or companies that are contracted to use it well, which means for the general good.*** To do this properly, as always, we need to dig deep: not least by fostering true respect for the natural world—gaiacentric and with a sense of the numinous—a sense of the sacred indeed—as outlined in chapters 4 and 14. Mindset is the *sine qua non.*

Then, I suggest, we need to emphasise the importance of ***community***, as discussed throughout this book. Land should 'belong' to society as a whole—in the sense that society as a whole is responsible for it—but in practice, the work of society as a whole should be carried out by communities, in the spirit of subsidiarity (chapter 9). It surely would not be desirable for society simply to boot incumbent landowners off their land like Henry VIII or Robert Mugabe but ***compulsory purchase*** is a less-than-perfect but widely accepted alternative to outright seizure. Governments readily resort to it when they want to run a freeway through some village or ancient wood.

I would like albeit whimsically to suggest that ***local communities could afford to buy all of Britain's farmland, even at current, inflated prices***, from the few who are deemed to own most of it. Thus Britain has 23 million hectares of farmland and a population of around 65 million. That's 0.35 hectares per person, or 0.86 acres—which, we might note in passing, is *easily* enough to support a human being, if it is well managed, so these figures alone suggest that Britain should easily be able to support its own population if we chose to do so. More immediately to the point: 0.35 hectares at current prices would cost around £8000. Few of us could put our hands in our pockets and pull out £8000 but £8000 taken out as a mortgage (from a community owned bank) and paid back over the lifetime would scarcely be noticeable (at least if the economy was more egalitarian). £8000 is, after all, roughly the price of a term (twelve weeks) at the school that I went to for free, in more enlightened times.

In truth, £8000 is the *most* we should have to pay—because, again, we should not throw out the babies with the bathwater. Many farmers and landowners already run their farms as well as they can reasonably be run. Some that I know (as written up in my earlier book, *Six Steps Back to the Land*) have invited new farmers on to their land and are helping them to set up enterprises of the agroecological kind that are geared primarily to local markets, in the manner of enlightened agriculture [chapter 6]. Some Trusts, too, like Britain's Royal Society of Birds and the National Trust manage some farmland, generally along agroecological lines. It is very hard to establish systems that truly serve the community *and* are good for the biosphere *and* pay their way, and those that do exist surely should not be disturbed. If it ain't bust, don't fix it. Thus we, society as a whole, would not need to buy *all* existing farmland. A lot could and should be left as it is. So the cost per head for a buy-out that is as cross-the-board as it needs to be comes down to around £5000 per head of population, the price of, say, a six-year-old Skoda Octavia.

Worldwide, community acquisition of land is already well in train—albeit still tiny compared with the might of the gentry and aristocracy in Britain and the still increasing might of the corporates and finance companies worldwide. Community Supported Agriculture—individual initiatives within it are called 'CSAs'—is growing in Britain and is strong in the USA and in Australia. Individual CSAs do not necessarily buy land; but they do ensure that it is used for the good of the community, either by working it themselves or in partnership with local farmers. Britain's Land Justice Network a 'a non-hierarchical network of groups and individuals including academics, housing activists, architects, ramblers, coders, musicians, planners, artists, landworkers and bird watchers' who seek by various means to ensure that land is used for the general good. Britain's Ecological Land Cooperative does buy land and rents it or sells it on to small start-up farmers. *Terre de Liens* in France is a nationwide movement designed expressly to buy farmland and to bring it in to public ownership. It has now acquired more than 5000 hectares—tiny compared to the whole but a fair slice of land nonetheless and a good base.

In short, the position is not good and is getting worse and there isn't much time to put things right. But, as always, there are plenty of good ideas out there and a lot of good people are on the case, worldwide. We are in desperate straits no doubt but there is still hope, provided enough people take a serious interest.

Part V

MINDSET

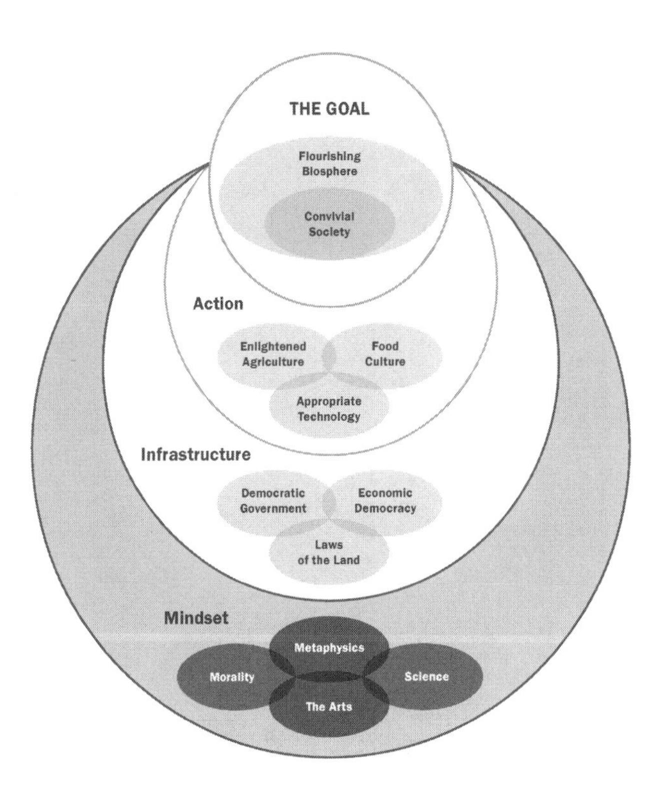

12

GOOD FOR EVERYONE: THE UNIVERSAL MORALITY

TO CREATE A WORLD THAT IS AS GOOD AS IT CAN BE for human beings and for our fellow creatures living in a state of nature we need to be guided by the bedrock principles of ***morality*** on the one hand—what is it *right* to do?—and ***ecology*** on the other—what is it *necessary* and *possible* to do? And—crucially—is it possible and/or worthwhile to devise a moral code that all human beings can subscribe to, and feel at ease with? Can we realistically envisage a universal morality?

Ecology is primarily a matter of science and science on the whole begins with clear premises: that the universe does indeed exist; that it works in an orderly fashion—according indeed to what are called 'laws'; and that our job is to find out what is actually in the universe—what does it consist of?—and how it all works, and what are the laws that keep it on course. This is difficult, but at least we have an agenda. There are also agreed ways of finding out—the so-called 'scientific method': in essence, quantified observation (data); hypothesis; then testing, as far as possible by experiment; all subject to the rigours of mathematical analysis; and then (in theory) pored over by anyone else who cares to take an interest in the following years and centuries. This is not as sure-fire as it may sound—in practice the process is often quite messy and as outlined in chapter 13 it does not and cannot lead us to absolute truth. Omniscience is beyond our reach. But it is at least *robust.*

Morality, studied by the discipline of moral philosophy, is far more slippery. What actually are we trying to achieve? Are we simply asking, in a pragmatic kind of way, what is the least harmful thing to do in any one situation? Or are we digging deeper and asking 'What is the *nature* of goodness?' What does 'good' even mean?

There seem to me to be two main questions:

First*: Is good or bad merely a matter of opinion?* Or is there something out there—some 'objective' entity that we might identify as goodness or indeed as badness (which we might call 'evil')? Was Hamlet right to say (Act II Scene 2):

There is nothing either good or bad but thinking makes it so?

Or is there more to it than that?

Secondly: *How do we—or should we—decide what's good and what's bad?* Can we arrive at sound judgements by a purely 'rational' route—just by 'weighing the facts' and allowing the conclusion to emerge on purely logical grounds, like an exercise in maths? Or is morality in the end a matter of feelings? Or is it (which seems sensible)—some combination of the two?

Philosophers, clerics and people at large have been pondering these issues for thousands of years—probably for many tens of thousands although we cannot know what our distant ancestors thought and felt. One thing is certain—or should be: because we are intelligent, because we have free will (or at least the illusion of free will), because we are social animals who *need* each other, and because as a species we are highly influential members of the biosphere, *none* of us can escape some measure of moral responsibility. To be sure, those who subscribe to the philosophy and faith of neoliberalism are content to leave morality to the market. What people will buy is deemed to be good since it seems to express general desire and aspiration, and what people will not buy is *ipso facto* undesirable and therefore bad. Thus, the neolibs like to claim, they remain morally neutral. Nothing to do with me, guv. That's just the way life is. But this way of thinking makes sense only if you believe in neoliberalism and the metadarwinian rhetoric that lies behind it—and as the one-time Anglican turned Catholic Cardinal John Henry Newman (1801-1890) put the matter in a letter to his friend Mrs William Froude in 1848:

We can believe what we choose. We are answerable for what we choose to believe.

In truth, the decision to leave moral decisions to the market is itself a moral decision. There is no ducking out.

How can we pick our way through the labyrinth of moral philosophising? Well, just to keep the discussion tidy, the Oxford-based philosopher and theologian Timothy Bartel suggests that in practice moral philosophers these past few thousand years have pursued three main lines of thought in their search for moral principles. They are:

Utilitarian (consequentialist)

Deontological

Virtue Ethics

So let us look briefly at each.

Utilitarianism

The Utilitarian approach to morality, as its name suggests, is very pragmatic and unimpeachably rationalist—very much a child of the Enlightenment. The essence of it was summarized by the philosopher who is often seen as its principal advocate, Jeremy Bentham (1748-1832). The point of morality, he said, is to achieve

The greatest happiness of the greatest number.

This arithmetical approach—'greatest happiness of the greatest *number*'—is useful up to a point but it has serious drawbacks. As outlined in chapters 9 and 10, governments and others in authority commonly assume that we are made happy by increasing wealth and so are wont to equate morality with *stuff*. Insofar as governments like to think that it is their job to make us happy, they emphasize the need above all to increase wealth—personal affluence and GDP. In similar vein modern ethical committees are wont to equate 'good' with 'cost effective.' Thus, like Trollope's villainous banker Melmotte, they make a *moral* virtue of wealth.

In stark contrast, many of the greatest moralists through all of human history have favoured poverty; not out-and-out deprivation, which prevents people from reaching their potential and achieving fulfilment, but at least avoidance of excess. In a finite world, as St Gregory warned, those who take much more than their fair share in the end deprive others—other people and other creatures. As individuals, as societies, as nations, we need always to acknowledge that 'enough's enough.' Gandhi emphasised simple living. Muhammad lived for most of his life in one room next to the mosque. The way of Muhammad—the *sunnah*—is simple and frugal. St Francis embraced poverty and urged others to do the same. In practice too the means by which wealth is maximized are often highly destructive. Indeed the most lucrative may be the cruellest and most destructive of all, including various forms of mining and hyper-intensive farming.

More broadly, it is indeed reasonable to argue in Benthamite style that the happiness of the majority matters more than the indulgence of a few, and that societies that favour the few over the many, as Britain and the US so obviously do, are morally deficient. But it matters too (does it not?) who the majority are and what it is that makes them happy. After all, if six Hooray Henries beat up one old tramp who nobody knows or cares about, we have six happy roisterers and one poor fellow who is very unhappy indeed. This may be a good bargain arithmetically yet those of us who are not Hooray Henries feel in our bones that it is wrong. The question is: ***What is this bone feeling, and where does it come from?***

In truth, although rationality clearly has its place in moral philosophy, matters of good and bad cannot be decided by rationality alone—as emphasized not least by David Hume (1711-1776), twin pillar of the Scottish Enlightenment alongside Adam Smith and one of the greatest rationalists of all time. In 1739 in *A Treatise of Human Nature* Hume wrote:

> *Morals excite passions, and produce or prevent actions. Reason of itself is utterly impotent in this particular.* ***The rules of morality, therefore, are not conclusions of our reason.***

Attempts to decide matters of right and wrong just by examining the facts always fall short, said Hume:

In every system of morality, which I have hitherto met with, I have always remarked, that the author proceeds for some time in the ordinary ways of reasoning, and establishes the being of a God, or makes observations concerning human affairs; when all of a sudden I am surprised to find, that instead of the usual copulations of propositions, is, *and* is not, *I meet with no proposition that is not connected with an* ought, *or an* ought not. *This change is imperceptible; but is however, of the last consequence. For as this* ought, *or* ought not, *expresses some new relation or affirmation, 'tis necessary that it should be observed and explained; and at the same time that a reason should be given; for what seems altogether inconceivable, how this new relation can be a deduction from others, which are entirely different from it.*

This paragraph is commonly paraphrased to become: 'We cannot derive an *ought* from an *is*.'

In similar vein the Cambridge philosopher G.E. Moore (1873-1958) dismissed the once popular idea that we can base our conception of right and wrong on what happens in nature. He called this ***the naturalistic fallacy***. Infanticide, rape, and cannibalism—all are widespread in nature. Genocide is practiced by some troops of chimpanzees and some ants (who also practice slavery). On the other hand, the Roman Catholics in particular are wont to talk of 'natural law.' Beyond doubt, all of us are wont to condemn behaviour that we perceive to be *un*natural—such as the parental neglect of children. And as argued later, in matters of morality intuition is crucial: and our intuitions derive in large part from our biology. We cannot follow nature mindlessly but neither can we simply ignore what it tells us.

Deontology

To the deontologist morality is a matter of duty and/or obligation. Again this is a strong and probably necessary idea but again it leaves open the question of whether the duty or obligation are themselves good. Thus fighting men and women in war have a duty to kill the enemy and may be required to bomb cities or set fire to villages—but is this really *good*? At its worst, obligation to some higher authority is used as an excuse to defend the vilest of actions—as in the infamous Nuremberg defence: 'I was only obeying orders.' Less dramatically but nonetheless perniciously corporate executives and politicians persuade themselves that it is good, morally, just to do what the company or the party requires of them even when conscience proclaims that the company or the party are behaving badly. This is called loyalty. Loyalty is good insofar as it is the opposite of treachery but not so good if it impels us to support the insupportable. It is not in itself a prime virtue.

At least traditionally, those who subscribed to one or other of the theistic religions (notably to the Abrahamic religions of Judaism, Christianity, and Islam) took it to be their duty to obey God, and many still do think in those terms. But does God always behave well? Some texts in the Old Testament certainly sound strange to modern ears. There's a great deal of smiting going on, which often seems gratuitous. The standard justification—'God moves in a mysterious way'—as neatly encapsulated by William Cowper (1731-1800) never seems entirely convincing (at least to me). Besides, although Christian Protestants urge us to study the Bible for ourselves, most followers of the Abrahamic religions rely in practice on prophets and priests, rabbis, and imams, to interpret the holy texts for them. Yet we are warned to beware of false prophets—and are the interpretations of religious authorities necessarily accurate? The wranglings of theologians these past few thousand years, and the violence that their disputations have often led to, suggest that there is plenty of room for doubt. Deontology, in short, like utilitarianism, has its uses, but doesn't quite meet the case.

Virtue Ethics

Aristotle simply asked 'What makes a good person?'—and the answer, he concluded, is that good people possess good qualities, known as virtues. This you might feel gets us nowhere since we then need to ask—'What are these good qualities?' and 'Why should we consider them to be good?'

Yet in practice, this deceptively simple approach to morality seems to provide the most satisfactory insights.

To answer the obvious questions (what are these virtues, and what makes them good?) we can appeal to the idea outlined at the start of this book: that of ***the Perennial Wisdom.*** For, I suggested, the Perennial Wisdom is taken to consist of all the ideas and attitudes that human beings have come up with and adopted during our long history and pre-history that seem at least to most of us to be true and important. These include ideas about the material universe and also, vitally, include a sense of what is good and what is bad. So one way to explore the concepts of goodness and badness is to ask what people at large through all of history have felt about them; what ideas on the matter really seem convincing and have endured. In other words we should trust humanity's own inner selves, our own intuitions, evolved and honed over many thousands and even millions of years of biological evolution and of culture. As St Augustine (354-439) put the matter:

> *Do not wander far and wide but return into yourself. Deep within man there dwells the truth.*
>
> Quoted by Pope John Paul II in *Faith and Reason (Fides et Ratio—Encyclical Letter)*. Catholic Truth Society, 1998, p.25.

Where, though, do these deep feelings come from? Some would say 'from God.' Others might say that our feelings are evolved like all other aspects of our being in Darwinian fashion and in the end are embedded in our DNA. Yet others might appeal to the hypothetical Universal Intelligence as discussed in the next chapter. Yet others might say that God and the Universal Intelligence are different names for the same thing. I am content for the time being at least to take the Perennial Wisdom—the best insights of all humankind through all of time—as our arbiter of good and bad. To be sure, some people treat the Perennial Wisdom as a *fait accompli,* like a fundamentalist religion, which they would impose in authoritarian fashion on all humanity for all time. I take it in contrast to mean a never-ending and ever-improving collective attempt to define what is true and good. Like religion in general, the search for the Perennial Wisdom should be seen as work forever in progress, a perpetual quest.

In practice, though, very few people acknowledge the idea of the Perennial Wisdom. Different societies have—or seem to have—different moral standards. In practice, those moral standards are largely or sometimes almost entirely set by religion—for even in those societies that no longer think of themselves as 'religious' the mindset has largely been shaped by the religion of their more devout ancestors. I believe that religious insight is vital but it does have drawbacks.

One obvious problem is that the different religions over the years have all gone their own ways and each one seems to have developed its own moral codes. Detractors in the form of atheists have seized on this. So it is for example that Richard Dawkins, perhaps the most high-profile of all modern atheists, has pointed out that whereas Jewish men are required to wear hats in the temple, Christian men must go bare-headed into holy places (unless they are bishops or other officiates). Thus, the detractors are wont to conclude on a note of triumph, 'They can't all be right!' Inevitably say the critics, moral codes in the end are arbitrary—matters of opinion. Hence, many conclude, there can be no universal morality.

But the wearing or non-wearing of hats is a matter of customs and manners, and customs and manners should not be equated with moral *principles*. Customs and manners are important because they symbolize a desire to be part of the society as opposed to being apart from it. Manners are an expression of respect, and respect has moral import. But they are not the core issue. Good mannered people may be rogues and rough-mannered people may be good. The real question is: Is there, or can there ever be, a truly *moral* code that *everyone* who is not a psychopath can subscribe to, whether or not they are 'religious,' and whatever their religion may be?

A universal morality

In reality—and very encouragingly—when we explore all the different religions we find that whatever their different traditions and outward show they all insist on three virtues in particular that have been accepted by most of humankind through most of known history and may indeed be seen as universal moral principles. These are:

Compassion

Humility

An attitude of reverence towards the natural world

You don't have to be 'religious' to feel in your bones that these are the moral principles that really matter. This universal morality may not rest on bedrock but it has robust foundations nonetheless—the shared, evolved attitudes of most of humanity, honed over millions of years of human and pre-human existence in response to pressures and vicissitudes of living, and in particular of social living. Thus:

Compassion

This, many feel, is the greatest moral principle of all. All big ideas come in clusters and compassion encompasses or at least is allied to *justice, kindness, unselfishness* and to what is commonly called *altruism* in the moral and not simply in the biological sense. Truly to be compassionate requires empathy; what Adam Smith called 'human sympathy.' If we are to cooperate fully and reliably in any activity then we need truly to care about other people's wellbeing and feelings or else we are liable to jump ship as soon as something better comes along. Compassion in short is properly seen as a virtue but also—like all virtues, in practice—it has an element of enlightened self-interest since cooperativeness is the best survival tactic of all (chapter 3). Thus cooperativeness, rooted in compassion, should enhance general happiness, and so it should appeal to the utilitarians too.

In Islam, compassion is seen as one of the prime attributes of God. Every chapter of the Qur'an (except one) begins, 'In the Name of God, the Compassionate, the Merciful'—a phrase devout Muslims utter day and night whenever they begin a fresh line of activity.

For the Dalai Lama, too, compassion is the core of all virtue. I was once privileged to hear him lecture at Oxford. From the floor, a world-renowned paediatrician asked him for his advice on a huge moral dilemma. For this paediatrician had worked for some years in South-East Asia, where there is a high incidence of thalassaemia; an inherited form of anaemia. The prognosis for children born with the full-blown disease is miserable in the extreme. Even with repeated transfusions, each one enormously traumatic for the baby and the family, seriously affected babies rarely live beyond about 18 months. But, said the doctor, it is now possible to diagnose the disease *in utero*. And, he asked, if I know that a baby carries the lethal genes, should I abort? Is it *right* to abort?

The Dalai Lama replied that of course it is not right. Abortion is always deeply regrettable. But, he said, in real life it is not always possible to achieve moral perfection. Sometimes we just have to do whatever is least bad. Always, he said, when faced with such a dilemma, ask yourself, 'What is the most *compassionate* thing to do?' It is, I suggest, very hard indeed to improve on that.

In similar vein, in June 2017 at the University of California at San Diego, the Dalai Lama entreated the 'Young people of the 21st century' to

> *... bring on the revolution of compassion! ... Many remarkable individuals have called for different kinds of revolution: technological, educational, ethical, spiritual. All are motivated by the urgent need to create a better world. But for me, the Revolution of Compassion is in the heart, the bedrock, the original source of inspiration for all the others.*
>
> Quoted in *The Dalai Lama. A Call for Revolution* by Sofia Stril-Rever. Rider, Penguin, 2017.

A Christian theologian once pointed out to me that the Christian concept of love is not identical with the Buddhist concept of compassion but they are clearly in the same camp and as St Paul famously observed (Corinthians, 13:1-8):

> *Though I speak with the tongues of men and of angels, and have not love, I am become as sounding brass, or a tinkling cymbal.*

In truth, if we do not have compassion, which I and many others are content to equate with love, then no social measure, no law, no economic or political system can work well. With compassion, many and various kinds of economic or political systems can work to everyone's benefit. Marxist societies can certainly be benign—although those that have been kindly in intent have generally been given short shrift by more aggressive rivals, just as Salvador Allende's Chile was put a stop to by the US. Capitalism can be extremely nasty but it doesn't have to be and indeed, with compassion and good sense, and with suitable modification, it can work very well. As the Nobel Prize winning economist Paul Krugman put the matter in *The New York Times* on January 10, 2011:

> *... welfare-state capitalism—a market economy with its rough edges smoothed by a strong safety net—has produced the most decent societies ever known.*

Even Feudalism can be among the least bad options in a society that lacks the infrastructure to manage democracy, provided the lords really do recognize the principle of *noblesse oblige.* They don't have to behave like Alan Rickman's Sheriff of Nottingham in the 1991 version of *Robin Hood.* Unfortunately, the one political-economic system that seems to me to be beyond redemption is the one that now prevails: the capitalist offshoot known as neoliberalism. It falls horribly short of what is needed precisely because, as outlined in chapter 10, dyed-in-the-wool neoliberals have shaken off what they see as the shackles of morality as a matter of what they would doubtless call principle. In the neoliberal mindset, to misquote *Wall Street*'s Gordon Gekko once again, compassion is for wimps.

What a pity it is that the world is dominated by people who as a matter of policy have abandoned the one outstanding quality—compassion—that is essential for our and the world's wellbeing. What a pity too that we spend so much time and intellectual effort on the niceties of economic theory and the soap opera of politics and so little on the thing that matters most of all, which is the underlying morality and its metaphysical roots.

Humility

Humility is a complex idea with all kinds of connotations. To the Greeks, the gravest sin of all was *hubris*: usurping the power of the Gods; presuming to have more knowledge and power than it is given to mere humans to possess, and presuming to run the world as if we really knew what we were doing and had the right to do whatever we want. Hubris was the principal theme of Greek tragedy. The Greeks were right of course. Much or most of what's gone wrong in the modern world can be traced to hubris—including or especially scientism (chapter 13), rooted in the idea that science really can tell us everything that is worth knowing, and to the uncritical technophilia (chapter 5) to which this gives rise, which gives people in positions of influence the impression that we human beings can manipulate the world and the life within it any way we want, and that we have a right to do so.

Humility is the antithesis of hubris; the antidote to it. Christians—including or especially Martin Luther (1483-1546)—have emphasized that whatever good things may come our way should be seen as a gift, granted to us by the *grace* of God. We, ultimately, are not in control and we should not claim the credit.

This idea too is at the very heart of Islam. The very word, 'Islam' means, literally, 'submission' and in particular, 'submission to the will of God.' The Qur'an (25:63) speaks of:

> *The servants of the Lord of Mercy are those who walk humbly on the earth, and who, when the foolish address them, reply 'Peace.'*

The concept of humility too throws light on the concept of ***rights***. The idea that all human beings should be credited with rights is surely vital. The UN Declaration of Human Rights, framed in 1948, is a key document: truly a milestone in human development. We surely should embrace the idea as the UN does that every human being has a *right* to the basics of life: food, clean water, clothes, clean air, a place to live. It is surely right too to extend the concept of rights to all living creatures,

Yet the concept of 'rights,' essential though it is and morally straightforward though it may seem, in practice has led all too often to a loss of humility: to arrogance and indeed to hubris. Thus the American Declaration of Independence of 1776 tells us that we have been

> *'... endowed by [our] Creator with certain unalienable Rights' including 'Life, Liberty, and the pursuit of Happiness'*

and this apparently unexceptionable sentence contains two deep moral/ metaphysical traps.

First there's the idea that our 'Rights' have been 'endowed' by God. In truth, it is far safer—both morally and socially—to acknowledge that whatever 'rights' we may care to lay claim too, and however precious—'unalienable'—we may take them to be, they are *not* God-given. They are a human invention, devised as a means to instil moral principles into our everyday lives. It is safer by far to acknowledge as Martin Luther did that all the good things that happen in our lives come to us by the *grace* of God; or, as the Muslims say, 'All praise and thanks be to Allah!' To assume that our perceived rights are more than a social or legal device—albeit a good and vital one—is at least borderline hubris.

You may feel that this is just an irritating theological quibble and for most practical purposes that may well be the case. But the idea that our 'rights' are indeed God-given and 'unalienable,' and indeed that we have a 'right' to pursue happiness, has all too often led people to suppose that they have a *right* to do more or less whatever they want to. I always remember a woman at Atlanta airport whose luggage had been lost proclaiming for all the world to hear that 'Ah have a *raht* to ma valise!' Well, actually, no. It is jolly bad luck that your suitcases have been sent to Helsinki or Vladivostok when you yourself are bound for Alabama but it is not a matter of cosmic significance. This is a minor example. But by the same token, billionaires who grow rich at other people's expense (and extreme wealth in the end is always at other people's expense), and nations that subjugate less powerful nations tend similarly to claim that they have a right to their excesses (it is always possible to think up some excuse) and further to imply that their right to conquer or to plunder was granted by God. In the US, ostensibly Christian zeal, extreme wealth, and military might often seem to go together. It is all very hubristic.

Often people add a conditional clause—that there should be no rights without responsibility. This in effect amounts to a *quid pro quo*: that is, I am obliged to respect your space only insofar as you respect mine, and if you don't respect my space then I am perfectly entitled—'within my rights'—to encroach on yours. But although this refinement seems reasonable enough it does not quite match up to reality. After all, people who are mentally impaired, or babies, or indeed animals do not necessarily understand the subtleties of the world and cannot properly be held to be responsible for anything.

To the ruling, 'no rights without responsibility' we should at least add the maxim of Karl Marx:

To each according to their needs. From each according to their ability.

Thus we should respect the rights of elephants or dogs or cows or chickens even though they may not formally recognize our own claim to rights. Animal rights is an important concept.

Still, though, the grand generalization applies: that the rights of human beings are not God-given, or at least we cannot assume that they are. The idea that rights are God-given, as the American Declaration of Independence implies, has led many people to conclude that they have an absolute right to be as rich as they are able to be, to manipulate the landscape as convenient—fell trees, drain marshes, shoot inconvenient predators—or to invade other countries and plunder whatever is going, including the land itself, or indeed to enslave their people. If we embraced the moral concept of humility we surely would shy from such enormities. We might still kill some animals and replace some forest with crops but only when strictly necessary—always choosing the least invasive of the options.

In short the concept of rights must always be underpinned, or contained within, the greater, moral concept of humility. Humility properly conceived is crucial, if we seriously want to live long term in a tolerable state, and to keep our fellow creatures in good heart.

A reverence for Nature

As discussed in chapter 4: if we take seriously the cause of wildlife conservation then we need to feel deep in our bones that the natural world is sacred, and that we are privileged to be alive in it. I reckon that most people would feel this if the feeling was not beaten out of them in the spurious name of rationality. Such is our—human—influence these days that it is not enough simply to lie back and enjoy our surroundings. We are obliged—*noblesse oblige*—to take active steps to protect and conserve our fellow creatures from our own rapacity, and for this we need as much understanding as we can muster, notably through the science of ecology; and we need sound policy to ensure that what needs to be done, and should be done, is possible. But most of all—the *sine qua non*—we need to care. I have met many fine scientists who have no truck with religion and reject (or misconstrue) the notion of spirituality who nonetheless care deeply about the natural world and spend their lives in its service, so I don't want to suggest that it is absolutely vital to go beyond this. But as I will argue at greater length in chapter 14, I do feel that our feeling of duty of care is at least reinforced by a sense of transcendence—the sense that what we can see and touch, wondrous though it is, is only the surface of things; that there is an underlying intelligence at work in the world, or indeed an all-pervasive intelligence, that we should feel answerable to.

In common with many millions of other people I very much like the Eastern concept of the ***dharma***. The basic idea is that the universe is fundamentally harmonious and that it is incumbent upon us to behave in ways that maintain or increase that harmony. This at least is the Buddhist interpretation. I am reliably informed that some Hindus have invoked the idea of the *dharma* to justify the caste system—arguing that caste is the natural harmony of society and is therefore good. We find the same kind of idea in the much-loved Anglican hymn, 'All Things Bright and Beautiful,' by Mrs C.F. Alexander (1818-1895). She presents the sun and the rain and all living creatures as part of 'God's almighty plan'—and so too, apparently, is the social hierarchy of Victorian England:

The rich man in his castle
The poor man at his gate.

Generations of poor men and women, and more especially their children, have sung this with gusto, apparently glorifying in their own subservient status (although Mrs Alexander, by all accounts, was a very kind and philanthropic woman). But all big ideas and the words that describe them are used in many different senses; and the Buddhist version of the *dharma*, as I understand it, seems spot on.

This idea of the *dharma* does not belong to science (it is not in theory disprovable) but it is in line with some ideas that are rooted in science including the idea of universal intelligence, outlined in chapter 14, and the idea that nature is at least as cooperative as it is competitive, discussed in chapters 3 and 4. To be sure, if we argue that *because* the universe is fundamentally harmonious we should *therefore* seek to maintain that harmony then we may seem to be flouting Hume's warning that we should not derive an ought from an is. But then: clever fellow though he was, we need not assume that Hume said everything that needs to be said. In any case, as Hume himself says in slightly different words, morality in the end depends on feelings; and the idea that the universe as a whole is harmonious (despite the surface turbulence) and that we as moral beings should seek to enhance the harmony seems to me very neatly to encapsulate the attitude that's required.

In short, although the concept of morality is indeed slippery, and we can never decide definitively on matters of good and bad, we need not simply conclude that it is all just a matter of opinion, or that might is right, or that it's OK to leave moral decisions to the market. The idea of *virtue* trumps the utilitarian approach to morality, and I suggest (taking my lead from the greatest religious leaders), the chief of all the virtues is compassion. We arrive at this account of morality both by engaging our intellect (rationality) and by listening to our own feelings. I love the idea of 'cultivated intuition,' discussed further in chapter 14. Ideas from the borders of science and metaphysics provide further reinforcement: the ecological idea of mutualism; the evolutionary idea that cooperation—the natural companion of compassion—is nature's principal survival tactic; the idea of one-ness, reinforced by the realisation that all Earthly creatures are related. All these ideas are encompassed in the idea of universal consciousness as outlined in chapters 13 and 14.

None of this amounts to a definitive account of morality but it seems to me to point us in the right directions.

In passing we might ask: do Donald Trump, or Vladimir Putin, or Xi Jinping, or all but a few of the world's most powerful leaders, have any conception at all of what compassion and humility actually *mean*, or have any interest in the natural world except as a playground and a source of wealth ?

No wonder the world is in a mess.

13

SCIENCE

For the world is not to be narrowed till it will go into the understanding but the understanding to be expanded and opened till it can take in the image of the world as it is in fact.

Francis Bacon (1561-1626) in *The Great Instauration* (1620).

SCIENCE HAS VERY ANCIENT ROOTS but it wasn't until the 17th century that it began to emerge in a recognizably modern form—and the term 'scientist' was not coined until the 1830s. Before that, those who studied the natural world were called 'natural philosophers.'

But over the past four hundred years, a twinkling in the long history of humankind, science has become a prime ingredient of the Perennial Wisdom, providing insights into the workings of the natural universe that were and still are beyond all imagining. Along the way, the 'high' technologies that flood from science have the power hugely to improve the individual lives of human beings and can, when appropriately applied, help us to take proper care of the natural world. Truly, modern science is a triumph of humankind—practical, aesthetic and spiritual, as acknowledged in recent years not least by the Dalai Lama and a succession of popes, especially John Paul II and Francis.

But human beings have a wonderful knack for despoliation and science, alas, has been widely misconstrued, misrepresented, and misapplied. To a large extent it has become the handmaiden of big business, high finance, and aggressive governments—ersatz food, ever more probing surveillance, 'more bang to the dollar.' Thus, one of humanity's and the world's greatest assets is now, at the same time, among its greatest threats. Misconstrued and misapplied it threatens to de-humanize humanity—which, surely, is the very opposite of what progress ought to mean.

For my part, I love science—it has been the *leitmotiv* of my life since I first toyed with spiders and centipedes in the parental back yard in the years after World War II—but I hate the thing that it has often become. For all our sakes, science needs to be rescued, re-conceived, re-taught: placed in its proper, metaphysical context. We need to recognize first of all what a succession of philosophers, not the least being Immanuel Kant, have been telling us for centuries: that we can never perceive and grasp things as they really *are*. All our understanding, or what we think is our understanding, is at best an account of reality (although 'reality' is itself a tricky concept). All our understanding in the end is *narrative*, a story that we tell ourselves about the world around us to help us get through life, to improve on total confusion: and what we call 'truth' is a story which, at any one time, we happen to find convincing. We might also suggest (more later) that the stories we tell ourselves are simply regions of apparent solidity and coherence within what an anonymous 14th century mystic called 'the cloud of unknowing.' We can never attain what is demanded of us—impossibly—in courts of law: the truth, the whole truth, and nothing but the truth.

Science too, in the end, is just a narrative like everything else we call knowledge: a very brilliant exercise in storytelling, but storytelling nonetheless. Only the mystic, achieving union with God, can claim to have experienced truth—though perhaps that too is an illusion. The ideas of science don't have to be applied to everyday life, for scholarship, knowledge, insight, should surely be prized in their own right. But insofar as science is applied it should be geared, like everything else, to the twin goals of conviviality and ecological wellbeing; and underpinned, like everything else, by the moral imperatives of compassion and humility.

To put things right we need, as always, to re-think from first principles: to ask what science really is and what it is not; how it differs from other ways of thinking and looking at the world; and how it came into being.

An overview of science: what it is and how it became

Modern science is, well, *modern*—but it has deep and multifarious roots, stretching way back into prehistory. It seems, after all, that our pre-*sapiens* ancestor *Homo erectus* learnt to harness fire more than a million years ago—and fire has been and still is a huge player in human affairs, helping us greatly to extend our understanding of the material universe, and our ability both to transform and to destroy the world we live in. Black Kites in Australia spread bush fires by taking burning twigs from place to place (they feed on the retreating insects) but they do not actually light the fires in the first place and apart from that the use and control of fire seems unique to humans. Metallurgy and metalwork, alchemy and modern chemistry, ceramics, and of course cooking could not happen without it.

In historic times science has drawn on all the resources of human imagination, thought, and crafts from East and West—Greek, Chinese, Indian, Arab; theology, philosophy, astronomy, mathematics, logic, metallurgy, ceramics, architecture, agriculture, folk medicine, alchemy, astrology, magic. The immortal pioneers of the 17th century stood, as Newton said of himself, 'on the shoulders of giants.' Those giants of course included the great thinkers of Greece (Pythagoras, Aristotle, Archimedes, and the rest)—and a variety of philosopher-theologians from the Middle Ages: Jewish, Christian, Muslim. Standard histories of science often gloss over the thousand years from the 5th to the 15th centuries as if they were simply a religious diversion but as outlined below, this is a huge mistake.

Knowledge never proceeds in a straight line—there are endless false trails along the way as ideas become fashionable, then for a time become the orthodoxy, and then, very often, are abandoned. Life and the universe in the end are beyond our ken and we are obliged, always, simply to feel our way. Yet, overall, the *content* of science, the canon, has expanded exponentially these past few centuries, and surely must continue to do so for centuries to come if research is not hijacked by special interests along the way, or curtailed by fiat or by lack of resource. The *philosophy* of science—our understanding of what it is and what it is not—has changed too, significantly, while *attitudes* towards science in any one society and from age to age have ranged from excitement and absolute faith through disillusionment and positive antipathy to what is very like fear. Thus:

A lightning history of science and of the philosophy of science

The following is a personal and very cursory sketch—of what science is and what it is not. I have picked out just a few thinkers from the scores who might have been cited. I am very aware too that my account is far too Eurocentric. In particular it misses out the huge contributions of Arab natural philosophers between the 9th and 16th centuries, in maths, astronomy, cosmology, and biology and in the practical crafts and proto-sciences of metallurgy, ceramics, glassmaking, alchemy, medicine, perfumery. These Muslim thinkers anticipated some of the ideas that we traditionally ascribe to westerners by 1000 years. It is far from obvious the extent to which the 'western' scientists borrowed directly from their Muslim predecessors but Copernicus in particular specifically acknowledged his debt to Arab astronomers of the 12th century and before. Truly the world needs a more complete, pancultural account to incorporate the contributions not only of Greece and the rest of Europe but also of Babylon, India, China, the Arab world and indeed, if we looked more closely, of all cultures. Science is and always has been a collective human endeavour, albeit with huge discontinuities.

The build-up: the European Middle Ages

Historians often skate over and sometimes ignore or even deride the contributions of natural philosophers and theologians between the 5th century (the time of St Augustine (354-430)) and the end of the 15th (leading up to the Reformation and first stirrings of the 'Italian' Renaissance)—but this is a huge mistake. Some vital technologies and crafts were wonderfully refined in the Middle Ages: clockwork, architecture, alchemy—and all were grist to later developments. Even more to the point, in those thousand years an honourable and not-so-short shortlist of theologians and other thinkers made fundamental contributions to the *philosophy* of science that have guided scientists ever since.

Thus, on the broad front, mediaeval thinkers, especially the Italian Dominican friar Thomas Aquinas (1225-1274), did much to sort out the difference between insight achieved by revelation (which is essentially intuitive), and insight achieved by observation and rational thinking. This discussion did not begin with them—Greek philosophers including Plato and Aristotle had much to say on it—and of course it continues, not least with Pope John Paul II's encyclical of 1998, *Fides et Ratio* (*Faith and Reason*). Some hard-nosed modern atheists are wont to dismiss faith as wishful thinking and muddle-headedness but as we will see later, the distinction between intuition and rational thought is nothing like as clear as the hard-heads like to suppose. Neither is it true—emphatically not—that science is rational all the way through. If it was, it would not work. There would be no progress at all. Intellectual progress needs leaps in the dark.

Hard-nosed apologists of science present it as a kind of edifice—a veritable ziggurat—of unequivocal truth. The stones of the ziggurat are *facts*, based on repeatable and effectively irrefutable observations and—crucially, at least wherever possible—on *measurement*. The facts are then interpreted, which is the first step towards explanation. Yet way back in the 14th century the French philosopher Nicholas of Oresme (1320-1382) pointed out that all is not so simple, for any one observation can always be interpreted in many different ways and it isn't always easy to see which one is 'true' (or any of them, come to that). In fact it is always impossible to know with absolute certainty that *any* of our explanations is 'true'—and in any case truth is a tricky concept (of which more later).

For example, said Nicholas, we can all agree that the Sun rises every morning—an observation which, provided the sky is clear, seems endlessly repeatable. But does the Sun appear to rise because the Earth is spinning on its axis, or because the Sun is orbiting around the Earth? (The idea that everyone in the Middle Ages believed the Earth is flat was a later, somewhat mischievous invention. History is full of them. People like to deride the past so as to make the present look better.)

All very well, you may feel, but that was then and now is now. More recent data shows beyond all reasonable doubt that the Earth goes round the Sun (the maths is simpler that way). Yet the same kind of problem still persists, in every context. Notably, the present 'standard model' of cosmology tells us that the universe began 13.8 billion years ago with the Big Bang. There is all kind of evidence for this, including the observation that the universe is expanding—which implies that it must be expanding from some initial point, starting a long time ago. Yet at least half a dozen physicists of equal standing have put forward half a dozen alternatives to the Big Bang which, they say, fit the observations equally well. The dissenting scientists all give eminently plausible—*rational*—reasons for choosing an alternative but in the end their reasons are intuitive. As one leading cosmologist said in a recent BBC TV documentary, 'I just feel that the Big Bang doesn't make sense.' Note 'feel.' In the end it is not, as we are brought up to believe, the 'facts' or more broadly the 'evidence' that carry the day in science. ***In the end scientists—like everybody else—rely on their intuition to tell us what is true—what we feel in our bones is the case.*** A wise person is not one with a bigger brain, but with more sensitive bones. I'm sure Einstein would have agreed with this. In roughly similar vein a QC once assured me that in a court of law, a fact is what the judge says it is. Always, some human being has to *decide* what to take seriously. Nature does not come with labels but we do come with preconceptions and predilections and see what we are primed to see. Nicholas Oresme, I suggest, would have had no trouble with any of this.

Hugely important was and is the polymath and long-time Bishop of Lincoln, Robert Grosseteste (1175-1253) who discussed, among much else, the importance of *experiment*. To be sure, he did not mean experiment in the modern sense—giving nature a poke, to see how it responds under (more or less) controlled conditions. He really just meant *experience*—actually observing nature to see how it behaves, and not just speculating on the basis of logic on how it ought to behave. Mediaeval thinkers were extremely keen on logic—but nature does not always behave the way that clever people think it should. Aristotle (385-323) in the 4th century BCE loved to observe nature but he apparently thought that he could infer how the world really works just by thinking about it and his physics led his successors astray for centuries. But Grosseteste preferred to *observe* what really happens and in particular he wrote very perceptively about light and colour. The Franciscan friar Roger Bacon (1219/20-*c.*1292) carried on his good work.

The English Franciscan friar William of Occam, or Ockham (1285-1347) provided a principle of inquiry that has played a huge part in modern scientific thinking ever since. His principle is known as ***Occam's razor,*** although this is not an expression he coined himself. In truth he simply issued a warning:

Non sunt multiplicanda entia praeter necessitatem

which means:

Entities are not to be multiplied beyond necessity.

This means what it says. We should always seek to base our explanations on what we know already is the case. We should not pluck new, unknown, *ad hoc* forces out of the air to explain whatever we happen to find puzzling. Don't assume that a conjuror must be using magic before exhausting the possibility that he may have been using mirrors. Emphatically, though, this does *not* imply, as is commonly taken to be the case, that the simplest possible explanation must necessarily be the true one. Occam was not trying to provide a sure-fire guide to the truth. He was simply telling us to clear our minds of unnecessary clutter, and not to jump to arbitrary conclusions. For Nature will not be second-guessed. Nature feels under no obligation to behave simply, just for our convenience. Sometimes explanations that really do explain what's going on are very complex indeed or (as with quantum physics) are hugely counter-intuitive, and sometimes it really is necessary to invoke new, previously unknown forces. Newton's gravity is a case in point. As Einstein commented six centuries after Occam:

Explanations should be as simple as possible, but no simpler.

Of key importance too was ***numerology***—the forerunner of modern maths. Pythagoras it was in the 6th century BCE who first formally drew attention to the extraordinary power of maths. Most obviously, it provides wonderful patterns in abstract thought. His most famous theorem tells us that in a right-angled triangle the square on the hypotenuse is equal to the square of the other two sides—which isn't exactly obvious at first sight. But more than that, mysteriously, the abstractions of maths often provide insights into the workings of the real, physical world—helping us not simply to explain the material universe, but also to *predict* how the material universe will behave in the future. In recent times mathematic calculations led physicists to predict the existence of black holes—and when astronomers looked they found that indeed, there are such things. In short, as Pythagoras perceived, maths seems to have magical, occult powers. Even today, no one can explain why maths has the power it has. Is the universe innately mathematical? Was it *designed* along mathematical lines? Is God a mathematician? Or are the mathematical patterns we perceive in the universe simply imposed by our own questing brains—in the same way that we see the signs of the zodiac in the pattern of the stars which (so modern astronomers tell us) are random; or see faces and strange beasts in the clouds? Opinion is still divided—and, I imagine, always must be.

Whatever the truth of the matter, maths has played a key role in natural philosophy/science ever since the time of Pythagoras. In about 400 CE St Augustine suggested that:

> *Numbers are the Universal language offered by the deity to humans as confirmation of the truth.*

And in the 1980s in an interview (with me) on BBC Radio 3 the Cambridge biochemist and sinologist Joseph Needham (1900-1995) *defined* science as

> *The ruthless mathematicization of ideas.*

Numerologists focused on the mysteries and so, like Pythagoras, they had and have one foot in the occult; and, some would say, the same might be said of modern mathematicians. Maths does indeed provide wondrous insights into the workings of the universe but why it should do so is a mystery.

Neither should we imagine, as some historians have suggested, that all these mediaeval proto-scientists were simply mavericks, out of the theological mainstream. Communications were extremely difficult in those days—what might they have achieved with email? But the nature of the material world, and how we can possibly *know* anything at all, and the relationship between science and religion, were matters of great concern in the Middle Ages, and were commonly approached with far more subtlety than is often evident today.

The brink of modern science: the 16th century

The 1500s saw the true beginnings of modernity. The European 'Enlightenment' got properly underway, with its emphasis on rationality and reason; the Protestant challenge to Roman Catholicism led to the Reformation; and we saw the first stutterings of recognizably modern science. In particular, this was the first great age of modern map-making—geared to navigation and exploration, and inspired by commerce and conquest—but of huge intellectual significance too, and at least quasi-scientific. Herbalism came on apace too as evident not least in the plays of Shakespeare (1554-1616), from *Romeo and Juliet* and *Midsummer Night's Dream* to *Hamlet*; and fostered by gardener-naturalists including the great John Tradescant the Elder (c.1570s-1638). All these various threads of inquiry, plus a good dose of magic, were combined in the arts and skills of the magus, the all-seeing quasi-magical intellectual, epitomised in England by Dr John Dee (1527-1608), treasured advisor to Queen Elizabeth. Dee spanned the worlds of the occult and *bona fide* science: numerologist, alchemist, astronomer, astrologist, crystal-gazer. He is commonly taken to be the role model for Prospero, in Shakespeare's *Tempest*.

But truly in the realms of bona fide science or at least on the edge of it was the Polish astronomer and polymath Nicholas Copernicus (1473-1543) who began seriously to establish the concept of the heliocentric solar system—that the Earth and the other planets orbit around the Sun. He was not the first to suggest this: as Copernicus himself acknowledged, the Greek Aristarchus of Samos beat him to it by 1700 years or so. But Copernicus was the first to put the idea on a firm basis. Basically he showed—very much in accord with Occam's principle—that a heliocentric model was far more elegant than the then widely-accepted geocentric model promulgated by Ptolemy of Alexandria in the 2nd century CE, which assumed that the whole universe revolves around the Earth. In particular, the maths needed to describe the heliocentric solar system was far simpler, with far less need for ad hoc adjustments. ***In practice, in science, the truth or otherwise of an idea is judged largely by the elegance of the maths used to describe it.*** Again this is not a sure-fire guide to the truth but it makes sense, and it's the way things are done. Copernicus's thesis was not published until after his death, however. The English astronomer and mathematician Thomas Digges (1546-1595), a pupil of John Dee, was the first to translate his ideas into English—and added the thought that the universe as a whole could well be infinite in extent. In this there are definite intimations of modernity.

The birth of recognizably modern science: the 17th century

Science really began to come into its own in the 17th century—the true beginning of what is commonly called 'The Enlightenment.' Again from among the blizzard of geniuses I will select just a very few to illustrate what seem to me to be the most salient insights.

In 1620 the English philosopher-statesman Francis Bacon (1561-1626) published *The Great Instauration*—which, I am pleased to report, roughly means 'the great re-think.' In it he argued that what counted as knowledge up to then was a rag-bag of more-or-less established 'fact' plus a liberal dose of armchair thinking—of the kind, he says, that we find in Aristotle (he was no fan of Aristotle). In fact, he said, (p. 7):

> *... the entire fabric of human reason is badly put together and built up, and like some magnificent structure without any foundation .... There was but one course left, therefore— ... to commence a total reconstruction of sciences, arts, and all human knowledge, raised upon the proper foundations.*

We should, he said, root our explanations of the world only in reliable observation of the real world, and on experiment. His approach—argue from established *fact* to explanation—is known as *induction*. In truth, he does not properly explain *how* we move from fact to explanation and as discussed later, it's now clear that this involves creative guesswork, followed by testing (the method known as 'hypothetico-deductive'). He also comes uncomfortably close to suggesting that we have a right if not a duty to achieve 'dominion' over nature as apparently advocated in *Genesis* (1:26)—although he also says (*The Great Instauration* p. 33):

Nature, to be commanded, must be obeyed.

All in all he is rightly placed among the earliest and greatest of the recognizably modern philosophers of science.

In ***physics*** Galileo Galilei (1564-1642) of Pisa did much to consolidate the importance of experiment, and also observed the planets through his new, improved telescope and came out in strong support of Copernicus. In this he famously fell foul of the Catholic Church—which is doubly unfortunate not least because the Pope at the time, Urban VIII, was very much in favour of scientific inquiry, and Galileo himself was a good Catholic, and the two had had a good relationship. The much-bruited notion that Galileo was a modern, forward-thinking 'rationalist' while Urban VIII was a primitive stick-in-the-mud is (yet another) gross distortion. The real point seems to be that Galileo lacked the skills of the diplomat. Enormous intelligence and common sense don't always go together. In the customary polymathic fashion of his age he wrote a play to illustrate his ideas—and his play seemed to satirize the pope. The Catholic Church in those very difficult and turbulent times played a big part in European affairs, further complicated by the rapid growth of Lutheran and Calvinist Protestantism, and Urban had a serious but delicate position to keep up, both political and religious. He could not afford to be seen to be mocked. So Galileo was put a stop to—albeit kindly: placed under very comfortable house arrest. If Galileo had shown a little more humility, not to say sense, the history of the past 400 years might have been very different. Today, the Pontifical Academy of Science, established in 1936 by Pope Pius XI in Vatican City, is a renowned centre of scientific research. The much-bruited idea that science and religion are inveterately at odds, which has launched not a few best-sellers these past few years, is crude in the extreme. Ideas that catch on are often crude. (Noel Coward said the same about 'cheap music.') More in the next chapter.

Galileo, incidentally, was born in the same year as Shakespeare—and, some say, his influence can clearly be seen in some of the later plays. (Dan Falk in *The Science of Shakespeare* (2014) draws special attention to *Cymbeline*. I haven't read it and can't comment.)

A few decades after Galileo, the Cambridge physicist Isaac Newton (1643-1727) proposed momentously that the 'force' that keeps the planets in their orbits around the sun is the same as the force that causes apples to fall towards the ground. He called it ***gravity***. Newton thus showed the limitations of Occam's rule—for sometimes it is *necessary* to propose quite new principles, or phenomena, in order to explain the realities of life.

But gravity was—and still is—mysterious. Truly, it has an occult quality. It is, as Newton conceived it, a force that operates at a distance—no observable contact is necessary—and how could there be such a thing? Albert Einstein (1879-1955) in the 20th century suggested that gravity isn't really a 'force' at all. It results from curvature of the space-time continuum. I'm not sure this really helps, at least for ordinary purposes. (Rocket scientists are content with the physics of Newton.) Nowadays we take gravity for granted but as the botanist and philosopher of science Rupert Sheldrake points out, nobody (not even scientists) can properly be said to *understand* it. As with many of the ideas of science, we (including the professional scientists) just grow used to them. It's the same with modern concepts such as Einstein's space-time and the more modern idea of the 11-dimensional universe. Einstein was so special because he could *envisage*, in his mind's eye, how things must be. Maths is needed to explain what he had in mind but he left a lot of the maths to other people.

The idea of gravity hugely advanced the idea that nature as a whole is orderly—that there is an overall unity. Indeed, Newton went on to describe the entire universe as a giant exercise in clockwork. On the back of this and other insights Newton did as much as anyone to establish the idea of scientific ***law***—another huge concept with momentous implications which, again, we now take for granted. Yet as the modern philosopher of science Nancy Cartwright points out, not least in *The Dappled World* (1999) the term 'law' implies that there must be a lawmaker—which means that this most fundamental of scientific concepts is rooted in theology (and Newton spent more time on theology than on science). To the atheist, of course, the idea of a law *maker* is an anathema. To the hard-heads, the laws of nature just *are*, just as the universe itself just *is*.

The idea that the universe works like clockwork (with or without a lawmaker) is archetypally ***deterministic***. It implies that once the laws and the mechanisms of physics are in place the whole caboodle will continue to run forever just as the ground rules dictate. The fate of the universe is sealed from the outset; and if only we understand the rules we can predict the future. This idea seems commonsensical and some found and find it attractive, and as outlined below, it was widely accepted until fairly well into the 20th century. But then, as discussed later, it was shown, emphatically, to be false.

The ***life sciences*** too made serious progress in the 17th century. Of pivotal importance was the English polymath Robert Hooke (1635-1703)—sometimes described as 'England's Leonardo,' although much overlooked. Hooke made substantive contributions across the sciences and in particular, as he recorded in 1665 in *Micrographia,* he looked through his decorated leather microscope and observed that the tissues of plants are divided into cells, like honeycomb. Thus he laid the foundations of ***cell theory***: the idea now universally accepted that all living flesh (animal, plant, fungus, seaweed) is cellular. There is no more significant idea in all of biology. Among much else cell theory illustrates the essential *unity* of life; an aspect of the grand metaphysical principle of oneness. Meanwhile in the Netherlands the Dutch businessman and natural philosopher Antonie van Leeuwenhoek (1632-1723) looked through his own newly-designed microscope and saw minute creatures milling about which in English were called 'animalcules': the first stirrings of modern microbiology.

Hugely important too was and is the English naturalist John Ray (1627-1695) who among much else laid the foundations of modern taxonomy—the craft and science of classification. The emerging science of taxonomy reinforced the idea of an orderly universe—and helped to show that *life* too is orderly, beneath the bewildering diversity.

Meanwhile the English physician (from Folkestone) William Harvey (1578-1657) built on the work of his Paduan teacher Hieronymus Fabricius (1533-1619) to show that the blood does not ebb and flow from the heart, as had been supposed, but circulates. This added weight to the idea that *at least at some level* the living body can be envisaged as a machine, subject as machines are to the laws of physics. This dealt at least a palpable blow to the concept of ***vitalism***: the idea that life partakes of special forces beyond the simple restraints of physics. Harvey's work suggested that at least at the most basic, physical level life does not march exclusively to its own special drum. That does not however mean that there is *nothing* special about life. We need not suppose that the laws of physics, or at least of physics as understood so far, provide a complete, rock-solid explanation of all life's phenomena. There is life in the concept of vitalism still.

So it was that the giants of the 17th century, of whom the above are just a sample, laid the foundations of modernity. Above all they put in place the grand philosophical concept of scientific *law*, and the idea that the universe, including the living world in all its multifariousness, is, at bottom, orderly. They also illustrated, inadvertently, how easy it is in our studies of the universe to be led astray. In particular, as discussed later, the universe emphatically is *not* deterministic. Cause and effect in reality is non-linear: no simple relationship between cause and effect. Randomness is built into the mechanism—and indeed is the mainspring of evolution; and although evolution does not necessarily imply progress, it does hold the promise of progress. Clockwork is the wrong model. Clocks, ultimately deterministic, do not evolve—or not at least without outside intervention. But we will come to that.

Note, though—which is I feel is crucial—that the scientific greats of the 17th century were all deeply devout, in their many different ways. They absolutely did not feel, as contemporary hard-nosed scientific atheists insist, that science and religion are inveterately at odds. As outlined above, the spat between Galileo and Pope Urban VIII has been much misrepresented (and so, too, as outlined in the next chapter, was and is the perceived clash between the church and Darwin's ideas on evolution). In the minds of the 17th century natural philosophers (and of many modern scientists) the orderliness of nature reflected the orderliness of God's mind. Overall, the great innovators of the 17th century felt about their scientific inquiries in the same way that J.S. Bach (1685-1750), a few decades later, felt about music, of which, he said,

> *The aim and final end ... should be none other than the glory of God and the refreshment of the soul.*

It would be good—at least advantageous—to revert to this way of thinking even if, for whatever reason, we chose to express the idea differently.

But the mood changed.

The 18th century

The 18th century, so is commonly considered, was the height of the Enlightenment. Up until then it was widely accepted in the Christian world that reason—rational thinking—and revelation should be of roughly equal status. Reason implied empirical truth, based on direct observation and calculation: the stuff of science. Revelation means that the truth of things is 'revealed' to us by some outside agency, which at least in the theistic religions means God. God's truths were and are transmitted directly to specially endowed prophets and then passed on to the rest of us. 'Faith' implies that we should take those revealed truths seriously even in the absence of material evidence. As the resurrected Jesus said to his doubting disciple Thomas (John 20:29):

Blessed are they that have not seen, and yet have believed.

Faith, for Roman Catholics, is perceived as a gift, the loss of which is keenly felt.

As knowledge built up in the 18th century it became more and more acceptable to explain the workings of the universe without reference to God. Rationality alone, it seemed—observation and maths—could tell us all we need to know. So it was that the French mathematician and physicist Pierre-Simon de Laplace (1749-1827) declared that if only we knew exactly what is in the universe and where all of it was at any one time, then we could predict with certainty how everything would turn out for the rest of time—the ultimate expression of determinism. History reports (although the reports seem to be apocryphal) that when Napoleon asked Laplace where God fitted in to his grand scheme of things Laplace replied:

Je n'avais pas besoin de cette hypothèse-là.
(I had no need of that hypothesis.)

It is probably wrong, though, to suggest that Laplace was an atheist, positively denying the existence of God. He emerges rather as a ***deist.*** Like Newton, he apparently believed that God had indeed created the universe, and put the laws of physics in place, but had then in effect retired, and left the mechanism that He had created to run itself. We can envisage Him outside His celestial garden shed basking in a celestial deckchair and gazing upon a job well done—not just upon his rows of runner beans but on the whole cosmos; although Newton suggested that God does need to intervene now and again, as a gardener does, or indeed a repairer of clocks, to keep the whole Creation on track. Nonetheless, the idea that the workings of the universe *can* be explained without reference to God is obvious fuel for atheism. It is one thing to believe in God if there is no other explanation, but if there is an alternative explanation, why resort to the supernatural? Such thinking seems to be in line with that of Occam—although Occam, as a Franciscan friar, clearly did not feel that God is surplus to requirements.

In short, the 18th century saw a huge shift in general worldview and in particular in the philosophy of science. It also of course saw some huge advances in the *content* of science and hence in its scope and confidence.

Thus the 18th century too saw the transition from alchemy to modern chemistry—quantitative and stripped of mythologizing. In particular—one of the great 'paradigm shifts' in science and hence in human understanding in general—scientists (though still called 'natural philosophers') began to formulate the modern concept of the 'element.' As outlined below, this idea came triumphantly to fruition in the 19th century and was considerably refined in the 20th.

For well into the 18th century, strange though it seems, natural philosophers still largely accepted the idea put forward in the 5th century BCE by the Greek Sicilian philosopher Empedocles (c.494-c.434) and embraced not least by Aristotle: that the material world is compounded of the four supposed elements—water, earth, fire, and air. But serious doubts grew as the century wore on. Notably, in the 1770s, the notoriously shy and extremely rich English aristocrat and natural philosopher Henry Cavendish (1731-1810) produced and isolated hydrogen by adding various metals to various acids—though he called it 'inflammable air.'

Bizarrely, though—just to show that the path to enlightenment never did run smooth—the study of air in the 18th century was bedevilled by a persistent belief in the non-existent gas phlogiston. The idea of phlogiston was first formulated in the 17th century by the German physician and alchemist Johann Joachim Becher (1632-1685) and further elaborated by another German physician and chemist George Ernst Stahl (1689-1734). Phlogiston was conceived as a—what? Substance? Anti-substance?—that was present in combustible materials and disappeared when the material was combusted. This idea persisted even after it was realized that materials often *gain* weight when burned—that the ash may sometimes weigh more than the original stuff.

So it was that the polymathic English theologian and chemist Joseph Priestley (1733-1804) discovered oxygen but failed to realize that he had. Instead he called it 'dephlogisticated air.' It was left to the (very rich) French tax collector and gentleman chemist Antoine Lavoisier (1743-1794) to refine Priestley's experiments and to coin the name 'oxygen.' He proposed that burning did not cause combustible material to lose phlogiston. Instead, burning happened when the material combined with oxygen in the air—what we now call 'oxidation'—with loss of energy in the form of heat and light. Lavoisier was very meticulous and had top-of-the-range instruments for weighing. He was not the first to measure and to quantify his experiments by any means but he was able to be very precise—and precision matters. This crucial chapter in the history of science ended badly, however, at least for the two main protagonists. Priestley was hounded out of England (or so he felt) because he had sympathized with the French revolutionaries, and those same revolutionaries cut off Lavoisier's head because they did not like tax collectors. But their heritage lived on. As outlined later, the new conception of 'elements' that they had helped to frame culminated in the 19th century with the Periodic Table, one of the great creations of all science.

Throughout the 18th century too a succession of physicists in England, Germany, America (Ben Franklin), Italy and France provided significant insights into the mysteries of ***electricity***. Not the least was Luigi Galvani of Bologna (1737-1798) who showed among other things that a frog's leg will twitch when touched with electrodes. In other words, life itself partook of this mysterious force; another blow to the idea of vitalism. Galvani's work inspired Mary Shelley (1797-1851) to write *Frankenstein* while sheltering from the rain in Switzerland in 1818.

The technologies of the Industrial Revolution also contributed huge insights—and prompted new lines of research. Key lines of interest were ***hydraulics***—this was an age of canals and of mines that were prone to flood—and ***steam power***. The first working steam engines of the 18th century were the work of engineers—essentially craftsmen, guided by their experience and good sense. But in the late 18th and early 19th centuries the work on steam engines gave crucial impetus to the growing science of thermodynamics, of which more later.

The 18th century too saw the birth of *bona fide* ***Earth science***, led initially by James Hutton (1726-1797). Among much else, Hutton concluded from his geological forays in his native Scotland that the Earth must be many millions of years old. In the 19th century Hutton's successor and fellow Scot Charles Lyell (1797-1875), great friend and geological mentor of Charles Darwin, independently reached the same conclusion. The world was not, as Archbishop James Ussher of Armagh (1581-1656) had previously calculated from the chronology of the Bible, created more or less in its present state on October 22, 4004 BCE. Again, though, both Hutton and Lyell were deeply devout. Hutton did much to clarify the physics of volcanoes but also asked, what was God's *purpose* in creating them? The answer, he suggested, was that volcanoes made mountains; and mountains, as they erode, give rise to soil, the support and life-blood of terrestrial plants on which all terrestrial animals depend, including us. In truth, mountains are created through the action of plate tectonics and it now seems that without plate tectonics to stir and re-circulate the minerals of the Earth's crust life on Earth could not be sustained. Hutton's idea was not mere whimsy.

In ***the life sciences*** we might single out the Swedish naturalist Carl Linnaeus (1707-1778) who built on the work of John Ray and laid the foundations of modern ***taxonomy,*** with the natural world divided into kingdoms and hence into orders and finally into genera and species. (Other subdivisions including phylum and family and, most recently, *domain*, came later). Linnaeus also—building on the work of mediaeval and 16th and 17th century herbalists—devised the binomial system for naming living creatures: first the generic and then the specific name as in *Bellis perennis* (the daisy) and *Homo sapiens* (us). It all contributed to the grand idea that life too, for all its diversity and complexity, is orderly.

The age of the scientist: the 19th century

In the 1830s the Cambridge polymath William Whewell (1794-1866) first introduced the term '***scientist.***' He coined the word expressly to refer to the Scottish physicist Mary Somerville (1780-1872) since he felt he could hardly call her a 'man of science.' But the label, 'scientist,' seemed to draw a line around both scientists and science, marking them off forever from the rest of human thought. The answer to Juliet Capulet's question 'What's in a name?' is, evidently, 'a great deal.'

The content of science romped ahead in the 19th century, on all fronts. Seventeenth and 18th century natural philosophers made huge strides in the science of ***electricity*** as outlined above but it remained little more than a curiosity until the Englishman Michael Faraday (1791-1867) showed that electricity and magnetism were two sides of the same coin and introduced the idea of the electric 'field'; and then the Scottish genius James Clerk Maxwell (1831-1879) established the idea of ***electromagnetism*** and ***the electromagnetic spectrum***, which includes gamma rays through x-rays to light to infra-red and microwaves to radio waves. Within decades, much or indeed most of the spectrum had given rise to a suite of technologies from x-rays to radio. The two transformative insights of the 20th century—Einstein's relativity and quantum mechanics—both derive from Maxwell's work (as Einstein was at pains to acknowledge).

The crucial science of ***thermodynamics*** derived in significant part from the attempts of the French physicist and soldier (Nicolas) Sadi Carnot (1796-1832) in the 1820s to increase the efficiency of steam engines—a fine example of a novel technology not simply making life easier but also prompting new fundamental insights. Early studies sought to clarify the relationship between heat energy and mechanical energy, but soon the field expanded to explore the relationship between all forms of energy. From thermodynamics emerged the idea of ***entropy:*** the rock-bottom state of absolute quiescence which, we are told, is the ultimate destiny of the whole universe (though I'm not sure people believe this anymore).

Computer science was born in the 19th century too. In the 1820s the English polymath Charles Babbage (1791-1871) began designing the world's first *bona fide* general-purpose ***computer*** and by 1837 had produced detailed plans for making one. Alas, he wasn't able to build the machine—too complex; too expensive—but engineers at London's Science Museum did produce a working model based on his plans in 1991. It works. Computing needed 20th century electronics to bring it to fruition—first valves, then transistors, then microchips—but Babbage had obviously grasped the principles. What difference would it have made to the course of history if IT had been available in the 19th century?

In ***chemistry***, the Cumberland-born Quaker-educated Englishman John Dalton (1766-1844) extended the idea that experiments must be quantified and confirmed an idea first conceived by the Greeks—that matter is composed of atoms. He concluded that all the atoms of each individual element are identical in all their properties, including their mass, which is not quite true but it is a crucial insight nonetheless. Hence, each element has its own characteristic ***atomic weight.*** From this observation, with a few refinements along the way, the Russian chemist Dmitri Mendeleev (1834-1907) laid the foundations of the ***periodic table***, showing how all the known elements are related to each other—and predicting the existence of several that were not yet known (but have been discovered since). His table, first published in 1869, is at the heart of all modern chemistry. (Dalton, incidentally, tells a wonderful story of lunch with a local family which ran into tea and then supper and lasted from midday to 10.00 pm when they all went to bed. It's good to be reminded that scientists are human.)

Organic chemistry too was born in the early 19th century. Thus in 1828 the German chemist Friedrich Wohler (1800-1882) synthesized urea—key constituent of urine—from inorganic salts (potassium cyanate and ammonium sulphate). This was another blow to vitalism, at least in its original form. It seemed that some materials of an organic kind could be knocked up on the laboratory bench. Indeed, 'organic' chemistry is now conceived not simply as the chemistry of living systems but as the study of carbon-based molecules and their interactions. Work on artificial fertilizers by Justus von Liebig in Germany (1803-1873) and John Bennett Lawes in England (1814-1900) further reinforced the notion that living flesh, and all that goes with it, can be construed as a complex exercise in chemistry. Some suggest indeed that all life should just be seen as complex chemistry—which is the basis of the agrochemical industry which Lawes, more than anyone, initiated.

Out of organic chemistry arose ***biochemistry***, specifically focused on the chemistry of living organisms. Many trace its birth to the research on fermentation by the German scientist Eduard Buchner (1860-1917) who in the 1890s showed that *juice* extracted from yeast could ferment sugar. Intact, living yeast cells are not required. Again, the idea is reinforced: that life *is* chemistry. Even so, the concept of vitalism is not quite dead. It is still impossible to pin down—at least in chemical terms—the difference between a living person and the same person, a few seconds later, who is declared dead. Death still seems to involve the departure of life, the snuffing out of some vital spark. More later.

We might reasonably suggest that ***molecular biology*** was born in 1869 when the Swiss physiologist/chemist Johann Friedrich Miescher (1844-1895) discovered a weird substance in the nuclei of white blood cells which he called 'nuclein'—and in 1881 the German biochemist Albrecht Kossel (1853-1927) described the primary structure of nuclein: that is, ways in which its various components are linked to each other. In fact there were two kinds of nuclein. One was and is a polymer of adenosine, cytosine, guanine, and thymine, each one linked to a reduced form of the sugar, ribose, with all the different components linked by phosphate radicals. The other kind contained uracil instead of thymine. The first he called deoxyribonucleic acid, or DNA; and the second was and is ribonucleic acid, or RNA. For this work Kossel was awarded a Nobel Prize in 1910.

Miescher surmised that nuclein must be involved in heredity and in this he was indeed prescient. In the 20th century DNA proved to be the stuff of genes (see below) with various kinds of RNA as its helpmeets. Miescher and Kossel should be better known than they are.

In the 19th century the ***Earth sciences*** moved ahead on two main fronts: in the study of rocks and landscapes, which is ***geology***; and in the study of fossils, ***palaeontology***. Charles Lyell (1797-1875), yet another devout Scot, essentially picked up where James Hutton left off. Like Hutton, among much else, he helped to establish the extreme age of the Earth—although he never came near to the current estimate, of 4.5 billion (4500 million) years. He inspired Darwin, who became a good friend, although Lyell never accepted the idea of evolution by means of natural selection. Outstanding among the array of 19th century palaeontologists was the Englishman Richard Owen (1804-1892). Among much else, Owen coined the expression 'dinosaur' and made huge contributions to vertebrate taxonomy. For good measure he founded London's Natural History Museum. Like Lyell, Owen helped to provide much of the evidence that underpins the idea of evolution—showing most obviously that ancient life forms were often very different from the present. But also, like Lyell, he was very reluctant to accept the idea of evolution. Unlike Lyell, however, Owen was not a friend of Darwin who he seemed to see as an over-privileged toffee-nosed upstart (surely most unfair).

The ***life sciences*** also leapt ahead in the 19th century—overlapping the advances in chemistry (and biochemistry) and the earth sciences. Five lines of development seem to me to be of outstanding importance:

1: ***Germ theory***. The French biologist and chemist Louis Pasteur (1822-1895), building on his own work on yeasts and wine-making and on the insights for example of van Leeuwenhoek, began to show that various diseases are caused by micro-organisms. Later in the century the German physician Robert Koch (1843-1910) showed that tuberculosis and cholera are caused specifically by bacteria. Thus Pasteur and Koch between them did much to establish the modern science and technologies of microbiology with huge, transformative implications in medicine and—as is now at last being properly appreciated!—in ecology (including the ecology of the human gut). Microbes of all kinds 'protists,' bacteria, archaeans, viruses—are key players in all ecosystems and for them, all other organisms are ecosystems in their own right—potential habitats in which to live, feed, and multiply.

2: ***Homeostasis***. Homeostasis is one of the defining features of living creatures—and integral to the concept of Gaia (chapter 4). It means that an organism (or the whole global ecosystem) is able to maintain a more or less steady state even in the face of changing conditions. So although on a hot day you could fry an egg on the pavement, if that was your fancy, you yourself may simply sweat or gently glow. In truth the term *homeostasis* was not coined until 1926, by the Harvard physiologist Walter Bradford Cannon (1871-1945) but the idea of it came from the French physiologist Claude Bernard (1813-1878) who in the 1860s framed the concept of the *milieu interieur*—the 'internal environment'; and the prime task for living organisms, he suggested, is to keep the internal environment constant. Indeed. That's it. Keeping our *milieu interieur* constant is what we (and mushrooms and oak trees) do, to a greater or lesser extent, and rocks don't.

3: ***Evolution.*** Truly pivotal is the idea of Charles Darwin (1809-1882) and Alfred Russel Wallace (1823-1913) of what Darwin called, in his *Origin of Species* in 1859, 'The origin of species by means of natural selection.' The essence of it is that all organisms produce offspring like themselves ('like begets like')—but there is *variation* nonetheless. No two kittens in a litter are exactly alike (said Darwin) and all are somewhat different from their parents. Some of the variants will inevitably be better suited to the environment than others and they will be more likely to survive and hence to have offspring of their own. Thus *nature* selects those that are best adapted just as farmers select the best bulls from which to breed. Hence 'natural selection.' In the 1860s the philosopher Herbert Spencer (1820-1903) summarized the notion in the phrase, 'survival of the fittest'—where 'fit' means 'most suitable' as in 'fit for purpose.' Darwin himself later adopted the expression. The idea of evolution by means of natural selection has changed not only the life sciences but the entire modern *Zeitgeist*.

The idea of natural selection is blindingly simple but has kept biologists, philosophers, and theologians occupied ever since, not least because it suggests a simple *mechanism* that seems to explain how it is that living organisms, by and large, are so well adapted to the conditions they live in. As with Laplace's concept of the cosmos, there seems to be no need to posit some designer God. Furthermore, Darwin (in line with Lyell's notions on the age of the Earth) suggested that evolution has taken place over many millions of years—that the world and all its creatures were not created in seven days as a simplistic reading of *Genesis* seems to suggest. Thus natural selection in particular and science in general have often been seen as grist to the atheist mill and Darwin has often been presented as a spokesman for atheism. This yet again is a simplistic half-truth, at best, or indeed is a straightforward and deeply pernicious misrepresentation, though it often passes as scholarship. More in the next chapter.

4: ***Genetics.*** In the 1850s an Augustinian friar called Gregor Mendel (1822-1884), at St Thomas's Monastery at Brno, now in the Czech Republic, began experiments on garden peas that initiated the modern science of genetics. He showed that when different varieties were crossed the features—'characters'—of the parents were not simply blended in the offspring. Instead, all the different characters—initially he looked at seed colour (yellow or green) and texture (wrinkled or smooth) height (tall or short)—were inherited as discrete units, in (almost) any combination. Each feature, he concluded, must be transmitted from generation to generation by discrete 'hereditary factors.' Early on he introduced the idea of dominance and recessiveness and later, working on a range of plants including runner beans and antirrhinums, he showed how some individual characters depended on combinations of factors and so could indeed have a blended appearance.

His work was published in 1866 but, as is so often the case, it was overlooked. He sent a copy to Darwin who apparently failed to read it (and blundered on with his own, somewhat crackpot interpretation of heredity; one of his few big mistakes). Mendel finally achieved recognition in the early 20th century (long after his death) when the terms 'gene' and 'genetics' were first coined. The liaison of Darwinian evolution with Mendelian genetics, finally capped off with molecular biology, was one of the great scientific developments of the 20th century (of which more later).

5: ***Psychology.*** Towards the end of the 19th century, psychology began to be brought into the scientific fold. From the beginning there were many different threads and still are, which do not always fit comfortably together—from the physiology of nerves to the quantification of behaviour (which led to ***behaviourism***) to anthropology and the psychoanalysis of Sigmund Freud (1856-1939). The whole field illustrates in spades that there is no clear dividing line between psychology and literature, or science and metaphysics. Despite the best efforts too of many excellent thinkers, the workings of the mind and the nature of consciousness remain mysterious and probably always will (as again is discussed further in the next chapter). This is perhaps the most profound and important lesson of all: that in the end, life and the universe are beyond our ken. It is dangerous indeed, as the old Greeks stressed, to assume that we really do *understand,* and that we know what we are doing. Such presumption is the sin of hubris, than which there is none deadlier.

6: Finally—and, I suggest, most importantly—the 19th century saw significant advances in the ***philosophy of science.*** Such was, and is, the faith in the methods of science that many began to believe, and many still do, that science is the only worthwhile game in town. All other ways of thinking are too woolly and speculative by half: just matters of opinion. In the 1830s the philosopher and sociologist Auguste Comte (1798-1857) in France presented this way of thinking as a formal philosophy, known as ***positivism.*** He argued that the observations we make through our senses are the only source of *certain* knowledge: which implies (a) that the knowledge thus obtained is indeed certain, and (b), in effect, that no other sources of knowledge could or should be relied upon or even taken seriously. Only science can provide truth that is really *robust*; truly trustworthy. Metaphysics, including religion, was, in effect, whimsy.

Such were the advances in knowledge and in confidence that in 1894 the German-American physicist Albert A. Michelson (1852-1931) declared with breath-taking chutzpah that in physics at least

> *... it is probable that most of the grand underlying principles have been firmly established ... the future truths of physical science are to be looked for in the sixth place of decimals.*

Together with his American colleague Edward Williams Morley (1838-1923), Michelson was the first to measure the speed of light accurately, and was the first American to receive a Nobel Prize for physics (in 1907). Deservedly, he was taken very seriously. But in this, he could not have been more wrong. Michelson's quote, incidentally, is often ascribed to the great William Thomson, aka Lord Kelvin, (1824-1907).

Into modernity: the 20th century and onwards

Michelson was too confident by half, not to say hubristic. Within a few years of his declaration—the ink was hardly dry—new ideas came on board that would turn all physics completely on its head. In all cases the thinking began seriously in the 19th century although the story really belongs to the 20th—and of course continues, for the ensuing confusion is far from resolved and perhaps never can be. Relativity and quantum physics illustrate a key principle of the philosophy of science: that we can *never* assume that we have a problem sewn up, whatever the problem may be. Humility is, or should be, a prime virtue in science. Nature is always a step ahead of us—or many steps. We could not know how far we fall short of perfect understanding unless we were already omniscient and could gauge the extent of our own ignorance—which of course is logically impossible. In any case, as discussed later, 'perfect understanding' is a nice idea, even a useful idea, yet it is in principle nonsensical.

We should look first at the main ideas of science itself and then—equally important!—at the twists and turns of the philosophy of science.

Two huge ideas in ***physics*** have very obvious implications in all fields of thought including all philosophy and theology. They are the idea of ***Relativity***, due mainly to Albert Einstein (1879-1955); and the whole field of ***quantum mechanics*** and the related discipline of ***particle physics*** initiated by Max Planck (1858-1947).

Einstein was of course a towering presence through most of the 20th century and still is. He was not the only great thinker in the history of physics by any means but (like Newton and Maxwell) he was outstanding among those that were. As noted above, he had a very special ability to *envisage* how the universe must work, applying what he called 'thought experiments,' where others merely calculate. He is best known for his twin theses on ***Special Relativity,*** published in 1905; and ***General Relativity*** published in 1916. But he had fingers in many pies and was awarded a Nobel Prize in 1921 for his insights into physics in general and especially for 'his discovery of the law of the photoelectric effect.'

Crucial to his thesis on *Special Relativity,* is the idea—consistent with the measurements of Michelson and Morley—that light moves at a constant speed through a vacuum. From this, after much thought experiment, emerged the idea of *space-time*: that space and time are not independent entities but are two sides of the same coin. Earlier thinkers seemed to have reached a broadly similar conclusion—including, it seems, Christopher Marlowe (1564-1593). For when, at a few minutes to midnight, the eponymous anti-hero in *Dr Faustus* is due to be dragged off to Hell he pleads:

Stand still thou ever-moving spheres of heaven
That time may cease, and midnight never come!

But Marlowe didn't think the idea through and could not begin to do the maths and it was Einstein who brought the idea into mainstream physics.

Out of special theory also came the ideas that for a stationary observer and a moving object, time moves at different speeds; that no physical thing can move *faster* than the speed of light; and, most famously, that matter and energy are interchangeable—again, are two aspects of the same phenomenon. This thought is encapsulated in the equation that has launched a million T-shirts: $E=mc^2$ (where E = energy, m = mass, and c is a constant equivalent to the speed of light).

Einstein's second thesis, on *General Relativity,* addresses in particular the notion of gravity. The main conclusion is that gravity is not an attractive 'force' as Newton envisaged, but simply describes the way that objects fall when unrestrained. Specifically, he conceived the idea that space-time is curved. This looks like, and in essence is, a giant metaphor—very few people can really *see,* in their mind's eye, what curved space-time really *means.* But the idea works anyway. It finds particular application in astronomy—contributing to the science of quasars, pulsars, and black holes. Here I am merely recording the fact that this is so. I would not attempt to explain how.

The second truly momentous insight of the 20th century that brought us properly into modern times came from the German physicist Max Planck (1858-1947). In 1900 he reported that radiation from a warm black surface takes the form not of a continuous spectrum of energy but is more like a stream of discrete particles—which he called *quanta.* Out of this came the twin disciplines of ***particle physics*** and ***quantum mechanics.***

In related studies, early in the 20th century, the Danish physicist Niels Bohr (1885-1962) described the structure of the atom not as indivisible blobs as Dalton had envisaged them but in effect as miniature solar systems with a nucleus of positively charged protons and neutral neutrons with orbiting 'shells' of negatively-charged electrons. Most of the atom, like most of the solar system, is space (though space, we now know, is far from empty). Bohr's model is now much modified but it still serves as a rough guide. Now, though, particle physics has shown that protons and neutrons—and the universe as a whole—are compounded from a whole zoo of smaller particles that are said to be 'fundamental.' (Electrons are fundamental particles in their own right.)

Particle physics studies the particles and quantum mechanics describes their interactions and general behaviour—which, it has emerged, is seriously weird. For the fundamental particles emphatically do not march to the drum of Newton's laws that so brilliantly describe the behaviour of immediately observable, middle-sized objects like billiard balls and planets. Indeed, fundamental particles behave in ways that seem impossible. Sometimes they behave as particles and sometimes as waves. They can, apparently, be in more than one place at the same time. Quanta can bore through apparently solid barriers as if they weren't there—a phenomenon known as *quantum tunnelling*. Two particles that originate from the same source remain coordinated and so they influence each other even though they may be on opposite sides of the universe—the phenomenon of *quantum entanglement* which, as discussed later, is now finding a place in biology and in psychology.

It also transpired early on that the behaviour of fundamental particles is *in principle* unpredictable; and since fundamental particles are (or seem to be) the ultimate stuff of which the whole material universe is made this suggests that the whole idea of a *deterministic* universe is no longer tenable, at least in detail. In this context Einstein famously observed that

God does not play dice

—but it seems that He does. It is also suggested that *unless* the Universe had an element of randomness built into it, it would grind to a halt. It needs novelty. The same applies in biology. More or less random alterations in genes—mutations—provide the novelty that natural selection works on.

Perhaps the weirdest idea of all, though, came from the Austrian physicist (later an Irish citizen) Erwin Schrödinger (1887-1961). In 1935 he published an Einstein-style thought experiment in which he proposed that a cat (say) at any one time is both dead and alive and becomes one or the other only when observed. It seems indeed that nothing really *exists* unless and until it is observed. This sounds like gobbledegook as much of modern physics does but again, the closer you look the more it seems to be so. The idea that things—all things—only truly exist when observed again belongs in the realms of metaphysics. It is related to the key idea (which many people, including me, now take very seriously) that the most fundamental stuff of all is consciousness which I am content to equate with 'mind.' More in chapter 14.

In short, all these contemplations, arising from early 20th century physics—the rigorous, maths-inspired study of physical reality—take us well beyond the almost cosy insights of Newton and truly into unknown territory. Although some of the key ideas are now more than 100 years old very few people indeed are properly to grips with them and only specialists dare seriously to speculate. A professor of particle physics once told me that he did not even attempt to envisage the kind of worlds that are now being described. 'I just do the maths,' he said. But then, Niels Bohr observed that anyone who claimed to understand quantum physics doesn't understand the problems.

Einstein's idea of relativity and his conception of space-time with all its ramifications, for all their exoticism, may be seen as the culmination (so far!) of *classical physics*. Basically, this is the physics of the macroworld; in effect, of atoms. Quantum mechanics deals with the subatomic world, of fundamental particles and all that they do—which is when we move beyond the merely exotic and into a realm that is truly weird. The two species of physics, classical and quantum, seem incompatible. The maths that describes classical ideas simply does not describe quantum phenomena. Yet they both describe aspects of the same universe, and a huge amount of observation and experiment suggests that both are right. So how can two sets of apparently robust ideas that apply to the same universe be so incompatible? Physicists have laboured long and hard on this and many have dreamt of a 'grand unified theory' that can bring the two incompatible strands together. As a non-physicist I wonder whether this is really such a great problem. After all, we might argue that the quantum world, weird though it is, is the *real* world. The everyday (or not-so-everyday) phenomena described by classical physics may then be seen as an 'emergent property.' Emergent properties in general do not necessarily or directly reflect the phenomena or the forces that gave rise to them. In the same way, the chemistry of common salt, an essential nutrient (if we don't overdo it) cannot be inferred from the chemistry of its parents—the highly flammable metal sodium and the deadly poisonous gas chlorine, a foul weapon of war in WWI. By the same token, why should classical physics bear any obvious relationship to the more fundamental physics of the quantum world? (But I am not a physicist and perhaps that question is too naïve.)

As all Trekkies and Whovians (aficionados of *Star Trek* and *Dr Who*) know, not to mention fans of *The Big Bang Theory*, the core ideas of quantum mechanics and relativity are key players in modern ***cosmology***, the study of the universe as a whole and of how it all began. I love the idea, now well established, that all the elements of the periodic table were generated in distant and ancient stars as they ran through their life cycles: birth, growth, and explosive death. Other modern insights include that of the expanding universe and the Big Bang itself; the 9- or 11-dimensional universe, as opposed to the standard four (three of space and one of time); black holes; the idea of quantum gravity; and the realization (long intimated) that 'space,' including the space between stars and within atoms, is far from empty. Weirdest of all perhaps is the 'multiverse' theory which says that there is in truth an infinity of universes that between them act out all that is possible. Such an idea stretches credulity and common sense well past breaking point but nonetheless, some say, it should be taken seriously. What then is fantasy?

Newton observed more than 300 years ago that

> *to myself I am only a child playing on the beach, while vast oceans of truth lie undiscovered before me.*

Today, despite the brilliance of modern science—or perhaps because of it—we are far closer to Newton than to Michelson, who claimed that physics is all but sewn up. Chris Isham, a leading exponent of quantum gravity at Imperial College London (and a serious Christian) is wont to suggest that we are 'a million miles' from anything resembling complete, coherent understanding of the physical universe. But then, as Socrates observed, to be truly wise is to realize how ignorant we are. It is, though, as he surely would have agreed, logically impossible to gauge the extent of our ignorance.

What is clear, is that the more we look at the universe the weirder it seems. It now seems for example that *most* of the universe—about 85%—consists of material that we know is present only because it clearly exerts gravity. The missing majority is called 'dark matter.' It's clear, too, that the universe is not only expanding but is expanding at an ever-increasing rate—which has prompted physicists to propose a new *and unknown* form of energy which they call, *faute de mieux*, 'dark energy.' Einstein's theories, which still seem novel although he described them 100 years ago, already seen inadequate—merely part of a far larger story; just as Newton's mechanics, which once seemed to tell us all there was to know, had to be subsumed within the larger vision of Einstein.

The word 'dark,' in dark energy and dark matter, primarily reflects the extent of our ignorance.

The Earth sciences in the 20th century and beyond have taken us well beyond Hutton and Lyell. I particularly like the idea, first set out in 1912 by the German Alfred Wegener (1880-1930) of ***continental drift***. Again there are pre-echoes, for way back in the 16th century the Spanish-Dutch map-maker Abraham Ortelius (1527-1598) pointed out how well the continents fit together if you put them all together like a jigsaw—suggesting that they might once have *been* together, and then shuffled apart; and others in the 18th and 19th centuries said much the same. But Wegener's account was by far the most solid. Alas, though—yet again!—after some initial enthusiasm his work was largely forgotten and even derided, mainly because no one could think how continents *could* move. Then from the 1960s onwards there emerged the idea of *plate tectonics*. It seems that the outer crust of the Earth is divided into a series of *tectonic plates* that float on top of underlying, molten *magma*; and the plates are borne hither and thither by convection currents. The continents sit on top of the plates so as the plates slither about the continents are carried along with them.

Plate tectonics is now the orthodoxy. It explains much that is otherwise difficult to explain, including earthquakes, tsunamis, and the way that mountains are built: and (a very important point of detail) how the rock of the rising Himalayas absorbed carbon dioxide from the atmosphere and thus contributed to the global cooling that led to the Pleistocene Ice Ages. Wegener was primarily a meteorologist and surely would have loved that idea. Alas, he did not live long enough to see his ideas accepted and developed.

The Earth sciences too include palaeontology, though that is best discussed under life sciences.

The Life Sciences were transformed in the 20th century and the transformation continues. Here, for what it's worth, is a lightning sketch—a shopping list of some the biggest ideas:

The modern synthesis

First, early in the 20th century, the English biologist William Bateson (1861-1926) coined the word 'genetics'—the study of Mendel's 'hereditary factors,' which became known as 'genes.' For a time it looked as if Mendel's genetics was incompatible with Darwin's theory of evolution but then from the 1920s onwards a group of biologists—including Julian Huxley, J.B.S. Haldane, and the statistician R.A. (Ronald) Fisher from England; and Theodosius Dobzhansky (1900-1975), Ernst Mayr (1904-2005) and Sewall Wright (1889-1998) in the US—showed how, in truth, the two fit perfectly together. The combined theories form what became known as ***'the modern synthesis'***; sometimes called 'neodarwinism' although the term 'neodarwinism' has other meanings as well.

Molecular biology

From the 1940s onwards, various biologists in various places showed beyond all doubt that DNA, the mysterious nucleic acid found in cell nuclei, is indeed the *stuff* of genes. Then, with interest thoroughly aroused, more scientists showed how the various bits of the DNA—the adenine, cytosine, thymine and guanine—fit together; and finally, in the 1950s, Rosalind Franklin (1920-1958) at King's College, London, produced *crystals* of DNA from which she created shadow-pictures showing how the individual atoms within the crystal were arranged. From these pictures, and all the other data, Francis Crick and James Watson at Cambridge devised their famous 'double helix' model, showing the complete 3-D structure of the DNA macromolecule. They also suggested, at least in outline, how DNA is replicated: then others showed how DNA collaborates with teams of RNAs to make proteins, which then provide much of the structure and do much of the work of the cell. This is the essence of modern ***molecular biology.*** Its ideas neatly complete the neodarwinian synthesis: Darwin's evolutionary theory; Mendelian genetics; and molecular biology.

I learned all this stuff at school and university from 1959 onwards and felt for a time as Michelson did about physics—that biology was now sewn up. All the rest was detail. I was just a student but a lot of senior scientists evidently felt that way too. How naïve! In truth, understanding has only just begun. In particular, it is clear that DNA is not a simple 'digital code' as has often been supposed. It is more like human language: highly syntactical; elliptical; full of cross-references. Yet digital thinking persists. It is the essence of genetic engineering, which is the core technology of modern biotech, which is the darling of technophilic governments, now sweeping through the world's agriculture.

Some enthusiasts indeed equate life itself with DNA. They suggest that life began when DNA was first on the scene. What nonsense! DNA is itself a highly evolved molecule. It clearly had many precursors; and such a molecule could not have evolved *except* in a living milieu. In truth the essence of life is as Aristotle said—metabolism: *action*. More particularly, we might say, the essence of life is the cycle—a cycle that is able to keep itself going by drawing energy from its surroundings. A modern cell is a consortium of cycles, and of cycles within cycles: wheels within wheels. DNA was and is both the day-to-day manager of the whole caboodle, and the librarian; repository of the information needed to replicate the cycles. Life must have been messy before DNA (or its functional precursors) came on the scene—but still, DNA must have come late to the party. DNA is now (almost) ubiquitous among living creatures not because it is essential (that is: 'of the essence') but because it is successful. Common sense, though, says that we cannot equate DNA with life. Corpses contain perfectly viable DNA. Vitalism is no longer fashionable but we still need to explain the vital spark.

Ecology

Wondrous as all this is, though, I suggest that the most profound biological advance of the 20th and 21st centuries lies in ecology: the first glimmers of understanding of how all organisms on Earth mesh together, and interact with their surroundings, each an individual with its own *milieu interieur* but each, too, absolutely dependent on the others, each part of a far larger whole. To me one of the greatest insights of the 20th century was and is James Lovelock's concept of *Gaia*, as outlined in chapter 4.

Palaeontology

Hugely important too have been the continuing advances in palaeontology: showing beyond all reasonable doubt for example that birds are not only descended from dinosaurs but *are* dinosaurs, as T.H. Huxley and Richard Owen surmised in the 19th century; and showing too, with profound metaphysical and theological ramifications, that the human ancestral tree is as branched as any other. We—*Homo sapiens sapiens*—are not the only kind of human there has been, and we did not evolve in one straight and unswerving line from our apish ancestors, as 19th century—and early 20th century—post-Darwinian accounts of our evolution were wont to suggest. Modern day humans are simply the kind that the world has finished up with (for the time being. Though perhaps we are the last.).

Taxonomy—and the three domains

All these evolutionary and genetic cogitations have given rise to the modern arts and science of taxonomy. Linnaeus in the 18th century suggested that all living creatures could be classed in two kingdoms—animals (Animalia) and plants (Plantae). Very cavalierly, he bundled the fungi in with the plants. Now it's clear among much else that Fungi need their own kingdom—and that we should recognize several more kingdoms too, including the one that contains the brown seaweeds, which include kelp, which emphatically are *not* plants. More profoundly, the American biologist/biophysicist Carl Woese (1928-2012), who I had the privilege of interviewing in the 1990s, showed on molecular grounds that all Earthly creatures should be divided into three *domains*. Two—the Bacteria and the Archaea—are 'prokaryotes,' meaning their cells lack nuclei. The third, the Eucaryota (eukaryotes) have elaborate cells with nuclei; and they include all the macroscopic kingdoms—animals, plants, fungi, and the rest; plus various single-celled eukaryotes that were called 'protozoa' and classed as animals. In truth, then, animals do not represent a half of Earthly life, as Linnaeus suggested. They are just one life plan among at least a dozen.

The modern classification also illustrates in graphic form that all Earthly creatures are, literally, related. Insects are our cousins and mushrooms are somewhat more distant cousins and oak trees are more distant again (fungi are more closely related to animals than to plants). Brown seaweeds and miscellaneous 'protists' are even further away but they are on the same tree too—and so, too, are the bacteria and archaeans. Indeed, thanks in part to Carl Woese and thanks too not least to the New

England biologist Lynn Margulis (1938-2011) it's clear that the eukaryotic cell *originated* as a coalition of various bacteria and of at least one archaean. Some ancient archaean provided much of the cytoplasm of the eukaryotic cell and the various 'inclusions'—mitochondria, chloroplasts, etc—originated as bacterial lodgers that became part of the fabric. Truly, life itself is a masterclass in cooperativeness. As I commented earlier—***competition is a fact of life, but cooperativeness is the essence.*** The metaphysical observation that all life is one is literally the case. If this idea had spilled over into the zeitgeist, rather than the deeply pernicious meme of 'the selfish gene' and that life inescapably is one long punch-up, the world's politics and daily life might have been significantly different, and far safer and more agreeable.

Animal psychology

Also of profound significance are the advances in animal psychology. The 20th century began dourly with the rise and rise of *behaviourism*: animals were conceived as machines whose behaviour is compounded from chains of reflexes. Any attempt to draw parallels with human behaviour was written off with snorts of contempt as 'anthropomorphism,' which was perceived as the great no-no; most 'unscientific.' The mood began to change in particular with Jane Goodall's (b. 1934) work on chimpanzees in the Gombe Stream National Park in Tanzania, beginning in the 1960s. In a nutshell, although the penny was slow to drop among biologists at large, she showed that the behaviour of wild chimps could not simply be explained away in behaviourist terms. At least: the attempts to fit their behaviour into the behaviourist 'paradigm' became just as convoluted and obviously absurd as the attempts of late Mediaeval astronomers to defend the idea of the geocentric solar system. Other studies in other contexts rammed home the point and by the 1980s the animal psychologist Patrick Bateson (1938-2017)—he a not-too-distant relative of William Bateson—declared that anthropomorphism within bounds is 'heuristic,' giving key insights into the behaviour (and indeed the minds) of animals. Today, in particular, the work of Frans de Waal in the Netherlands supports the general idea (though I paraphrase) that it is more fruitful to assume that intelligent creatures such as chimps and honey badgers are like us, than to assume or indeed insist that they are really just elaborate clockwork toys. We need to acknowledge that other intelligent animals really can be happy or miserable or jealous or sad, just as we can, and just as our intuition tells us is the case. There are some signs that such thinking is now having an influence on animal welfare and on conservation. But the wheels of legislators and big business grind very slowly and they, in practice, call the shots.

Quantum biology

Some biologists are beginning to perceive that a great many fundamental biological processes, from photosynthesis to bird migration (at least in some of its forms), cannot be understood without reference to the very peculiar, totally counter-intuitive manifestations of quantum mechanics: wave-particle duality; superposition; quantum tunnelling; and quantum entanglement. Hitherto, both biologists and physicists have dismissed this idea because they say these peculiarities are simply not possible in 'normal' conditions, such as are found within living organisms. Quantum phenomena are very delicate and are generally swamped by the noise and jostling of atoms and molecules that are the norm in what we experience as everyday life.

But physicist Jim Al-Khalili and molecular geneticist Johnjoe McFadden argue in *Life on the Edge* (Black Swan, 2014) that it's the ability to enable quantum tunnelling and entanglement and all the rest to happen among the bustle of 'normal' chemistry that makes life special. Indeed, they more or less define life as the state that exists on the border between quantum mechanics on the one hand and classical physics on the other. *How* living systems manage to do this is one of the great unknowns of science. Science does not lead us to omniscience and absolute certainty. It takes us instead to the limits of what is knowable at any one time, and this special quality of life—the exploitation of quantum phenomena within a macro-environment—is a prime example.

Al-Khalili's and McFadden's idea remains speculative but to me and a growing number of *bona fide* scientists it has the ring of truth. It makes perfect sense. It certainly deserves to be taken seriously—which, as suggested in the next chapter, in the end is the best we can hope for any idea.

Consciousness

Finally, even more radically, many scientists and others are now re-visiting the ancient idea that consciousness, not the measurable, tangible, visible, *material* world that we experience and is the subject of conventional science, is the basic *stuff* of the universe. Conventional science treats the material world as the prime 'reality' and sees consciousness simply as an epiphenomenon. But the truth may well be the other way around. More in the next chapter.

All in all, biology and indeed all science looks very different now from what it did when I was introduced to it at school in the mid-20th century, and it surely will look very different again in a few decades' time. I hope the shift will continue to be for the better—the subject becoming broader, more open-minded, more morally and aesthetically aware. I do hope that science is not reduced to biotech and the space race, to enrich corporate shareholders and to tighten the grip of the superpowers. This could happen all too easily.

The modern philosophy of science: omniscience, or the cloud of unknowing?

Science should never be taught without the philosophy of science. Conventional education explains the content of science and tells us how wondrous it is (quite rightly). But the 'phil of sci' is needed too to tell us what science really *is*, and what it is not, and to point out its limitations—and indeed to point out that it does have limitations.

In the 20th century the phil of sci confronted us with hugely contrasting points of view, and it still does. At one extreme we are given to understand that science can tell us all we need to know, and indeed that in the fullness of time, if we keep up the good work, it will make us virtually omniscient; and that out of this omniscience will come high technologies that will make us omnipotent. Indeed we will be gods. Some scientists and science commentators evidently believe this, or behave as if they do, and some politicians too—usually of the kind who read classics or history or some such at university and came to science late in life and feel that it might make them more grounded.

At the other extreme we still find people who, frankly, fear science. Scientific knowledge, they feel, erodes God's mystery—and this, they suggest, is blasphemous: like Adam and Eve seeking to eat from the tree of forbidden knowledge.

Both extremes, I suggest, are nonsensical. Absolute or exaggerated faith in the power of science to reveal all is known as ***scientism*** and lies behind the uncritical technophilia that is now so threatening, as outlined in chapter 5. At the other extreme, the idea that scientific enquiry is blasphemous seems itself to be blasphemous. It diminishes God. It puts God on a level with conjurors, whose tricks seem tawdry once the secret is revealed. In absolute contrast the intricacies of life and the universe grow *more* wondrous the more we look at them—and in the end we just have to acknowledge that all our explorations end in mystery (as Einstein said).

The only sensible position, I suggest, is to acknowledge that science really is wonderful and everyone should at least be given the chance to get to grips with it. The reasons are both personal and cultural (it is at least a shame to go to the grave without at least an inkling of what Darwin or Einstein *really* said) and political; for science really is powerful and democracy cannot function as it should unless people at large have some feel for what science can do and what it cannot. No one can govern well—whether the governors are autocrats or oligarchs or people at large—unless they have at least some feel for what is *possible,* and what is not. This is what science can provide.

The 20th century began on an ambivalent note. Thus on the one hand the first intimations of relativity and quantum physics opened up whole new vistas of human knowledge and insight, suggesting that our powers of inquiry might indeed be unlimited. At the same time the combination of Mendelian genetics and Darwinian evolution seemed, to some, to 'explain' life. So too did the evermore confident and precise inroads into psychology—the buttoned-down mechanistic approach of the behaviourists on the one hand, and the grand sweeping anthropological insights of Freud and others on the other. What more was there really to know?

Yet the very fact that Einstein and Planck's revelations followed so hard on Michelson's suggestion that physics was already sewn up, should have sounded a very loud note of caution. For the ideas of physics that emerged in the early 20th century revealed the most telling truth of all: that ***how-***

ever much we think we know, and however clever we may think we are, reality is always one step ahead of us—and once we have made that step, we will find a whole new Jacob's ladder opening up before us, reaching towards the heavens but never quite getting there. In truth, many of the leaders of 20th century science, including Einstein and Bohr, retained the necessary humility. As Einstein remarked in *Living Philosophies* (1931):

> *The most beautiful experience we can have is the mysterious—the fundamental emotion of which is the cradle of time and true science.*

Yet science as a whole seemed to grow in confidence. There was great faith in the *method* of science—a method somewhat different from that advocated by Francis Bacon but similar in spirit: a feeling that as long as we follow the rules, we can't go wrong, and must arrive eventually at *truth*, both certain and unequivocal. The modern method—dating from the 20th century—was and is to collect as much data as possible (*facts*) based on repeatable, reliable observation; to come up with various *hypotheses* to explain how all the (known) facts might fit together; and to *test* the various hypothesis by experiment and/or by making predictions about the way the world would be if the hypothesis was correct. All the observations are *quantified* and the quantities are then subjected to the most rigorous *mathematical* analysis—for maths can't be wrong, provided we make no mistakes (can it?). Then the whole story is subject to *peer review* and if it gets past this is published in a respectable journal for all the world to scrutinize and criticize forever and ever. Only those ideas that survive such battering are granted the status of *theories*. 'Theory' in science does not mean 'hunch' or 'wheeze' as it does in common parlance. A scientific theory is an idea that has been through the most rigorous intellectual mill that human beings can subject it to, and survived. Tried and tested theories are added to the grand ziggurat of irrefutable knowledge which, apparently, a great many people in positions of influence, and many others too, imagine science to be.

This way of thinking led, by the time of World War I, to ***logical positivism***: clearly an echo of Comte's early 19th century positivism, though apparently a separate initiative. In particular the logical positivists developed the idea of ***verifiability***. That is, they said, the only ideas that are truly robust, and should be taken seriously, are those that can be verified—which in effect means *proved*; and in practice, they said, the only ideas that *can* be verified are those of science.

Thus, science was and in some circles still is conceived and presented as a sure path to certainty and indeed as the royal road to omniscience. In the words of one of the leading logical positivists Rudolf Carnap (1891-1970):

> *... there is no question whose answer is in principle unobtainable by science.*
>
> [Quoted by Peter Coates in *Ibn 'Arabi and Modern Thought*, ANQA, Oxford, 2002, p. 61]

Of course, some questions don't seem answerable by science, such as 'Does God exist?' but the logical positivists got round this simply by declaring that such questions are nonsensical (since we cannot agree on how to define God) and therefore should not be asked. Metaphysics, which does address such questions, thus was kicked most emphatically into the long grass, where the fairies live; and so too therefore was religion, which in essence is metaphysical. Logical positivism was in large measure the culmination of 18th century Enlightenment atheism. Again it was and in some circles still is taken to be self-evident that science and religion must be at odds.

Logical positivism began to fall out of favour as a formal discipline in the 1960s (it still seemed to reign supreme when I was at university) and was more or less defunct by the 1970s when its leading British proponent, A.J. ('Freddie') Ayer (1910-1989) at Oxford, finally gave up on it. Yet the essence of it persists in the minds of many scientists. Thus the renowned physical chemist Professor Peter Atkins of Oxford (b. 1940) famously wrote in a book published in 1995:

> *Science, the system of belief founded securely on publicly shared reproducible knowledge, emerged from religion. As science discarded its chrysalis to become its present butterfly, it took over the heath. There is no reason to suppose that science cannot deal with every aspect of existence. Only the religious—among whom I include not only the prejudiced but also the underinformed—hope there is a dark corner to the universe, or of the universe of experience, that science can never hope to illuminate. But science has never encountered a barrier, and the only grounds for supposing that reductionism will*

fail are pessimism on the part of scientists and fear in the minds of the religious.

['The Limitless Power of Science' in *Nature's Imagination—the Frontiers of Scientific Vision*. Ed. John Cornwell, Oxford, Oxford University Press, 1995, p. 125. Quoted (disapprovingly!) by John Lennox, Oxford professor of maths and a devout Christian, in *God's Undertaker* (Lion Hudson, Oxford, 2007, p. 8)]

I feel that Francis Bacon was nearer the mark when he observed in his essay 'On Atheism' that

... a little philosophy inclineth man's mind to atheism; but depth in philosophy bringeth men's minds about to religion.

[From *Essays, Civil and Moral,* 1597]

And yet: even while logical positivism was still on the rise, seen by many as the key to modernity, it was being eroded at the roots.

First, beginning in the 1920s, the Austro-Hungarian mathematician Kurt Gödel (1906-1978) began to show that maths isn't quite as sure-fire as was generally taken to be the case. He showed, to paraphrase cruelly, that mathematical equations that aren't just tautologies (in effect, matters of definition) are bound to be incomplete or internally inconsistent or uncertain. That is, they are bound, always, to contain some assumption that, in effect, is arbitrary. Maths in short is not so 'objective' as is supposed. Mathematicians don't after all have a hotline to objective truth, whatever objective truth may be. This means that the theories of science, rooted in and 'verified' by maths, are not quite so secure as they seem.

Neither—to take a practical example—can we simply throw maths at problems and hope that it will tell us all we need to know. For example, modern taxonomists try to work out which creature (alive or dead) is related to which by assessing as many features as possible—including, of course, nowadays, the sequence of their DNA. But the resulting analyses typically produce many thousands of possible evolutionary trees. Statistics of a very fancy kind are then employed to work out which of the many possible trees are the most likely to be true. However, the data always lend themselves to several different forms of statistical analysis—different statistical *algorithms*. The taxonomist is left to decide which of the algorithms is the most appropriate for the task in hand—which he or she does on the basis of their own expertise, which in turn is based on their day-to-day work and their education and on their own predilections. In short, we can never escape the need for human judgement; and judgement that can properly be considered *wise* cannot be based simply on formulae.

In the 1930s came a serious challenge from the Austrian-British philosopher Karl Popper (1902-1994). He pointed out that in practice *no* big idea about the material world can be shown to be true beyond all possible doubt. We can show with absolute certainty only that certain ideas are *un*true. Thus, he said, we cannot prove the proposition that 'all swans are white' because however many we find we can't be sure that there is a swan somewhere that is not white, that we have so far failed to find. This example is not actually very convincing but it will do. It tells us that the principle of verification—the centrepiece of logical positivism—is not appropriate because in practice *nothing* can be verified beyond all doubt. Ideas that qualify as scientific are not those that can be verified but those that could in theory be ***falsified***. Scientific 'truths' are ideas that have survived rigorous testing and not been shown to be false. The canon of science as a whole, said Popper, is not founded on bedrock certainties because there are no bedrock certainties. Like the city of Venice the edifice of scientific truth is built on mud: or, rather, on supports that are driven into the mud until they can be driven no further. Like Venice, science is indeed wonderful but is not as secure as it looks.

A further caveat was provided in the 1960s by the Brazilian-born British zoologist and immunologist Peter Medawar, a Nobel Prize-winner and a friend and fan of Popper, who simply suggested that

Science is the art of the soluble

—an artful adaptation of Bismarck's comment that 'Politics is the art of the possible.' Scientists, in short, focus primarily—or in practice exclusively—on problems that they feel reasonably sure they can solve in the time and with the resources available. This strategy has clearly been very fruitful. But is it remotely likely that by exploring just what is within reach at any one time we can ever arrive at anything approaching omniscience? There are all kinds of reasons for thinking that this cannot be so.

The proposal of hypotheses is an essential step in the search for truth—but a hypothesis, as quantum physicist Richard Feynman (1918-1988)

put the matter, is, in the end, just a 'guess.' Indeed, as Isaac Newton said nearly 300 years earlier:

No great discovery was ever made without a bold guess.

Guesses in practice are leaps in the dark—albeit, in practice, informed leaps in the dark. Among the most spectacular leaps of the 20th century was one made by the American geneticist Barbara McClintock (1902-1992) who, from her studies of maize, concluded that genes must be able to move from one part of a genome to another—what she called 'jumping genes.' It was a wild idea but further studies suggest that she was right. How did she arrive at such an insight? McClintock's general approach was to cultivate a kind of empathy:

I start with the seedling, and I don't want to leave it. I don't feel I really know the story if I don't watch the plant all the way along. So I know every plant in the field. I know them all intimately and I find it a real pleasure to know them.

[Quoted by Jay B. McDaniel in 'Christian Spirituality as Openness to Fellow Creatures.' *Environmental Ethics* (1986) 8(1) 34.]

More broadly, science is commonly supposed to be rational all the way through—the epitome of rationality—but guesses based on empathy is not what is normally meant by rationality. Fruitful inquiry requires something altogether more mysterious: intuition; imagination. In truth the geniuses of science are *not* mere rationalists. They are masters of rationality but what makes them special is what makes poets and prophets special: a vibration in the whiskers, a feeling in the bones, that such-and-such an idea *must* be true. The rationality—the testing and the maths—comes later.

However—another huge however!—although rational thinking aided by maths can tell us what is *likely*, it can never tell us what is actually *true*, or at least it can never give us the whole truth and if it does then we cannot know for certain that it is the whole truth. Neither should we suppose that scientists are themselves guided to what they perceive to be true simply by thinking rationally. In the end, what makes a scientist say 'That's it!'—the grand eureka moment—is the feeling in the bones that such-and-such an idea must be *right*. This feeling is in essence aesthetic.

As the great British theoretical physicist Paul Dirac (1902-1984) commented:

It is more important to have beauty in one's equations than to have them fit experiment.

Or as John Keats (1795-1821) wrote in 'On a Grecian Urn' in 1819:

Beauty is truth, truth beauty,—that is all
Ye know on earth, and all ye need to know.

Crucial too to the modern view of science was and is the ideas of the American philosopher Thomas Kuhn (1922-1996). In *The Structure of Scientific Revolutions* in 1962 Kuhn pointed out that science does not build stone by irrefutable stone into permanent ziggurat of truth. Instead he introduced the idea of the *paradigm shift.* At any one time, he said, scientists in each field have a particular worldview—a paradigm—of what the world is like, and what is true and untrue. But over time, more and more ideas come on board that seem at odds with the existing paradigm, or at least fit too awkwardly for comfort. So there is a growing desire for a new paradigm. The shift from Newton's idea of a deterministic, mechanical universe to the modern view rooted in Einstein's relativity and quantum physics was and is a prime example. Note, however, that Newton's physics is not considered to be wrong. It is merely subsumed within a larger vision—a larger paradigm. As intimated throughout this chapter, in physics and in the life sciences the present paradigms are already looking creaky. Overall it seems that the solid edifice of truth should rather be conceived as a landscape painting, worked on constantly by a thousand different hands, that will never be finished. More generally it is clear, as some philosophers have been pointing out for some millennia, that absolute knowledge of absolute truth is not in our gift. All our knowledge, including scientific knowledge, is narrative—a story that we tell ourselves; and what we call 'truth,' in practice, is a story that (we hope) reflects reality reasonably accurately, whatever reality may be. Or at least, we might say, it is a story that, for the time being, we happen to find convincing.

In the early 20th century the French playwright and philosopher Gabriel Marcel (1889-1973) proposed that there are three levels of unknown: puzzles, problems, and mysteries. Puzzles, like jigsaws and

Rubik's cube, contain all the information needed to solve them. It's just a question of rearranging what's there. Problems too can be solved but require some research—more information than is provided. Mysteries are beyond final solution.

Science treats the world as a series of problems, to be solved. Some scientists still dream of final solutions, in the spirit of Michelson. In truth, though, our understanding is beset not only by unknowns but by what Donald Rumsfeld famously called 'unknown unknowns': things we don't even know we don't know—and we could not know what we don't know unless we were already omniscient. In truth, life is not merely a series of problems. For all our research and vaunted rationality, and for all our leaps of imagination, life and the universe will always be mysterious. What we think we know is always uncertain and provisional and always falls far short of what *is*. Again it seems abundantly obvious that science should never be taught without the philosophy of science. Science taught in isolation leads all too easily to scientism and hence to arrogance and hence to hubris, the most dangerous sin of all. Science is wonderful and indeed indispensable but it is not the royal road to truth. It is a key component of the Perennial Wisdom but it is not the whole of the Perennial Wisdom and neither is it as distinct as some seem to think from all other areas of inquiry. The borders of science are leaky, and science has its own limitations. Human affairs must be led not by mere rationality but by morality, and especially with compassion that must embrace all living creatures; and insofar as science is 'applied' at all to day-to-day affairs, it must help us to achieve what I suggested at the outset must be our goal—to create 'convivial societies in a flourishing biosphere.' In the end, too, for all our striving and the insights of genius, life and the universe will always be beyond our ken. Science, like human beings in general, cannot escape the cloud of unknowing.

Too often, science is taught purely or primarily as a utilitarian pursuit, intended simply to provide high technologies, of a potentially profitable kind. Thus it becomes the handmaiden of single-minded governments, like Britain's, and of big business. In truth, science should be taught as a cultural pursuit—factual of course insofar as we can discern the facts but also aesthetic, moral, and metaphysical. Metaphysics may be seen as the attempt to make sense of mystery, or at least to do the best we can. That is the theme of the next chapter.

14

Metaphysics: The essential ingredient that's gone missing

BEYOND DOUBT, THE ENLIGHTENMENT WAS ENLIGHTENING. It brought us new ideas and, perhaps even more importantly, it helped us to sort out the old ones and prepare the ground for new thinking.

But it had its downside too. Above all it emphasised rationality, which is fair enough—but at least in some people's hands it thereby diminished other, more intuitive, ways of interpreting the world. Rationality itself has serious limitations and drawbacks. It all too easily becomes equated with calculation, leading us into the trap of logical positivism, an exercise in materialism and quantification. We banish intuition at our peril. As we saw in chapter 13, science itself of a creative kind *depends* on intuition and on the related quality of imagination. A strictly materialist, quantified, 'rational' view of the world is altogether too skeletal. It misses out much that is important. Also, of course, a strictly hard-nosed approach cuts us off from spirituality—a much misused word that nonetheless has meaning, as discussed below. The combination of rationality and spirituality is what makes us truly human, and to be truly human is surely a good thing. Popes John Paul II and Francis said and say the same kind of thing, and so does many a scientist, from Barbara McClintock and Rachel Carson to Albert Einstein.

In particular, buttoned-down Enlightenment thinking of the kind that still prevails has seriously undermined the pursuit of metaphysics. Indeed, at least as an independent discipline, metaphysics has largely or almost entirely gone missing from western thinking, which means from world thinking, except when embedded within the various religions, when it is entwined with theology. Sayed Hossein Nasr, Professor of Islamic Studies at the George Washington University, Washington DC, suggests that the loss of metaphysics is the single greatest cause of the world's present ills. I think he is right.

What is metaphysics?

Science is about fact and explanation thereof. Philosophy is about thinking straight. Metaphysics is about meaning. Metaphysics is the search for truth. Metaphysics partakes of philosophy but it is not the same thing at all.

'Metaphysics' literally means 'beyond physics.' It addresses what are often called ***the ultimate questions***—questions that cannot be satisfactorily addressed by science alone, and to each and all of them it brings special insights and ways of thinking.

As I see things the ultimate questions are:

1: What is the Universe really like?

2: How do we know what's true?

3: What is 'good'?

And:

4: How come?

The 'ultimate questions' are surely the most fundamental of all so metaphysics should (should it not?) be at the heart of all our thinking and of all formal education—but instead it is marginalized. The ultimate questions cannot of course be answered with absolute certainty. All attempts to do so in the end are mere dogma. Indeed as outlined in chapter 13 there *are* no bedrock certainties. We can, though, throw light on the areas of uncertainty. So here is my own rough guide:

1: What is the Universe really like?

To this first question, metaphysics contributes four very big ideas. They are:

Transcendence

Oneness

The sense of mystery

Intuition—for we cannot get properly to grips with the issues that really matter by observation and calculation alone.

So:

Transcendence

The question—'What is the universe really like?'—has largely been delegated to science; which indeed over the past 400 years in particular, has given us and continues to give us wondrous insights. It is a privilege to be alive in this age of science. But science has clear limitations. In particular, as Peter Medawar pointed out, science in the end is and can only be 'the art of the soluble,' and the problems that are most soluble are those that have to do with the material world, which we can measure and mathematicise.

This is fair enough. Science succeeds as well as it does largely *because* scientists limit their field of inquiry to areas in which they think they can make most progress. But many scientists and philosophers then make a huge and quite unjustifiable leap—one that seems to me to be both arrogant and naïve. They have apparently decided that what they find convenient to study *is all there is*. Why should it be so? *(Continues on page 328)*

THE CORE IDEAS OF METAPHYSICS

Metaphysics addresses 'the ultimate questions'—shown below in bold type—each of which gives rise to and is informed by various subsidiary or related notions. (This summary is my own personal take on things. Others may see things differently). Thus:

1: WHAT IS THE UNIVERSE REALLY LIKE?

Transcendence:

- The numinous (divine presence)
- A sense of the sacred
- Universal consciousness

Oneness *(advaya).*

Harmony *(dharma; shalom).*

2: WHAT IS GOODNESS?

Compassion/ love:

- Kindness
- Generosity *(zakat)*
- Justice

Humility.

True concern for and a sense of oneness with the natural world.

3: HOW DO WE KNOW WHAT'S TRUE?

Rationality:

- Scholarship
- Science
    - Observation/empirical knowledge
    - Logic
    - Mathematics

Intuition:

- Revelation
    - Meditation
    - Ritual
    - Prayer
- Mystical experience

4: HOW COME?

The realization and acceptance of ultimate mystery.

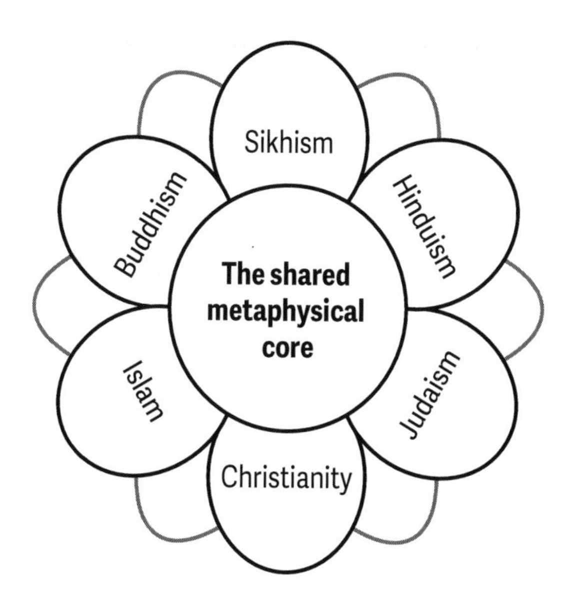

The diagram shows the relationship between metaphysics in general and the world's various religions in particular. The whole diagram looks like a flower—which is serendipitous; each 'petal' represents a different religion but all share the same central core of essentially metaphysical ideas. The six main petals are the global religions; the ones behind are regional religions like Shinto and the indigenous religions such as Maori.

The idea and the value of the Interfaith movement (as I see things) is both to explore the special features of each different religion and to contemplate and develop the core metaphysic—bringing to bear the special insights of all the religions. It is eminently possible to be a good Christian or Muslim or Hindu and also to partake of, benefit from, and delight in the special qualities of all other bona fide religions. The all-too common conceit that any one religion is true and all the others are heretical and blasphemous, is deeply destructive and can never be justified. All should be seen as quests with a common goal—a goal that might be seen as enlightenment in the broadest sense.

The core metaphysical ideas are summarized in the table on the left.

After all, science itself tells us that our brains are evolved organs: evolved under the pressures of natural selection to help us to survive—basically to feed, stay out of trouble, and reproduce. On the woodland edges and open savannah of Africa on which our first recognizable ancestors first appeared that meant finding suitable roots and seeds, hunting porcupines and (on a good day) wildebeest, avoiding hyaenas, and attracting mates. Why should an organ that evolved to cope with such earth-bound exigencies enable us to probe the deepest secrets of the universe? How could it be so?

It seems safer—more *logical*—to acknowledge that there could well be aspects of the universe that our brains did not evolve to cope with; that indeed *there is more to the universe than meets the eye*. Or, more accurately (since a great deal of the material universe including dark matter doesn't actually 'meet the eye'), it is very reasonable to suggest that some serious and indeed vital aspects of the universe may well quite literally be beyond our ken. We might then suggest, misquoting Medawar, that 'metaphysics is the art of the unknowable.' This—the idea that significant aspects of the universe are beyond the reaches of science—is what I mean by ***transcendence***. (I say 'what I mean by transcendence' because, like all big words, the term transcendence is used by different people to mean different things.)

Some philosophers declare that if something is unknowable then it is simply conjectural and therefore is not worth studying. Indeed, the logical positivists insisted that whatever cannot be pinned down—defined, observed, and mathematicised—is *ipso facto* nonsensical. A.J. Ayer used to say that the word 'God' is literally 'gibberish' (his word). But the idea that there is a transcendent world behind what we can see and touch and measure is perfectly reasonable ('rational'); and although we cannot pin down matters of a transcendent nature as precisely as we can pin down the physical universe (there is no metaphysical equivalent of $E=mc^2$) we can nonetheless talk sensibly about transcendent things. Metaphysics doesn't have the solidity of science but it is not entirely nebulous either, and it certainly is not vacuous. In any case, as we saw in chapter 13, science itself is not as solid as it looks.

Finally, those who say 'There is no evidence' for any phenomena at work in the universe beyond what we can see, touch, and measure simply do not know what evidence is. For evidence is not proof. If it was there would be no need for courts of law. Evidence is merely an observation that is compatible with a particular idea. Is there nothing about the universe to suggest there is more to the universe than meets the eye? Indeed there is so much that it took humanity a very long time to suppose otherwise.

Plato felt that the hypothetical transcendent world—the world behind the scenes—is in truth more 'real' than the world we can see and touch; that the visible and tangible world is merely the outward face of things. Embedded in this is the idea that there is or may be an intelligence at work behind the universe. Indeed, ***consciousness may be a principal component of the universe itself***. This idea may be wrong but there is no *reason*, apart from dogma, to reject it out of hand. Indeed it should be taken very seriously indeed. A little expansion is called for:

Universal consciousness

When we think it seems to us (does it not?) that the thinking emanates from our own selves, and in particular from our own brains. Too much thinking, after all, makes your head hurt. From this it seems to follow that thought and feeling, consciousness and 'mind' would not exist at all were it not that sentient creatures like us, brought it about.

But there is an alternative notion, embraced by some philosophers and theologians and also increasingly by scientists—including some anthropologists, psychologists, and in particular by *avant garde* physicists. It is that ***consciousness is a quality of the universe***, embedded in effect in the fabric of the universe. According to this idea, we do not generate consciousness inside our own heads, like a battery generating electricity. We *partake* to a greater or lesser degree of the universal consciousness that is around us all the time, in the same kind of way that a radio receiver partakes of the all-pervasive and ever-present radio waves. To put the idea even more strongly: the stuff of which the universe is made is not simply matter and energy, or space-time, but is mind-matter.

The idea of universal consciousness does not seem to pass the logical-positivist test. It is hard to see how it could be *validated* beyond all reasonable doubt. It is not clear either how it could pass the Popper test of scientific respectability, for it is not obvious how such an idea could be *dis*proved. One trouble is that if universal consciousness is indeed all-pervasive, then it is impossible to get away from. After all, a prime way to test whether some 'Factor X' does or does not exist is to create conditions in which we know for sure that Factor X is absent. If things really are different when X is not there we can reasonably infer that X must be making a difference when it is there—which is proof enough that it exists. But if we cannot create conditions in which we can be certain that X is not there at all then this acid test is not available to us. But life's like that. If universal consciousness exists at all then it is a material fact, and some philosophers and some scientists feel that all material facts should be testable. But some material facts, it seems, are not. In truth the bounds between the testable and the untestable are not as clear as some would like. The borders of science are fuzzy.

But why take an idea seriously that is intrinsically elusive and untestable? For a whole string of reasons, is the answer.

For one thing, consciousness itself—whether it is generated inside our own heads, or is part of the fabric of the universe—*is* a fact. Indeed it is the only fact of which we can truly be said to be aware because we could not be aware at all in the usual sense of the word unless we were conscious. Yet science and philosophers have so far produced no satisfactory theory of consciousness. We feel its existence but we don't know what it *is*. Some say that what we call consciousness isn't really anything at all—it is just the sound of neurones firing. The Boston philosopher Dan Dennett wrote a whole, large book along these lines (*Consciousness Explained,* 1991). But that when you boil it down is just an assertion. The idea of universal consciousness does not by itself tell us what consciousness is either, but at least it might broaden our inquiries and, with luck, push us in the right direction. In short, the idea of universal consciousness may help us to fill a huge conceptual gap—and filling huge conceptual gaps is what science and philosophy are for.

Secondly, like the even grander idea of transcendence itself, the idea of universal consciousness is perfectly plausible; and if it is true then it is of huge conceptual (and spiritual) importance, with all kinds of ramifications: a paradigm shift indeed. A plausible idea that is also potentially of huge importance should not be lightly abandoned.

Thirdly, potentially at least, the idea of universal consciousness could help to explain various phenomena that some are content simply to dismiss out of hand but which seem to demand to be explored. How for example do we account for the Dream Time which anthropologists have so widely reported among Australian Aborigines and other groups? How is it that two or more people dream the same thing and, when they wake up, share the experiences they shared in their dreams? We could just say that the anthropologists are mistaken, or self-delusory, or out to make a splash, or that they are being lied to (all of which of course have happened from time to time). But there is no good reason, apart from over-zealous scepticism, *aka* closed-mindedness, to refuse even to look.

The idea of universal consciousness seems to throw fresh light too on the phenomenon of telepathy. Again, the waters have been muddied by charlatans of one kind or another, and stage magicians who create illusions for entertainment (and sometimes though by no means always pretend that they have real psychic powers). It is the case, too, that attempts in the laboratory to demonstrate telepathy under controlled conditions in the way that scientists demand have commonly produced equivocal or negative results. But one reason for that may simply be that telepathy is difficult—especially for the westerners who are commonly roped in as subjects for such experiments; and so it is not easily replicated to order, even by adepts. Similarly (though at first sight it may not seem similar) only four athletes in the history of the world have ever jumped more than 29 feet (8.9 metres), the first being Bob Beamon who jumped 29 feet 2¼ inches at the Mexico Olympics in 1968, and never managed it again. If scientists tried to demonstrate to the accepted standards of science the somewhat outlandish claim that human beings can make such prodigious leaps they would fail, since no-one can do it to order. In any case, in *The Sense of Being Stared At* (2011) Rupert Sheldrake describes experiments which certainly seem to suggest that telepathy in some form is a fact (or at least the results are highly significant and cannot easily be explained in any other way).

Finally—and most intriguingly—the idea of universal consciousness chimes well with some of the key ideas to emerge from quantum physics—and especially from ideas that sprung, before World War II, from the pioneer studies of Niels Bohr, Werner Heisenberg, and Irwin Schrödinger. They showed that the behaviour of fundamental particles in any one experiment depends crucially on the observer: the conditions that the experimenter creates, and indeed, most strikingly, on whether or not the trial is observed by a conscious being. As the physicist turned philosopher Peter Russell described in *From Science to God* (New World Library, 2000), a whole range of scientists since have echoed the thought. Thus, in the words of the British-American physicist Freeman Dyson (1923-2020):

At the level of single atoms and electrons, the mind of an observer is involved in the description of events. Our consciousness forces the molecular complexes to make choices between one quantum state and another.

Or in the words of the Austrian-Swiss American Wolfgang Pauli (1900-1958), a Nobel Laureate:

We do not assume any longer the detached observer, but one who by his indeterminable effects creates a new situation, a new state of the observed system.

And this from yet another Nobel Laureate, the Hungarian Eugene Paul (E.P.) Wigner (1902-1995):

It is not possible to formulate the laws of quantum mechanics in a consistent way without reference to consciousness.

All this is revolutionary enough. Yet as the idea was bounced to and fro between physicists (science is and should be one long conversation) it grew ever stronger. Many indeed argue not simply that consciousness influences physical events (at the level of the quantum) but that physical matter itself would not *exist* without consciousness. Consciousness, not matter, or matter and energy, is the fundamental stuff of the universe. Max Planck himself kicked off the whole subject. Although he is commonly regarded as a conservative thinker, he declared:

I regard consciousness as fundamental. I regard matter as derivative from consciousness.

In more modern times, the Irish physicist John Stewart Bell (1928-1990), known especially for Bell's Theorem, said:

As regards mind, I am fully convinced that it has a central place in the ultimate nature of reality.

Or this from the English physicist Sir James Jeans (1877-1946):

The Universe begins to look more like a great thought than like a great machine.

And here perhaps is the strongest statement of the idea from Britain's former Astronomer Royal, Martin (Lord) Rees (b. 1942):

The universe could only come into existence if someone observed it. It does not matter that the observers turned up several billion years later. The universe exists because we are aware of it.

Yet the idea that consciousness is fundamental did not begin with the quantum physicists. It is the basis of the philosophical tradition known as ***idealism.*** The word 'idealism' in the philosophical sense derives from 'idea' and is intended to mean more or less as Max Plank said—that consciousness, not matter, is the fundamental stuff (or at least are co-equal; aspects of the same phenomenon). Idealism in this sense is quite different from 'idealism' in the political sense, meaning 'driven by moral or political ideals.' The general idea of it is ancient—embraced by various Pre-Socratic Greeks and in Hindu philosophy; and it has re-surfaced in many forms ever since, not least in the work of the Irish philosopher and theologian Bishop (George) Berkeley (1685-1753), and of Immanuel Kant. I like to think that this is the idea that lies behind the opening line of the Gospel of St John:

In the beginning was the Word and the Word was with God and the Word was God.

The original Greek says 'In the beginning was the *logos.*' 'Word' is not the only possible translation and surely not the best. 'Consciousness' seems to express the idea more accurately.

Clearly, then, there are parallels between concepts of a spiritual kind and those of *bona fide, avant-garde* physics—parallels which were brought to the world's general attention in 1975 by the Austrian-American physicist Fritjof Capra in *The Tao of Physics.*

In truth, for hundreds, not to say thousands of years, philosophers, religious teachers, and now scientists have debated and continue to debate the status of consciousness (mind) in the universe and the relationship between consciousness and material, measurable 'stuff.' René Descartes in the 17th century famously proposed the idea of what is now known as 'dualism': that the universe contains, or consists of, matter *and* mind—which remain as separate entities but work in combination. He envisaged that in the human body the material self interacts with the mind in the pineal gland, a discrete pea-shaped body embedded in the brain. Indeed he saw the pineal not simply the meeting place of body and mind but as the physical location of the soul.

Many others have preferred to take a 'monist' line: feeling that the universe must in truth be made of just one kind of stuff. As outlined above, some monists, including some philosophers and many scientists, have argued and continue to argue that measurable, observable matter is the primary stuff of the universe, and that consciousness is an 'emergent property' or an 'epiphenomenon' which somehow swims into being as material structures—particularly living systems—become more complex. Indeed they argue that mind (consciousness) is in effect an illusion. On the other hand the 'idealists,' who include some physicists, have argued and continue to argue that mind, or consciousness, is primary: that mind brings matter into existence.

Personally, I like the (monist) idea that mind and matter are two sides of the same coin; that the basic ground-stuff of the universe should be seen as mind-matter. The idea of mind-matter is at least analogous with Einstein's notion of space-time or with the quantum physicists' idea that the stuff of the universe may behave like a particle or a wave—since in reality it is both at the same time.

The discussions are endlessly intricate, sometimes heated, and (at least in the physicists' version) are inveterately mathematical, and so in the end are beyond the reach of non-mathematicians. I would love to understand all the arguments in all their subtleties but I cannot cope with the maths and it's too late to start now. I comfort myself with the thought that in the end, probably, the arguments about realism and idealism and mind-matter can never be resolved. The answers are and probably always must be beyond our ken. We really do live in a cloud of unknowing. So, at least *faute de mieux*, I will settle for the idea of mind-matter, granting consciousness and material stuff equal status, as complementary aspects of a unified reality. All the various arguments and shades of opinion are excellently summarized by the philosopher Jeffrey J. Kripal in *The Flip* (Penguin London 2019). Kripal also recommends the writings of the computer scientist Bernard Kastrup , beginning perhaps with *Brief Peeks Beyond* (2015), and so do I.

In the end, indeed, as Charles Williams observed (as cited earlier), we must each of us *decide* what to believe—or as I would say, what to take seriously; although as Cardinal Newman warned, we must all in the end accept responsibility for what we choose to believe. There is and never can be definitive 'proof' of the idea that the universe is compounded of 'mind-matter' but there are plenty of straws in the wind. The idea too is eminently plausible, and it has enormous explanatory power and considerable moral and metaphysical import—wonderfully reinforcing the idea of 'oneness.' In short, the idea of 'mind-matter' may be wrong, and certainly is a great simplification, but it is powerful and plausible and surely a great improvement on the simplistic materialism that now prevails. It surely is a worthy addition to the Perennial Wisdom.

The idea of the numinous

The idea of universal consciousness—an underlying intelligence—seems to raise the possibility that the universe has purpose; and it seems very reasonable (I stress *reasonable*) to equate the idea of an underlying intelligence with the idea of God. God need not be reified or personified—portrayed as an idol or as a muscular old man with a beard. Indeed, Jews and Muslims consider it blasphemous to depict God at all. He, She, or It (none of these earth-bound pronouns is really suitable) is conceived simply as a presence. Many, including many clerics, are content to see the word 'God' as a metaphor, to describe whatever it is that makes the universe tick and keeps it on course, and we cannot assume that this unifying force is adequately described by what we perceive to be the laws of physics.

The core idea of transcendence is, though, captured in the word '***numinous***,' a term first coined in the 17th century but brought to the world's attention in the early 20th century by the German theologian Rudolf Otto (1869-1937). It derives from the Latin *numen* meaning 'divine presence,' and describes the intimation of such presence that we feel especially in nature—for which Otto invoked the Latin expression *mysterium tremendum et fascinans*—'mystery both terrifying and fascinating.' The idea of the numinous thus conceived is central to mysticism (of which more later) and appears therefore in all religions (for all religions have a seam of mysticism) including or perhaps especially those known as pagan or shamanistic. It runs through all literature too, particularly of the kind known as Romantic. Indeed we may wonder whether true Romantic literature is possible at all without a sense of transcendence, even when the author claims to be an atheist. As the arch-Romantic Samuel Taylor Coleridge (1772-1834) commented in one of his essays:

> *... every being capable of understanding must be mad, who remains, as it were, fixed in the ground in which he treads ... Much more truly might it be said that an undevout poet is mad: in the strict sense of the word, an undevout poet is an impossibility ...*

Coleridge's friend William Wordsworth (1770-1850) shared the general feeling of divine presence as revealed in *The Prelude* (11, 66-73)—the monumental poem that he began in 1798 and worked on until his death:

> *A meditation rose in me that night*
> *Upon the lonely mountain when the scene*
> *Had passed away, and it appeared to me*
> *The perfect image of a mighty mind,*
> *Of one that feeds upon infinity*
> *That is exalted by an under-presence*
> *The sense of God, or whatsoe'er is dim*
> *Or vast in its own being ...*

Wordsworth expanded this thought in *Lines Written a Few Miles above Tintern Abbey* in 1798. But I reckon the general idea of divine presence and of universal consciousness was most beautifully conveyed by Coleridge in *The Eolian Harp*—a harp played by the wind—published in 1796:

> *And what if all of animated nature*
> *Be but organic Harps diversely fram'd,*
> *That tremble into thought, as o'er them sweeps*
> *Plastic and vast, one intellectual breeze,*
> *At once the soul of each, and God of all?*

All of which leads us to the true meaning of the term ***spiritual***. It means, or should mean, I suggest, 'a sense of transcendence'—or, more precisely, 'a feeling of divine presence.' In sociological surveys, most people claim to be 'spiritual' but many of those who make this claim simply mean that they are emotionally stirred by the music of Schubert, say, or of Nina Simone; and some of the harder-nosed kind insist that such emotional response is just a matter of hormones—adrenalin and serotonin and the rest—which, like all hormonal responses, can be explained away on evolutionary grounds, since appropriate emotional responses have survival value. But the term 'spiritual' should mean an intimation of some transcendent spirit—of the numinous, indeed; and we need not suppose *a priori* that this feeling is simply illusory.

All this, I suggest, throws new light on the meaning of ***mysticism,*** the often apparently dream-like state in which it seems the veils are lifted and the mystic is brought face to face with reality or with God. Perhaps the mystical experience is what we feel when our own consciousness is in perfect tune with the consciousness of the universe as whole: when indeed individual mind and the universe as a whole are as one.

Oneness

The idea of oneness is found in all religions to a greater or lesser extent: the oneness of humanity; the oneness of all living creatures; the oneness of all that is. Some indeed would say that every individual person and living creature, and indeed every fundamental particle, is an aspect of God. The concept of oneness is paramount in Islam. Indeed my good friend Ziauddin Sardar, founder and editor of *The Critical Muslim*, tells me that—'... *the* main concept of Islam—the concept above all other concepts—is: *tawheed*: an all-pervasive notion which includes the oneness of God, the oneness of humanity, the oneness of man and nature, the unity of knowledge...'

In the words of the 13th century Andalusian Muslim mystic Ibn-al Arabi (1165-1240):

> *God is essentially all things ... The existence of all created things is His existence. Thou dost not see, in this world or the next, anything besides God.*
>
> Quoted by Peter Russell in *From Science To God.* New World Library, Novato, California, 2003. p.114

Some decades later the German philosopher and mystic Meister Eckhart (1260-1328) said in very similar vein:

God is everywhere and is everywhere complete. Only God flows into all things, their very essences ... God is in the innermost part of each and every thing.

Ibid p.114

And in the 19th century one of England's most original poets, Gerard Manley Hopkins, (1844-89), who was born into a devoutly Anglican family but became a Roman Catholic priest, wrote:

The world is charged with the grandeur of God.

It seems to me, too, that many aspects of modern science reinforce the idea of oneness, even though, sometimes, the opposite has been inferred. Thus Darwin's idea of natural selection—especially Spencer's 'survival of the fittest'—is commonly taken to imply that all individual creatures and indeed all individual genes are doomed to be at odds with one another, each fighting their own individualist corner. Yet as discussed in earlier chapters, individual organisms and ecosystems are in the end more cooperative than competitive—not necessarily or usually seeking consciously to work for the common good but combining to create harmony nonetheless. If this were not so there would be no organisms, or ecosystems, and indeed no universe. Nothing would cohere.

Darwin pointed out too that if evolution is a fact, then, logically, all Earthly creatures must trace their ancestors back to a common ancestor. St Francis of Assisi (1181-1226) is reported to have said that all living creatures were his brothers and sisters—and if for brother and sister you read 4th cousin, or 27th or 136th cousin, then this is biologically accurate. Dinosaurs, whelks, mushrooms, and oak trees are our literal relatives. Modern evidence suggests that in reality there was never some single, ancestral creature that is ancestor to us all—but that idea, paradoxically, further reinforces the sense of oneness. For it now seems that life and the constituents of life did not originate just in one place with one primordial creature but in many places—but then the different constituents, and indeed entire creatures cooperated, coalesced, and eventually merged to form the life-forms we see today. Our own body cells, it seems, are a coalition of quite different life-forms: various bacteria embedded within and merged with the cell of an Archaean, which is a fundamentally different life form. Neither did the different species, once formed, simply diverge like the branches of a tree, as is commonly depicted. Often (far more often it seems than was ever traditionally envisaged) what seem like separate branches of the evolutionary tree come together and recombine—'anastomose,' as botanists say—as members of apparently separate lineages hybridize or simply fuse. It now seems that modern humans incorporate genes from up to five hominine lineages that once were more or less separate.

Then, too, there is the psychological (and moral) point expressed by writers such as Satish Kumar in *You Are, Therefore I Am* (2002) or by the Scottish philosopher John Macmurray in *Persons in Relation* (1961), or by psychologists like Sue Gerhardt as in *Why Love Matters* (2003), all of whom say from different standpoints that human beings cannot become fully human unless they are connected to other human beings and bound by love. Adults may choose to live as hermits but a child raised in total isolation can never be more than unrealised potential. I think the same is true of the whole human race *vis a vis* the natural world; that we cannot be or feel fully human if we are cut off from our fellow species. We evolved to be part of the whole. The same is true of all creatures.

The concept of oneness—that in the end all is one: that everything including ourselves is interdependent, hardly existing at all except in the context of the whole—obviously has profound moral and political implications; whether we think of ourselves as part of a whole or as isolates locked in perpetual rivalry. The idea is captured in the Sanskrit word *advaya*. The Buddhist interpretation of the *dharma*—of universal harmony—as outlined in chapter 12, also embraces the idea of oneness.

However—the huge and universal 'however'—not everyone agrees with the above analysis. Many thinking people, of the hard-nosed, materialist-positivist kind, reject the idea of the transcendence altogether. I have met a few. This raises the second grand metaphysical question:

2: How do we know what's true?

We don't, is the short answer. We can but do our best, making best use of our obviously limited faculties.

And our faculties, it seems, are of two qualitatively different kinds, which have often been seen to be at odds—bitter rivals indeed—but should be entirely complementary. The first of course is ***rationality***, including the principal devices of science: empirical 'evidence' based on observation; measurement; calculation. The second may be called ***intui-***

tion—a very broad category of prehension that extends from instinct to revelation. ***Imagination***—which, said Coleridge, is the essential quality of the poet—may be seen as intuition in active mode.

To take revelation seriously even in the absence of empirical evidence is to have *faith*. Scientists of the hard-nosed kinds are wont to dismiss faith out of hand but all thinking creatures have to have faith in something—if not in the word of God then at least in the power of mathematics to point us in the right direction. Indeed we cannot hope to understand anything at all unless we have faith in some premise or other. As St Anselm (c.1033-1109) put the matter:

> *Nor do I seek to understand that I may believe, but I believe that I may understand. For this, too, I believe, that, unless I first believe, I shall not understand.*

In this there are obvious echoes of St Augustine (354-430) who wrote in his *Ten Homilies on the First Epistle of John*:

> *Therefore do not seek to understand in order to believe, but believe that thou mayest understand.*

Both took their lead from *Isaiah* (7:9):

> *If you do not believe, you will not understand.*

Committed atheists are wont to greet such advice with snorts of derision. They take faith to mean 'blind faith,' to be arrived at only by a 'leap of faith'—prompting the polymath and wit Jonathan Miller (1934-2019) to ask what athletic training is needed to prepare for such a leap. But I think we should look more closely at the word 'believe.' Frankly, I'm not sure what I believe. I don't want to say that I believe in God in the way that so many Jews, Christians, and Muslims obviously do. But I do think that the underlying idea needs taking seriously; and if we replace the word 'believe' with the expression 'take seriously' then Augustine's and Anselms's recommendations make perfect sense, for we cannot hope truly to understand *anything* of substance—science, religion, art, cricket—unless we first take it seriously, and approach it in a spirit of true inquiry and humility. As the art and film critic Mark Kermode commented in *The Guardian*, (*G2*, December 11, 2009, p.15):

With almost any genuine art form, the most important works can rarely be taken at face value, and are only fully appreciated by those who have an affinity for the medium.

Thus, we cannot hope to get to grips with Picasso if after one glance we simply opine as many have done that their six-year-old could do better, and we cannot make any serious inroads into any religion if we simply pour scorn on odd turns of expression and apparently unsavoury anecdotes from ancient texts in the style of fundamentalist atheists such as Richard Dawkins.

Intuition is informed by the rational mind of course but in the main it is *felt*—at least as the popular expression has it—*in the bones*. We can think and argue till the cows come home, and well beyond, but in the end, to borrow the language of parliamentary debates, the bones have it. Theology as a whole emerges as a never-ending dialogue between rationality and intuition—brain and bones (more conventionally expressed as head and heart)—leading to what might be called ***cultivated intuition.*** Thus the 'Romantic' German theologian Friedrich Schleiermacher (1768-1834) described religion as

... the sensibility and taste for the infinite ... The essence of religion is neither thinking nor acting but intuition and feeling.

(Quoted by Keith Ward in *God: A Guide for the Perplexed, Oneworld, Oxford, 2003. p.19*)

In short, although some scientists, such as Peter Atkins (chapter 13) are wont to claim that science is nibbling away at mystery, and so in passing is undermining the whole idea of transcendence, and thus is delivering a mortal blow to religion as a whole, we might rather suggest that the more that science expands, the deeper it leads us in to the realms of mystery. Some—including Albert Einstein—relish this. Thus in *Living Philosophies* (Simon and Schuster, 1930), he wrote:

The most beautiful thing we can experience is the mysterious. It is the source of all true art and science. He to whom this emotion is a stranger, who can no longer pause to wonder and stand rapt in awe, is as good as dead: his eyes are closed. This insight into the mystery of life, coupled though it be with fear, has also given rise to religion. To know that what is impenetrable to us really exists, manifesting itself as the highest wisdom and the most radiant beauty which our dull faculties can comprehend only in their most primitive forms—this knowledge, this feeling, is at the centre of true religiousness.

Einstein's 'wonder and ... rapt in awe' clearly echoes Rudolf Otto's '*mysterium tremendum et fascinans.*' Einstein also said:

It is enough for me to contemplate the mystery of conscious life perpetuating itself through all eternity, to reflect upon the marvellous structure of the universe which we can dimly perceive, and to try humbly to comprehend even an infinitesimal part of the intelligence manifested in nature.

Also pertinent here is Gabriel Marcel's idea, cited in chapter 13, that we should distinguish between puzzles—which can be solved just by working through what's given; problems—which can be solved but need more evidence; and mysteries—which can never be fully resolved whatever we do.

Traditional scientists have approached the universe as if it were a puzzle or a set of problems, that can be solved with enough research. However, once we get deeply into science we see that the things we really want to know are forever beyond our ken. The murky world of quantum physics in particular poses questions that seem intrinsically unanswerable. To be sure, some of those questions could in theory be resolved if we had big enough instruments—telescopes to see right to the ends of the universe: accelerators to illuminate the most fundamental of particles—but some of the questions seem intrinsically unanswerable (including the idea of universal consciousness). In truth, as Einstein perceived almost a hundred years ago (and as Newton intimated some centuries before that), the Universe is, and ever will be, innately mysterious. Some scientists hate this thought. To them it is a betrayal of their calling. Many though by no means all agree with Professor Atkins that as science spreads its boundaries it will throw light into every 'dark corner,' and replace all mystery with certainty. The reality, though, may well be the other way around. The more that science reveals, the more mysterious the universe is seen to be. Some scientists, including some of the greatest, revel in the sense of mystery, like any Romantic poet. Metaphysics might be seen as the art of the innately mysterious.

So to the third of the ultimate questions:

3: What is 'good'?

All of moral philosophy, it seems to me, is essentially an exercise in metaphysics. Most members of ethical committees, however, do not think of themselves as metaphysicians. They generally are concerned with practical issues such as the rights of embryos or age of consent. They are often chaired by lawyers—who may indeed be very clear thinking, which is obviously desirable, but they tend to deal in the pragmatic rather than the transcendent. They often include clerics but clerics are inclined mainly to ask whether a particular course of action is or is not compatible with their own particular theology. Metaphysics addresses the more fundamental questions: 'What actually *is* "goodness"? What is this abstraction that gives rise to the adjective "good"? Where does the idea come from? How come we have such a concept? How much importance can we—or should we—attach to it?'

As intimated in chapter 12, there are many answers to these questions, and many *kinds* of answers. Some say that goodness emanates from God, as everything does, but this seems to raise as many questions as it answers. Not the least of them is the one that has occupied Christian theologians for the past 2000 years: How do we know, when a prophet or a seer claims to have heard the voice of God, that it was God who was talking to them, and not some deceiving demon? Some have died at the stake for claiming too much. In any case, why do we suppose that God is saying the right things—given that, especially in the Old Testament, He sometimes seems to make some strange moral decisions? Was all that smiting really necessary? Are there super-divine standards by which to judge God? If so, what are they—and where do they come from?

Evolutionary biologists have been wont to argue that moral codes have evolved, like everything else, because they have survival value. They help us to get along together which, as discussed in chapter 3, may be the most useful survival skill of all. Any idea that helps a creature to survive and/or to reproduce, is likely to persist, while ideas that cause us to die prematurely will die with us—and many kinds of moral idea obviously do have survival/reproductive value, including the moral imperative that parents feel to look after their children (or indeed, though to a lesser extent, to look after their parents as in the 5th Commandment—'Honour thy father and thy mother'). Religion as a whole with all its public rituals and affirmations has survival value because it helps to bind communities together, and there is safety in numbers—and this is true (and perhaps is especially true) even if the religion contains a great deal of stuff that outsiders would consider nonsensical. In a sense, at least up to a point, such evolutionary arguments obviously have weight. Certainly the negative is true. A moral code that caused us to die before we have passed on our genes would surely die out as we ourselves died out.

Evolutionary arguments, though, seem to ignore David Hume's idea outlined in chapter 12 we that 'we cannot derive an *ought* from an *is*.' They can also lead us to fall foul of the naturalistic fallacy, as conceived by G.E. Moore. As the staid Katharine Hepburn as the staid Rose Sayer in *The African Queen* says to the wayward Humphrey Bogart as the wayward Charlie Allnut when he polishes off the gin because, he says, it is 'natural' to get drunk,

The point, Mr Allnut, is to rise above nature.

However, many have taken issue with Hume and Moore. Whatever the philosophers may tell us it is obvious that in practice all of us, to some extent, do take nature as our guide. At least, people at large and the law take special exception to crimes that they perceive to be *un*natural—as when parents reject their children.

But if we cannot rely on the authority of governments or of clerics to tell us what is right, and if rationality won't do, what can we rely on? For my part, like many millions of others, I choose to take seriously the idea of the ***dharma***, the universal harmony, and the idea that it is good to act harmoniously, and bad to upset the harmony. This idea applies to each of us as individuals and to governments that endorse economic systems that lead to inequality and hence to strife, and to anyone that does avoidable harm to the biosphere. In the end, as the English poet and critic Charles Williams (1886-1945) remarked:

No one can possibly do more than decide what to believe.

[Quoted by Humphrey Carpenter in *The Inklings*, Harper Collins paperback 2006 (1st published 1978), p.217]

Finally:

4: How come?

A few years ago physicists began to get very excited about ***superstrings***. These were conceived as loops of energy that were *the* stuff of which all matter is composed. Just as material objects are seen to be compounded of atoms, and atoms are built from fundamental particles, so fundamental particles are built from superstrings (or are they manifestations of superstrings?). Superstrings, the theory has it, or had it, are the most fundamental things of all. Superstrings cannot be reduced to anything smaller. Thus, some felt, if only we had a theory—a mathematical formula—to describe the behaviour of superstrings we would then, truly, understand the material universe. Michelson's somewhat premature declaration (chapter 13) that the only remaining task in physics was to fill in the details, would be vindicated.

Superstring theory no longer seems to be quite as fashionable as it was—but that is not my point. The point is that even if superstrings are as important as some *avant garde* physicists have suggested, that would still not fully *explain* why the universe is as it is. We would still want to ask, '*How come* there are these things called superstrings, apparently endowed with the potential to form matter, which in turn gives rise to life, which in turn may be sentient? How did such things come about?'

This yet again is a modern variation on an ancient theme—for philosophers have been asking at least for the past few thousand years: 'How come the universe exists at all? If everything that exists was caused by something else, what was the first cause?' Theologians asked, 'If God made the universe and everything in it—then who made God?' Aristotle in the 4th century BCE came up with the idea of the 'unmoved mover'—the cause of everything that came after, but without cause itself. He did not try to envisage what the unmoved mover is like. He just said that, logically, there ought to be such a thing. About 1600 years later St Thomas Aquinas argued that God is Aristotle's unmoved mover—and argued accordingly that God must necessarily exist, or nothing else could. St Anselm, a century before Aquinas, made very similar arguments.

Many would say (probably including Aristotle!) that Aristotle's unmoved mover does not really explain anything. It is just a neat way of expressing ignorance: of acknowledging that we really don't know how it all began, or why. For the same kind of reason few now feel that Aquinas's various proofs of God's existence really stand up. Something that we feel logically *ought* to exist does not, in reality, necessarily exist. In short, the question 'How come?' is unanswerable, no matter what angle you come at it. Always we are left asking what came before the very first things that we know about, and how come there was anything there in the first place with the qualities needed to give rise to all that followed—and what does 'the first place' mean in this context anyway?

Finally: it is not quite true to say that metaphysics has been allowed (or encouraged) to die out. It lives on at the heart of all religions that are worthy of the name: all that are more than cults or politics dressed up. All religions indeed are metaphysical in nature—and religions are very much a part of modern life, just as they have been, so the archaeological evidence suggests, at least since recognizably modern human beings first appeared. We should look, then, at the relationship between religion and metaphysics; and between both of them and science.

Metaphysics, religion, and science

All human understanding in the end is narrative—a story that we tell ourselves about the way things are. What we call 'truth' is a story that we find convincing—one that 'rings true.' Beyond doubt, some stories describe reality more accurately and completely than others—whatever 'reality' may be; but as many a theologian and philosopher has pointed out, we, feeble human beings with our evolved brains, can never hope to grasp the whole. We can only aspire, over time, to provide a more satisfying narrative, more complete, more accurately encompassing the things that we feel are the case, and which matter. The best, most complete, most robust story that we can devise at any one time is what might be called the ***Perennial Wisdom.***

All bona fide ***religions*** attempt to provide us—either just their own society or the whole world—with a complete narrative: a complete account of how the world is and how we should live in it. To this end, all religious narratives have three fundamental components:

First, they all include what might at least loosely be called a ***cosmology.*** That is, they all have some idea of what the universe is really like—how it operates. Some but not all include some kind of creation myth; an account of how it all came into being.

Secondly, all religions have a ***moral code.*** All aspire to tell us how we ought to behave.

Thirdly, and some would say most importantly, religions require particular ***practice.*** At least in the Abrahamic religions (Judaism, Christianity, and Islam) the practices are intended to be transformative. They leave us in a new state of mind—and indeed, as some would express the matter, they help to put us in touch with God. To some extent too—even to a large extent—the various rituals serve a social purpose. They express solidarity: intended to show that the performer understands and respects the rules and is truly part of the gang.

In short, *bona fide* religions (as opposed to arbitrary cults) tell us or aspire to tell us all we really need to know about the universe and how to live in it, and why.

The cosmologies of religions generally differ somewhat from the cosmology of science. Thus we are told in *Genesis* that God created the Universe in seven days whereas geologists over the past two centuries have shown, surely beyond reasonable doubt, that Earthly life took billions of years to evolve. Then again, some religious zealots condemn Darwin's vision of evolution by means of natural selection because it seems to make the Creator redundant—which they say is blasphemy. At the opposite extreme, dyed-in-the-wool atheists, including some scientists, some of whom are well-known, argue that since Darwin's ideas are obviously *true,* the idea of the Creator God is thereby discredited, anachronistic, left over from a less sophisticated age. The myth has been perpetuated that when Darwin first published *Origin of Species* in 1859 biologists rallied to his flag while clerics, particularly those of the Church of England, who were Darwin's peers, rose up as one against him.

As always, it seems, the truth is far different, and far more nuanced. Modern theologians—and some more ancient ones—are wont to point out that religious texts in general including the Bible were not written as literal accounts. They are commonly based on historical events and memories but they are intended to convey deeper truths about the nature of the universe and the purpose behind it and the moral implications. Ancient religious texts to a large extent are metaphorical, poetic—and they need to be because the things of which they speak, notably God, are not immediately visible and tangible. They cannot therefore be captured in the language and thoughts of everyday life that is applied to everyday objects and activities.

Neither is it true—far from it—that all scientists rallied around Darwin and that all clerics were outraged. In truth, many geologists and biologists were appalled by Darwin's evolutionary ideas, including the geologist Charles Lyell who was a friend of Darwin and the palaeontologist Richard Owen who definitely was not—even though their own discoveries and ideas added weight to Darwin's own theory. On the other hand, Charles Kingsley (1819-1875), who is best known as the author of *The Water Babies* and *Westward Ho!* but was also a Church of England vicar, wrote, *re* Darwin's account of evolution (very perceptively, I think) that:

> *We knew of old that God was so wise that he could make all things; but, behold, he is so much wiser than even that, that he can make all things make themselves.*
>
> From a lecture of 1871 'On the Natural Theology of the Future' in *Westminster Sermons*, London, Macmillan, 1874.

More broadly, atheists like Oxford's Richard Dawkins suggest that since the Creation accounts in *Genesis* seem at odds with the findings of geology then all the Abrahamic religions are thereby undermined and indeed that the whole edifice of religion comes crashing down. Once we see that the Bible was never intended to be reportage and apply a little theology, and indeed common sense, as Kingsley and many others have done, such arguments simply seem silly.

Many atheists gleefully point out too that different religions seem to have different views on morality ('so they can't all be right') although as pointed out in chapter 12, the critics commonly confuse morality with manners. What really matters is that all the great religions agree on the fundamental moral virtues—of ***compassion, humility,*** and ***a sense of the sacredness of nature***. All agree too on the central tenets of metaphysics: the idea of transcendence, and hence of underlying intelligence and purpose (which some equate with God); the sense of oneness; the acknowledgement that all in the end is mystery. Life and the universe are not just a series of problems, to be sewn up once and for all.

Although there have been and still are terrible and bloody conflicts between the different religions, all their greatest representatives tend to get on very well together. The Dalai Lama and Archbishop Desmond Tutu are the best of friends, bound by a huge common understanding, as evident in *The Book of Joy*, a dialogue between the two of them (edited by Douglas Abrams. Hutchinson, London, 2016). As part of his training the London-based Sufi leader Pir Zia spent several years with the Dalai Lama, until the latter told him he was ready to go off and be a good Sufi. More broadly, as the Arab Andalusian Muslim mystic Ibn 'Arabi (1165-1240) put the matter:

> *My heart is a pasture for gazelles and a convent for Christian monks; a temple for idols and the pilgrim's Ka'aba, the tables of the Torah and the book of the Qur'an. I follow the religion of Love. Whatever way Love's camels take, that is my religion and my faith.*
>
> From *Tarjuman al-Ashwaq*

For my part, I reckon that Interfaith is one of the most promising movements of our times (although 'Interfaith' is a ghastly name on several counts). At its most basic the movement tries simply to organize friendly discussions between Muslims and Christians and Hindus etc, which of course is well worth doing but, as many agree, is not enough. In more sophisticated vein, interfaith aficionados seek in effect to establish a 'syncretic' religion drawn from all the great religions and on the traditional religions of the kind commonly and derogatorily called 'pagan'—and out of the amalgam to create a form of religion that can serve all humanity. Each *bona fide* religion has its own special strengths, so why not try to bring them all together? Thus (it seems to me) Christianity is particularly strong on compassion, which it tends to call 'love'—or that at least was the prime message of Jesus. Islam emphasizes humility (and as Ziauddin Sardar points out, the Qur'an also emphasises compassion, even if many who call themselves Muslim very obviously do not). The Eastern religions in general, and those of say the Maoris or the native Americans which are commonly classed as Pagan, stress oneness with nature.

Many feel at one with the core ideas of metaphysics (the sense of transcendence, oneness, and ultimate mystery) and yet reject the particular doctrines and constraints of any one religion. Thus, in the spirit of Ibn 'Arabi and Meister Eckhart, the Portuguese-Dutch philosopher Baruch Spinoza (1632-1677) declared:

> *Whatsoever is, is in God, and without God nothing can be, or be conceived.*

This may seem like the ultimately 'religious' sentiment yet Spinoza was thrown out of the Jewish religious community because he seemed to be suggesting that God *is* nature, which struck the Jewish authorities as a suspiciously pagan idea. Einstein, unlike Spinoza, abandoned Judaism of his own volition but he did not, emphatically, abandon his spiritual leanings. In 1929 he wrote to Rabbi Herbert S. Goldstein to say:

I believe in Spinoza's God, who reveals himself in the harmony of all that exists, not in a God who concerns himself with the fate and the doings of mankind.

However, this more general embrace of spirituality—the sense of transcendence and mystery—need not mean, and surely should not mean, that the traditional religions are abandoned. It is possible to be a good Christian or a good Muslim or whatever *and* be part of a wider, interfaith movement, just as it is possible to be a good Italian or German—or indeed to be a *better* Italian or German—*and* be a good European. In our own time the Dalai Lama, Archbishop Tutu, and many others demonstrate the principle.

Darwin is often co-opted by dyed-in-the-wool atheists as a champion of their cause. *Obviously*, they seem to feel, the idea of evolution by natural selection wipes God off the map, and all talk of transcendence. In reality, as the chemist and historian of science John Hedley Brooke has pointed out (he the author of the seminal *Science and Religion* of 1991), it is very hard to pin down Darwin's religious views. He did at times express anti-religious sentiments but at least as often he revealed a deeply spiritual underpinning. Darwin died in 1882 and was interred in Westminster Abbey, and Dean (Frederick) Farrar (1831-1903) said in his eulogy that:

This man, on whom for years bigotry and ignorance poured out their scorn, has been called a materialist. I do not see in all his writings one trace of materialism. I read in every line the healthy, noble, well-balanced wonder of a spirit profoundly reverent, kindled into deepest admiration for the works of God.

Quoted in 'The Impact of Darwin on Conventional Thought' by Robert M Young in *The Victorian Crisis of Faith*, edited by Anthony Symondson; SPCK, London, 1970, p.26.

In truth, as A.N. Wilson describes in *God's Funeral* (1990), a whole raft of western intellectuals in the 19th century from Dostoevsky to George Eliot and beyond lost their faith in orthodox Christian teaching. Many were left bereft as a result, as beautifully captured by Matthew Arnold (1833-1888) in *Dover Beach* (1867):

The Sea of Faith
Was once, too, at the full, and round earth's shore
Lay like the folds of a bright girdle furled.
But now I only hear
Its melancholy, long, withdrawing roar,
Retreating, to the breath
Of the night-wind, down the vast edges drear
And naked shingles of the world.

The modern-day tension between science and religion is largely, and regrettably, a battle between the austerity of naked shingles, and crude dogmatism.

The rise and rise of science and particularly of geology and evolutionary theory was only part of the reason for the westerners' loss of faith in the 19th century, and perhaps only a minor part. As shown by the quote from Charles Kingsley, some religious people at least found it easy to come to terms with Darwin's ideas. The real sticking point, as the much neglected novelist Mrs Humphry Ward (1851-1920) describes in *Robert Elsmere* (1888), was the rise of Biblical scholarship, which was revealing severe inconsistences in Biblical texts. The penny does not seem seriously to have dropped at that time that religious texts are *not* reportage but are intended to convey deeper truths, and are largely metaphorical. Neither were westerners so familiar in the 19th century with the Eastern religions. Buddhism in particular is deeply spiritual and yet, at least in its best-known forms, has no conception of a reified, personified God. I feel that if Darwin had lived in the 20th century, when such ideas were far more familiar, he would have taken the same kind of view as Einstein: perhaps rejecting the details of the religion he was born into, but with a strong sense of transcendence and of mystery—what Otto called the numinous. This squares entirely with Dean Farrer's analysis. I am sure, too, that many other scientists feel exactly the same, although it became fashionable in the 20th century to feign a kind of hard-nosed materialist atheism. Incidentally, A.N. Wilson took his title, *God's Funeral*, from the title of an early 20th century poem by Thomas Hardy (1840-1928), one of many who lost his orthodox faith and suffered deeply as a result:

And, tricked by our own early dream
And need of solace, we grew self-deceived,
Our making soon our maker did we deem,
And what we had imagined we believed.

Finally, it is often assumed—particularly by Christians—that a 'religious' person is one who believes in God. But the word 'believe' and the word 'God' carry far too much baggage. A more cautious and in the end informative question would be: ***'Do you take seriously—or are you prepared to take seriously—the ideas of transcendence and of oneness?'*** A great deal of evidence, including various sociological surveys, suggests that most people do. Regrettably, however, this feeling does not necessarily translate into political policy or day to day action even though many political leaders (George W. Bush comes to mind) claim to be devout, and some of them are.

What then is, or should be, the role of religion/spirituality in the world at large?

What do we want religion to do?

It has been said of the Church of England that it is in favour of change so long as it does not make any difference.

From *Free to Believe* (BBC Books 1991, p.181) by David Jenkins, former Bishop of Durham, and his daughter, Rebecca Jenkins.

Should religion serve simply to provide comfort for the already devout? Should it seek more actively to 'spread the word,' to infuse humanity at large with feelings of compassion and a sense of transcendence? Or should it, in addition to such functions, seek actively to engage with everyday life—indeed to engage directly with politics?

Many attempts by clerics to intervene politically have not been encouraging. Present-day theocracies, dominated by religious dogma, are rarely convivial; sometimes anything but. In Northern Ireland in recent decades the Protestant cleric Ian Paisley openly stirred hatred against the Catholics. England's civil wars in the 17th century were mainly about ambition, property, and right to rule as all wars are but they were fired too by religion. Many feel therefore, including many clerics and most of the mainstream press, that religion should 'keep its nose out' of secular affairs. As David Jenkins wrote in *Free to Believe* (p183) the Church of England has often behaved with

> *... the sociological naivety that moral leadership is keeping the lower orders in their subordinate places.*

As Bishop of Durham from 1984 to 1994 Jenkins represented communities of miners in the 1980s during the reign of Margaret Thatcher and the deeply traumatic miners' strike. He had no doubt that clerics often appreciate the realities of people's lives much better than politicians generally do, especially those of the government ensconced in the capital city far away and hearing what they want to hear. He said (p.160):

> *Miners going through the agony of the end of a way of life are branded hooligans and anarchists; street protestors against an unpopular government are labelled criminals ...*

The causes have changed but the same still applies. Jenkins argued that clerics have a *duty* to draw attention to the facts and at least to point out the moral implications of government policy. Religious leaders have sometimes intervened far too clumsily but many too have hit the nail right on the moral and spiritual head including Mahatma Gandhi in India, Desmond Tutu in South Africa, the many clerics who helped to lead the CND movement and the brave Roman Catholic priests in South America who faced up to the dictators that western governments tended to support.

A feeling for transcendence and a sense of oneness, and of the numinous and the sacred, are surely needed to underpin the fundamental principles of morality and ecology. In short, the ideas of metaphysics and more specifically of religion must be taken very seriously indeed, and acted upon, if we and our fellow creatures are ever to enjoy the long, secure, and convivial future that ought to be possible.

Coda

Truly we are in the throes of a paradigm shift, or should be: one led and driven by metaphysics, albeit sometimes in the guise of science. It is transforming our understanding of what the world is really like, and of our place within it. If the new thoughts were widely known and taken seriously (or indeed the ancient thoughts that lie behind the apparently new ones) then surely they would prompt us to create a far better and more secure world—one in which science, moral philosophy, religion and the arts work in harmony to bring us closer to the goal and the ideal of the Perennial Wisdom.

But the oligarchs who dominate our lives and are settling the fate of the world are not aware of the shift, or if they are, they prefer to pretend that it's not happening. The ideas that prevail in politics and in finance are crass on all fronts. All are driven by the crude and anachronistic urge to dominate and to acquire the trappings of material wealth. Those who in the autumn of 2020 hold decisive power—Donald Trump, Vladimir Putin, Xi Jinping, and all the lesser lights from Bashar-al Assad to Joao Bolsanaro and Benjamin Netanyahu to Narendra Modi, not to mention Boris Johnson and his familiars—are exemplars of ego and vanity. Directly and indirectly they are adding fuel to the fires of racism, chauvinism, class distinction, and the crudely materialist, short-termist attitude to and treatment of the natural world.

Truly we need a Renaissance, and it will not be led by the people, or the kind of people, who now and through most of history have assumed the right to rule—and to whom, for some reason, the rest of us have granted that right. What at least should be the first stirrings of the Renaissance are outlined in chapter 16.

First though we should look briefly at the ways of thinking and feeling that can appeal most directly to our own inner selves: the arts.

15

THE ARTS

All human understanding in the end is narrative—a story that we tell ourselves. What we call 'truth' is a story that we happen to find particularly convincing.

It follows, then, that our whole worldview, what we take to be true and important, our perception of ourselves and our relationship with other people and with our fellow creatures, and in the end our *attitude*, is shaped in very large part by the stories that we ourselves invent, or are presented to us as we progress through life. *In practice*, what matters most is not whether the stories are literally true (whatever it means to be 'literally true') but whether they strike a chord with us. And whether a narrative registers with us or not depends at least as much on its form and presentation as on its content. The Greeks and Romans, and scholars well into the Middle Ages emphasized rhetoric: the art and science of persuasion. The modern equivalent is advertising, marketing, and the wiles of PR.

But the greatest storytellers of all, the ones that get to the heart of us, to the soul, are the ones we acknowledge to be artists: wordsmiths; painters; sculptors; architects; actors; composers; musicians; dancers. They express their thoughts and feelings particularly well.

Good narrative is not required to follow a strictly *logical* path. It should run smoothly and convincingly from point to point yet leave the reader's imagination to fill in the gaps. The artist doesn't so much tell the reader, or listener, or the viewer what's intended, in the manner of a pedagogue. The artist triggers the thought; or triggers the train of thought that will lead in the required direction. It's a mysterious process—truly an art rather than a science. Often, though, the meaning cannot be expressed in straightforward prose but only in metaphor—or, perhaps, the meaning cannot be expressed in words at all; only in forms that by-pass the intellect and appeal directly to our intuitions and emotions. Poetry does this. So too do the all the non-verbal arts. This is potent indeed for in the end, our *feelings* determine how we see the world, and behave in it. David Hume said this: and he was among the clearest thinkers of all.

Scientists are story-tellers too but their aims are different and their methods are more constrained. Scientists *are* concerned primarily with literal truth. They seek to provide accounts of the world that as far as possible encapsulate aspects of what we conceive to be reality. If they seek truly to bring new ideas to bear, they must at least from time to time allow their imaginations to run free. But in the end, scientists qua scientists must rein themselves in. They must wherever possible subject their ideas or their flights of fancy to mathematical analysis, test them against observable reality, and present them to the world in a strictly logical form.

Artists need feel no such constraint. To be sure, some artists of all kinds are very much concerned with literal truth but others are not, and although some are great thinkers they never, in their capacity as artists, confine themselves to mere cerebration. Art is the human soul in free flight—the imagination let off the hook. Thus set free, the imagination of the artist leads us to places we would not otherwise have conceived.

In the end, though, the point of art is to communicate. Art that remains locked in the artist's head or heart is stillborn. Art that is too obscure (or perhaps too *avant garde*) fails as art—although, as with the paintings of Van Gogh or the music of Mahler, what seems unacceptable to one generation may be meat and drink to the next. To appreciate art we must always meet the artist halfway. In the end (as Wittgenstein said is true of all attempts to communicate) *meaning* is where the intention of the speaker (or the composer or the painter) meets the receptive efforts of the reader (or listener or viewer). As discussed in the context of religion, too, we cannot hope to understand art that has any depth to it unless we first at least take it seriously. But once get a feel for what an artist is saying and get drawn in, whether it's Schubert or Brubeck, Rembrandt or David Hockney or Picasso, we see the world differently and sometimes see it afresh, as if for the first time. This is how our minds and sensibilities expand, and how the world can be changed.

The arts, in short, are not a luxury. In the end, whether we realise it or not, and beginning with nursery rhymes and continuing through comics and cartoons, and so perhaps into literature and intricate jazz and recondite painting, the arts largely determine—perhaps more than anything else, did we but know it—our *attitude*; and attitude is all important, the *sine qua non*. Attitude transforms ideas into mindset. Attitude is what makes the difference between the desire to dominate and the felt need to work as one with the rest of society, or indeed with all humanity, or indeed with all of nature. Governments that fail to support the arts in all their forms are seriously deficient. Governments that seek to harness the arts to enhance their own power as many in the history of the world have done, are positively evil.

Part VI

THE FUTURE

16

WHERE DO WE GO FROM HERE?

Or

THE RENAISSANCE HAS BEGUN

...if it did work, it would be a good thing, wouldn't it?

Jim Henson (1936-1990), creator of *The Muppets*

THE VISION OF THIS BOOK IS UTOPIAN—and therefore, some would say, is not worth considering. 'Convivial societies with personal fulfilment in a flourishing biosphere' is simply not 'realistic.' It is a dream. Hippie-dom. Life's not like that. We should put aside such childish things and face up to the grim realities of life. After all, when Sir Thomas More first conceived Utopia in the 16th century he intended the word to mean 'no-where.'

But is the dream really so fanciful?

Well, 'utopian' is often taken to mean 'perfect' and perfection is certainly not possible and neither is it truly desirable—not at least if we conceive perfection to be a static state. Life above all is dynamic. Absolute stability even in a state of perfection seems to mean death. Yet dreams can be valuable and indeed are essential—always to be kept in mind; something to be worked towards. Everything we do, I suggest—all technologies, all politics, the economy—should be geared to this conceptual goal: ***that everyone should be able to achieve personal fulfilment, and live in harmony with everyone else and with all our fellow creatures.*** It is essential, too, to acknowledge that human beings are not the only creatures that matter. As far as we are able we should strive to keep the biosphere in good heart, or at least to impose upon it as little as possible. Ideas qua ideas, including those of science, philosophy, the arts, and religion, must be given free rein to go where they will. But insofar as we *act* on those ideas—translate science into high tech, or moral philosophising into politics and economics—we need to direct them towards the vision of abundant and diverse life and universal harmony.

Even so—can this ever be more than an idle dream to be glimpsed through the bottom of a glass, or a haze of smoke, before reality kicks back in? Is it *wise* to live our lives in a dream? If people are not really capable of conviviality except with a few friends—or don't even want it; and if life is innately non-harmonious, and indeed is red in tooth and claw as Tennyson suggested, or one long punch-up as Darwin is often taken to have meant—then is it half-way sensible, or indeed *safe*, to suggest otherwise? Shouldn't we just accept that people are fickle and ultimately self-centred, and that nature plays nasty tricks, and arm ourselves accordingly? Isn't it the case that all attempts to create utopian societies—and there have been many—have ended in tears? Doesn't dreaming simply lead to chaos? This is how politicians and others in power defend the status quo. Admittedly, present policy is not perfect, but it is realistic, and it would be dangerous to change course. That at least is the standard rationale. Or as Mrs Thatcher put the matter, 'There is no alternative.'

Yet, I suggest, it is the status quo that's unrealistic. While Henri IV of France dreamed of a chicken in every pot the people who make policy in the present world have been holding out the promise, albeit vaguely and in some distant future, of untold riches for all; private pools and unlimited travel (yea, even unto outer space!). Meanwhile, all too obviously, the uncritical pursuit of wealth is leading us to the buffers. How is that realistic? On the other hand, as I have tried to show throughout this book, if we got our ideas straight and acted accordingly, then we and our fellow creatures could live agreeably and harmoniously far into the future—starting with the next million years.

But how could such an ambition succeed now when so many in the past with similar dreams have fallen short?

For three reasons, I suggest:

1: The ingredients are all in place

New knowledge is always desirable. Research on all fronts must surely continue. We can expect—and welcome—more paradigm shifts, especially in science. Techniques and technologies can always be improved. Besides, the search for new knowledge and insights and for better, more helpful and less damaging aids to living is one of life's greatest pleasures; a prime route to human fulfilment. Scholarship should again take centre stage. If we stop seeking to find out more or to do things better we will frizzle up and die.

And yet:

> **We surely already know enough to put the world back on its feet and to keep it and ourselves in good heart.**

Furthermore:

> **Although some of what we need to know is new, not to say hot off the presses, much is deep-rooted in traditional knowledge and needs only to be re-invoked and built upon.**

In particular, as argued in chapters 6 and 7, everyone who is ever liable to be born on to this Earth could have access to food of the highest standard, nutritionally and gastronomically. We need only to practice Enlightened Agriculture, aka Real Farming, based on the principles of agroecology and food sovereignty, and to develop a food culture that is geared to what Enlightened Agriculture provides—as opposed to the kinds we have now which are designed to maximize wealth and to concentrate that wealth in fewer and fewer hands (the hands of corporates and hedge fund managers and so on). Beyond doubt, truly enlightened farming needs modern science and there's a great deal more to find out. Yet the kinds of farming and cooking we really need are rooted in all the world's ancient cultures and need, at best, only to be refined. The role of science should be to enhance what's already out there and is known to work—not gratuitously to replace; and the science that matters most right now is the one that has often been most neglected, which is that of ecology.

Moral philosophy needs refinement too—underpinned by the metaphysical concepts of transcendence, sacredness, and oneness. Again, constant re-thinking and re-working is desirable and necessary but again, the necessary ideas have been with us for thousands of years. The basic moral principle is in *Leviticus* (19: 9-18):

> *Love Your Neighbour as Yourself.*

Jesus went one very considerable step further as St Matthew recorded (5:44)

> *But I say unto you, Love your enemies, bless them that curse you, do good to them that hate you, and pray for them which despitefully use you, and persecute you.*

This sounds very difficult and even perverse but the underlying idea, that our attitude towards humanity as a whole should be one of compassion, is widely acknowledged. It is emphasized particularly by the Dalai Lama and is a prime theme of the Qur'an. Indeed, as Buddhists, Jains, Hindus, and Sikhs—and *some* Christians—insist, compassion must be extended to life as a whole, reinforced by a sense of the sacred. In short, the essential idea is already out there, firmly embedded over thousands of years—for it was surely well established in the oral traditions of pre-history, long before such sentiments were written down. We know, too, from everyday experience, that human beings are eminently capable of compassion. Compassion is evident all around us in the spring of 2020 as the world does battle with Covid-19, and in the recurrent struggle against racism. Encouragingly, too—contrary, again, to what we have often been told—biology is on our side. Compassion underpins cooperativeness and as argued in chapter 3, cooperativeness is the most powerful of all survival tactics and therefore should be favoured by natural selection. That human beings are innately compassionate is a Darwinian prediction.

What's lacking above all is the ***infrastructure*** and the will to translate compassion into action. Governments should be coordinators, facilitators—enabling good things to happen. Instead for the most part they see themselves and are seen as elites, indeed as a special caste of humanity, intending not to serve but to rule—and, more often than not, to rule in ways that are primarily for the benefit of those with the most wealth and power. The prevailing, 'neoliberal' economy is designed not to serve humanity and the biosphere but simply, single-mindedly, to compete for material wealth by whatever means and in practice if not by direct intent to concentrate that wealth in fewer and fewer hands. The neoliberals argue when pressed that an economy that has no moral framework—one that makes its own moral rules—is somehow better for the world than one that has moral intention; an illusion based on a misreading of Darwin and of Adam Smith. Nowadays in the US and in Britain a degree from Harvard or Oxford in neoliberal economics—it's not called that but that's what it is—is the passport to high office. God save us.

As described in chapters 9 and 10 we need governments that are truly on our side—'of the people and for the people' as Abraham Lincoln put the matter; and an economy that can properly be called 'Green Economic Democracy.' Such an economy must be complex. It cannot be based on simple algorithms such as the neoliberals' 'free market' or the Marxist idea that the workers should own the means of production. Simplicity is always a great desideratum but to misquote Einstein, 'ideas should be as simple as possible *but no simpler.*' As an engineer once told me, all great machines are based on simple ideas but machines that actually work are always complicated.

2: The Net

In chapter 3 I argued that humanity's greatest asset is our ability to share and essentially to pool our thoughts rapidly and precisely. This enables us to cooperate to the nth degree. Human evolution and the history of civilization is largely the history of communication: speech, pictograms, writing, printing, the telephone, radio and TV. And now we have the internet, and mobile phones and Zoom; the whole 'social media.' To quote Tim Berners-Lee once more:

Hope in life comes from all the interconnections among all the people in the world ... The experience of seeing the Web take off by the grass-roots effort of thousands gives me tremendous hope ... .

Of course, the social media have a downside. They enable all kinds of bad things to happen on a scale that was not possible before: insults, threats, intimidation, manipulation. But that's life. All technologies can be misused. On the plus side, the web enables new, radical and essential ideas to spread like wildfire—or like a virus—between all people everywhere. Thus it becomes possible for people living very different lives in very different places all over the world not simply to communicate but truly to converse and to form working partnerships; and every partnership can communicate more or less instantly with every other to form global networks. This, surely, is just what the people-led Renaissance requires: worldwide civil society; a network of networks. With the social media it becomes possible for the first time truly to make democracy function as it should, on the large scale.

Indeed the new forms of communication make the new Renaissance possible as was never the case before. In fact—

3: The Renaissance has already begun

Paul Hawken estimates in *Blessed Unrest* (2007) that there may be as many as 10 million not-for-profit organizations in the world that are seeking in some way to make the world a better place—or at least as they perceive this to imply. They range from small wildlife trusts to giant NGOs like Oxfam and, the biggest of all, *La Via Campesina*, the worldwide farmers' and peasants' movement that represents more than 200 million peasant farmers. One study shows that about 40% of the world's people—about three billion—would like the world to be very different, with a different structure and different mindset. Less than half that number is enough to form a critical mass, able to bring about radical change. By the same token, governments in titular democracies like Britain commonly achieve power—which often seems like absolute power; the power of life and death—after winning only a quarter and certainly less than a third of the available vote.

In short: there are easily *enough* people and organizations in the world to bring about the Renaissance. If the necessary ideas and the techniques are already out there, then what's stopping us? Why do we put up with inadequate governments that often are not on our side and with an economy that is at best ill-conceived?

One thing that's lacking, I suggest, is ***coordination***. The individuals and groups that want the world to be different don't necessarily talk to each other, at least to the extent that is necessary, and so they don't work together to anything like the extent that is necessary. Sometimes indeed, in metadarwinian vein, they see each other as rivals and deliberately stay at arm's length. Sometimes, too, different groups really are incompatible. More often than not, however, the people who want the world to be a better place (as opposed to the extreme right-wingers and xenophobes who simply want to dominate) would benefit from cooperation. The internet has the power to bring them together or at least has the potential.

More seriously, what Hawken calls 'the blessed unrest' lacks a truly ***coherent philosophy***. Those who want the world to be a better place don't all agree on the kind of world we should put in its place. That is the purpose of this book: not to lay down the law and tell everyone else what to think and how to behave for that would be too hugely presumptuous, but to suggest an agenda for further thought and action for others to improve upon.

The College for Real Farming and Food Culture

The Renaissance we need now must be cross-the-board: everything needs to be re-thought, and re-thought furthermore in the light of everything else. But the grand Renaissance has to begin somewhere and as outlined in chapter 2 the best place to begin is with food and farming. That is: the Renaissance we so desperately need can sensibly begin with an ***Agrarian Renaissance.***

For agriculture affects everything else and is affected by everything else. Get it right and we could, with luck and a following wind, get everything else right as well. In truth, though, we cannot develop the kind of agriculture the world really needs *unless* we get everything else right as well: the economy; governance; mindset. Contrariwise, if agriculture is inappropriate then *nothing* else can work properly—and the neoliberal-industrial agriculture that is beginning to dominate worldwide is all too obviously *in*appropriate. In short, Enlightened Agriculture—Real Farming—is the *sine qua non*, right at the heart of all the world's affairs. Appropriate farming needs, though, to be complemented by an appropriate food culture which means in effect by people at large who know what good food *is,* and care about it enough to support enlightened farmers. This in turn of course requires a far more egalitarian economy to ensure that everyone can *afford* good food. The kind of economy we have now which leaves a large proportion literally out in the cold is a moral disgrace and even in crude material terms is counterproductive. The successive governments that have encouraged this economy and the academics who have promoted it should be ashamed, though of course they are not.

With all this in mind in about 2008 my wife, Ruth, and I, with help and generous support from friends, set up the Campaign for Real Farming, aiming to develop and promulgate the ideas needed to bring about the Agrarian Renaissance. The following year Graham Harvey, who I worked with at *Farmers Weekly* and for a long time advised and helped to script *The Archers,* suggested that we should try to mount a farming conference in Oxford. This would be the counter-voice, the antidote, to the established Oxford Farming Conference that has convened every January since 1936 primarily to promote mainstream farming—which, in recent years, had meant neoliberal-industrial farming. So one afternoon in January 2010 the Oxford *Real* Farming Conference (ORFC) with about 80 farmers and other interested parties was launched in a mediaeval library to discuss the ideas we feel are *really* interesting, with emphasis on agroecology (including organic farming, agroforestry, and pasture-feeding). Thanks mainly to Ruth's heroic efforts, we have come a long way since then. At the 11th ORFC in January 2020 well over 1000 farmers and others with a stake in farming met in Oxford's splendid town hall, plus a large church and conference centre, and a pub. We had to call off the 2021 gathering because of the Covid-19 lockdown and instead, led by Ruth and Fran Ryan, the ORFC became the ORFC Global: an international gathering made possible by Zoom. We will have to wait and see how this evolves.

The Campaign and the ORFC in turn gave rise to the College for Real Farming and Food Culture. It is focused of course on food and farming but also has a very broad curriculum to include all the lines of thought needed to make enlightened agriculture happen. This book essentially summarizes that curriculum—or at least sets out the kinds of ideas that need to be worked through. More on the College on our website (http://collegeforrealfarming.org/). The ORFC and the College, together with a few other ventures, are now coordinated by the Real Farming Trust—conceived as part of a cooperative global movement to bring about the Agrarian Renaissance and kick-start the grand Renaissance that we need to turn the world around.

Ideally, some time in the future, I would like the College to become a bricks and mortar entity, with its own model farm, exploring and demonstrating new approaches. But the College should always be a 'college' in the traditional sense: not a dispensary of acceptable and accepted ideas but a forum, a platform, a meeting ground where people from many or all regions and disciplines can discuss the ideas needed to bring about the Agrarian Renaissance and so contribute to the grand Renaissance. As such, it needs no dedicated premises, desirable as that could be. Of course, though, the Renaissance must not stop with discussion. The real task is to turn the good ideas into action. That requires political power. That is the next hurdle to be approached worldwide by whatever means are deemed necessary and are possible. The ideal route, I suggest in this book, is by renaissance: creating the world we want to see *in situ*, with or without assistance from the powers-that-be. Once there is an alternative, more and more people will feel able to jump ship, to abandon the status quo, to start life afresh, doing different things with different goals and a very different mindset.

To summarize the entire thesis in one sentence: What's needed is Enlightened Agriculture with complementary Food Cultures, within a framework of Green Economic Democracy, guided by moral principles centred on Compassion and underpinned by excellent science and particularly the science of Ecology, all rooted in the Buddhist conception of the Dharma and a sense of the Sacred. This is very different indeed from the present norms and in important ways is the precise opposite. So to put the world to rights we need radical, global, cross-the-board change—Renaissance indeed—and we, people at large, Ordinary Joes and Jos, have got to make it happen. But it is do-able. The essential elements are already in place and to some extent are being acted upon. Truly we are on the brink of catastrophe but still there is hope.

Further reading

The following is not a formal bibliography. It is a personal shortlist of texts and websites that I have enjoyed and been informed by over the past half century or so—plus a few of my own. Almost all on the list were written for the general reader, but they cite more scholarly works that may take the reader to PhD status and beyond.

1: What's the problem? The human condition and the state of the world

Ehrlich, Anne H. and Ehrlich, Paul R. (2004) *One with Nineveh: Politics, Consumption, and the Human Future.* Washington, DC: Island Press.

Pearce, Fred. (2011) *Peoplequake*. Eden Project Books.

3: Can human beings really be convivial?

Gerhardt, Sue. (2003) *Why Love Matters*. London: Routledge.

Kumar, Satish. (2004) *You Are, Therefore I Am*. Cambridge: Green Books

MacMurray, Sir John. (1961) *Persons in Relation*. London: Faber & Faber.

Noble, Denis. (2006) *The Music of Life*. Oxford: OUP.

Tudge, Colin. (2012) *Why Genes Are Not Selfish and People Are Nice.* Edinburgh: Floris Books.

De Waal, Frans. (2009) *The Age of Empathy: Nature's Lessons for a Kinder Society*. London: Souvenir Press.

4: A flourishing biosphere: morality, ecology, and a sense of the sacred

Empson, Martin (ed). (2019) *System Change not Climate Change.* London: Bookmarks Publications.

Lovelock, James. (2016) *Gaia: A New Look at Life on Earth*. Oxford: Oxford Landmark Science, OUP.

Sorrell, Roger D. (1988) *St Francis of Assisi and Nature*. Oxford: OUP.

Tudge, Colin. (2005) *The Secret Life of Trees*. London: Allen Lane. (2006) London: Penguin Books. (2006) published in the US as *The Tree*. New York: Crown Publishers.

5: Jobs, crafts, computers and robots. When is technology 'appropriate'?

Illich, Ivan. (1973) *Tools for Conviviality*. New York: Harper & Row. (2000) London: Marion Boyars Publishers.

Morris, William. (1993) *News from Nowhere and Other Writings.* London: Penguin.

Schumacher, E.F. (1973) *Small is Beautiful*. London: Blond and Briggs. (2011) London: Vintage.

6: Enlightened Agriculture and the Agrarian Renaissance

Cobbett, William. (First published 1822.) (1979) *Cottage Economy*. Oxford: OUP.

Evans, George Ewart. (1974) *The Farm and the Village*. London: Faber & Faber.

Fairlie, Simon. (2010) *Meat: A Benign Extravagance*. East Meon, Hampshire: Permanent Publications.

Fukuoka, Masanobi. (1985) *The One-Straw Revolution*. Toronto: Bantam Books.

Gregory, Christine & Hine, Sheila. (2019) *The Land That Made Us*. Sheffield: Vertebrate Publishing.

Harvey, Graham. (2016) *Grass-fed Nation*. London: Icon Books.

Lymbery, Philip with Oakeshott, Isabel. (2014) *Farmageddon*. London: Bloomsbury.

Pimbert, Michel (ed). (2018) *Food Sovereignty, Agroforestry, and Biocultural Diversity*. Abingdon, Oxon: Routledge.

Rebanks, James. (2020) *English Pastoral*. London: Allen Lane.

Shiva, Vandana. (2014) *The Vandana Shiva Reader*. Kentucky: Kentucky University Press.

Smaje, Chris. (2020) *A Small Farm Future*. Vermont and London: Chelsea Green.

Tree, Isabella. (2018) *Wilding; The Return to Nature of a British Farm*. London: Picador.

Tudge, Colin. (2016) *Six Steps Back to the Land*. Cambridge: Green Books.

— (2011) *Good Food for Everyone Forever: A People's Takeover of the World's Food Supply*. Pari, Italy: Pari Publishing.

— (2007) *Feeding People Is Easy*. Pari, Italy: Pari Publishing

— (2003) *So Shall We Reap: The Concept of Enlightened Agriculture*. London: Allen Lane. (2004) London: Penguin Books.

— (1998) *Neanderthals, Bandits, and Farmers*. London: Weidenfeld & Nicolson. (1999) New Haven, CT: Yale University Press.

— (1977) *The Famine Business*. London: Faber and Faber. (1977) New York: St Martin's Press.

7: True food culture: 'Plenty of plants, not much meat, and maximum variety'

Barrett, Louise. (2011) *Beyond the Brain: How Body and Environment Shape Animal and Human Minds*. Princeton, NJ: Princeton University Press.

Burnett, John. (1968) *Plenty and Want: A Social History of Diet in England from 1815 to the Present Day*. Harmondsworth: Penguin Books.

Hartley, Dorothy. (1954) *Food in England*. London: Macdonald.

Hsiang Ju Lin. (2015) *Slippery Noodles: A Culinary History of China*. London: Prospect Books.

Spector, Tim. (2016) *The Diet Myth*. London: Orion.

Tudge, Colin. (1980) *Future Cook*. London: Mitchell Beazley. (1980) published as *Future Food*. New York: Harmony Books.

8: What's gone wrong with the way the world is run?

Havel, Vaclav. (1987) *Living in Truth*. London: Faber and Faber, p.43.

9: Governance

Bevan, Aneurin. (1952) *In Place of Fear*. London: Simon & Schuster.

Hardie, Keir. (2015) *From Serfdom to Socialism*. London: Lawrence and Wishart.

Hartmann, Thom. (2004) *Unequal Protection: The Rise of Corporate Dominance and the Theft of Human Rights*. Emmaus, PA: Rodale Press.

Inglis, Brian. (1971) *Poverty and the Industrial Revolution*. London: Hodder & Stoughton.

Mason, Paul. (2013) *Why It's Kicking Off Everywhere*. London: Verso Books.

Wilkinson, Richard and Pickett, Kate. (2009) *The Spirit Level: Why More Equal Societies Almost Always Do Better*. London: Allen Lane.

10: An economy fit for purpose

Keen, Steve. (2011) *Debunking Economics*. London: Zed Books.

Large, Martin. (2009) *Common Wealth*. Stroud, UK: Hawthorn Press

Mayer, Colin. (2018) *Prosperity: Better Business Makes the Greater Good*. Oxford: OUP.

Norman, Jesse. (2018) *Adam Smith: What He Thought and Why it Matters*. London: Allen Lane.

Pettifor, Ann. (2014) *Just Money*. Margate, Kent: Commonwealth Publishing.

Raworth, Kate. (2017) *Doughnut Economics*. London: Penguin.

Springer, Simon, Birth, Kean, and MacLeavy, Julie (eds). (2016) *The Handbook of Neoliberalism*. London: Routledge.

Yueh, Linda. (2019) *The Great Economists*. London: Penguin.

11: The law of the land

Linklater, Andro. (2014) *Owning the Earth*. London: Bloomsbury.

Pearce, Fred. (2012) *The Landgrabbers*. London: Transworld Publishers.

Prebble, John. (1963) *The Highland Clearances*. London: Secker & Warburg.

Shrubsole, Guy. (2019) *Who Owns England?* London: HarperCollins.

12: Good for everyone forever: the universal morality

Murphy, Nancy and Ellis, George E.R. (1996) *On the Moral Nature of the Universe*. Minneapolis, MN: Fortress Press.

13: Science: the wonder and the threat

Al-Khalili, Jim, and McFadden, Johnjoe. (2014) *Life on the Edge: The Coming of Age of Quantum Biology*. London: Bantam Press.

Carey, Nessa. (2012) *The Epigenetics Revolution*. London: Icon Books.

Gottlieb, Anthony. (2016) *The Dream of Enlightenment*. London: Penguin.

Hannam, James. (2009) *God's Philosophers*. London: Icon Books.

Medawar, Peter. (1982) *Pluto's Republic: Incorporating the Art of the Soluble and Induction and Intuition in Scientific Thought*. Oxford: OUP.

Sheldrake, Rupert. (2012) *The Science Delusion*. London: Coronet.

Tudge, Colin. (1993) *The Engineer in the Garden*. New York: Hill &Wang.

14: Metaphysics: the essential ingredient that's gone missing

Capra, Fritjof. (1982) *The Tao of Physics*. London: Flamingo.

Davies, Brian, (ed) (2000) *The Philosophy of Religion*. Oxford: OUP.

Fellows, Andrew. (2019) *Gaia, Psyche, and Deep Ecology*. London: Karnac Books.

Goswami, Amit. (1995) *The Self-Aware Universe*. New York: Tarcher/Putnam,

Harding, Stephan. (2006) *Animate Earth*. Cambridge: Green Books

Jenkins, David, and Jenkins, Rebecca. (1991) *Free to Believe*. BBC Books.

Kastrup, Bernardo. (2015) *Brief Peeks Beyond*. Winchester: Iff Books.

Kripal, Jeffrey J. (2010) *The Flip*. London: Penguin.

Murphy, Nancy and Ellis, George F.R. (1996) *On the Moral Nature of the Universe*. Minneapolis, MN: Fortress Press.

Russell, Peter. (2005) *From Science to God*. Novato, CA: New World Library.

Sardar, Ziauddin. (2011) *Reading the Qur'an*. Oxford: OUP.

Wilson, A.N. (1999) God's Funeral. London: John Murray.

16: Where do we go from here?

Hawken, Paul. (2007) Blessed Unrest. London: Viking Books.

Pari Publishing is an independent publishing company, based in a medieval Italian village. Our books appeal to a broad readership and focus on innovative ideas and approaches from new and established authors who are experts in their fields. We publish books in the areas of science, society, psychology, and the arts.

Our books are available at all good bookstores or online at **www.paripublishing.com**

If you would like to add your name to our email list to receive information about our forthcoming titles and our online newsletter please contact us at **newsletter@paripublishing.com**

Visit us at **www.paripublishing.com**

Pari Publishing Sas
Via Tozzi, 7
58045 Pari (GR)
Italy

Email: info@paripublishing.com